Crystals, Insects, and Unknown Objects

A CREATIVE APPROACH TO THE TEACHING OF SCIENCE TO INTERMEDIATE SCHOOL CHILDREN

Crystals, Insects, and

A CREATIVE APPROACH TO THE TEACHING

John McGavack, Jr.

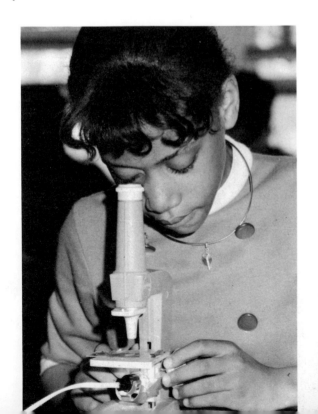

Unknown Objects

OF SCIENCE TO INTERMEDIATE SCHOOL CHILDREN

Donald P. LaSalle

THE JOHN DAY COMPANY / New York

The John Day Company, 257 Park Avenue South, New York, N.Y. 10010

An Intext Publisher

Published on the same day in Canada by Longman Canada Limited.

Library of Congress Catalogue Card Number: 73-135279
Printed in the United States of America

To Jynny and Nancy

ACKNOWLEDGMENTS

The authors gratefully acknowledge the teachers and administrators of the New Haven Public Schools and the schools served by the Talcott Mountain Science Center for Student Involvement Inc. in Avon, Connecticut, for their cooperation and aid in the testing of the material in this book.

In particular we are indebted to John Dommers and to Sheldon Glick for once again contributing their time and expertise in the photographic department; to Esther Danielson for her excellent drawings; and to Adele Davids for her typing of parts of the manuscript. Special thanks are extended to George C. Atamian, Eric Bill Danielson, Robert Judd, and Frank Milbury for many of the original ideas which were later developed into the existing units and for their further willingness and thoroughness in reviewing constructively the material within. We further acknowledge Dr. Laurence G. Paquin, Dr. Alvin Liftig, and Dr. Francis Driscoll for their faith and confidence in our ability and for showing us the way.

Lastly a tribute to the many students who made this book possible.

John McGavack, Jr.
Donald P. LaSalle

Preface

Young children are akin to scientists in that both possess insatiable curiosity about the world in which they live. Our intention is to have young children, freely exercising this built-in curiosity, explore new and exciting paths opened by the teacher, all the while using simple and easily available materials. The authors maintain that a creative approach to the teaching of science means making it possible for children to behave in the classroom in ways very similar to the way true scientists themselves operate.

Using science units which have been successfully tested with intermediate school children, we present here what we consider is a guide to the development of workable science programs adaptable to varying local needs. The first section, titled "How to Begin," constitutes a point of view embodied throughout. A second portion is devoted to "Why Do It This Way," in which a justification for this particular approach is explored. The nucleus of this book, the third section, deals with the nuts and bolts of really designing child-oriented science experiences. It is appropriately labeled "How to Do It." Last, an entire section is devoted to resources for the teacher and student and covers the broad spectrum from reading materials to science equipment and audio-visual aids, and is called "Where to Find Out."

Crystals, Insects, and Unknown Objects is the second in a series of books designed to meet the challenge of individualizing science for all elementary school youngsters. The first book in this series, *Guppies, Bubbles, and Vibrating Objects* (1969), is for use in the primary grades. *Crystals, Insects, and Unknown Objects* is for the intermediate grades.

This book can serve two major functions. One is as an instrument used in preparing prospective teachers for teaching science at the intermediate level and the other is as a ready guide for classroom teachers already engaged in the daily task of guiding intermediate school children in their classroom experiences. Every effort has been made in this book to aid teachers in developing materials, experiments, and investigations which will permit students an opportunity to uncover as well as discover the excitement and wonder of science. The immediate goal is to get science happening in as many classrooms as possible throughout the nation. The units herein are planned with this thought in mind and have been designed to permit children many chances to make mistakes and to use their senses in creating, experimenting, analyzing, measuring, recording, and observing, while having fun in the process.

Many activities have no real ending but are left to the imagination of both teacher and student. It is our intention to "stir children up—not tie them up."

John McGavack, Jr.

Donald P. LaSalle

Contents

HOW TO BEGIN   17

Teacher Attitude   17

School and Community   18

Observe—Hypothesize—Test   18

The Science Curriculum   19

Contemporary Issues   21

    Sex Education   22

    Drug Abuse   22

    Environmental Pollution   23

Textbooks   23

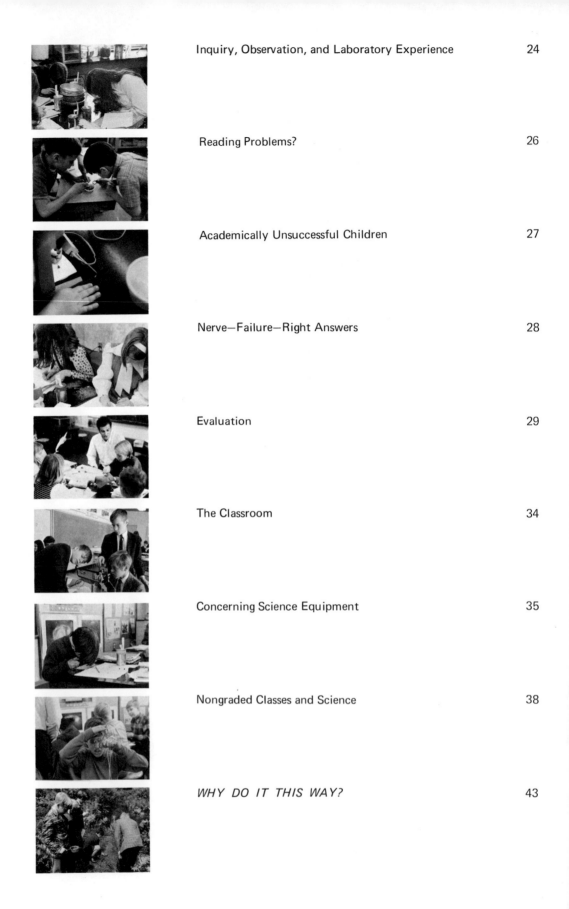

Inquiry, Observation, and Laboratory Experience   24

Reading Problems?   26

Academically Unsuccessful Children   27

Nerve—Failure—Right Answers   28

Evaluation   29

The Classroom   34

Concerning Science Equipment   35

Nongraded Classes and Science   38

WHY DO IT THIS WAY?   43

Science Units and Curiosity   43

The Senses and Autonomous Learning   44

Testing a Unit   45

Content versus Process   46

Individuality and the "System"   46

HOW TO DO IT   51

Aerospace   53

Air Pollution   86

Commonplace "Things"   97

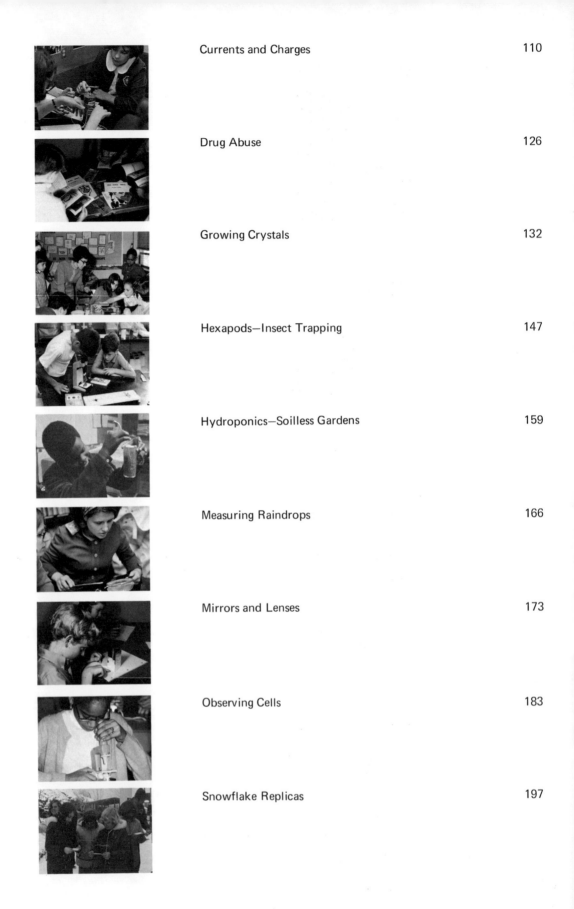

Currents and Charges 110

Drug Abuse 126

Growing Crystals 132

Hexapods—Insect Trapping 147

Hydroponics—Soilless Gardens 159

Measuring Raindrops 166

Mirrors and Lenses 173

Observing Cells 183

Snowflake Replicas 197

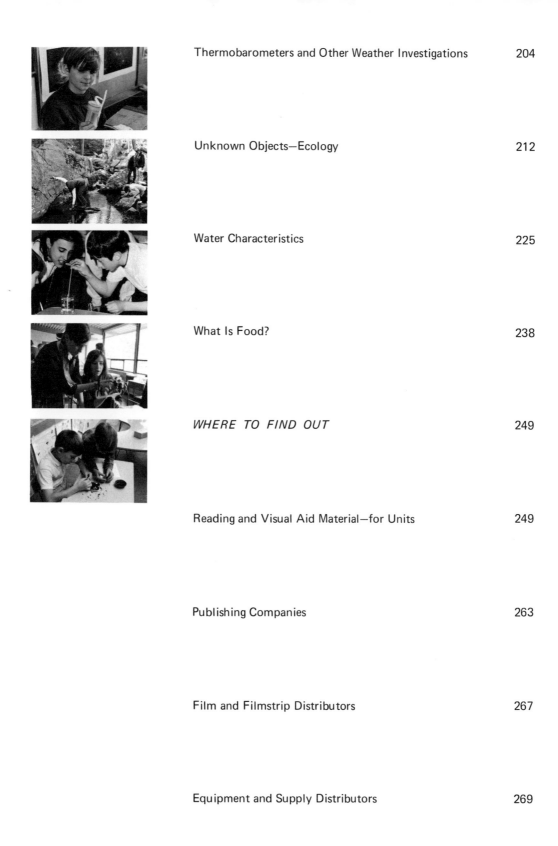

Thermobarometers and Other Weather Investigations   204

Unknown Objects—Ecology   212

Water Characteristics   225

What Is Food?   238

WHERE TO FIND OUT   249

Reading and Visual Aid Material—for Units   249

Publishing Companies   263

Film and Filmstrip Distributors   267

Equipment and Supply Distributors   269

13

How to Begin

How to Begin

We must begin at the beginning—and the beginning is the student. There are no convenient prescriptions for converting dependent learners into independent inquirers. Ultimately only you, the teacher practicing open inquiry, can find a way to make room for inquiry in your classroom.

Teacher Attitude

In order to bring about change in education and to alter the direction in which we are moving, we first have to bring about change in teachers—in the attitudes, qualification, competencies, and expectation levels of teachers. It has been said that while some teachers have taught for twenty-five years, they have gained only one year of experience—twenty-five times! Teacher education is not dependent on pre-service education or on in-service education, but on service by the teacher. This means being daily aware of his actions and their consequences in the classroom—utilizing the infinite number of classroom opportunities to regularly theorize about learning and learners in an attempt to formulate patterns which predictably alter children's behavior.

Ancient as the concept of individualized teaching and learning may be, educators still, for the most part, put students in prescribed rooms of prescribed sizes where teachers teach at them—the same things at the same time in the same way. As teachers we may know better but we don't have either the know-how to perform otherwise or the setting that lends itself to other approaches, or both.

The sensitive, competent, energetic teacher still remains as the primary vehicle for creating sub-

stantive progress in the rate and effectiveness of how children learn.

A good program of science instruction for young children must do more than acquaint students with facts and content. It should resist turning students into walking encyclopedias of supposedly important scientific information. Instead, the greatest concern should be with helping chil-

dren to learn rather than to have them just follow the rules of the game as prescribed by the teacher.

The "educational system" continues to focus on cognitive learning, particularly on stories and retrieving facts. In the final analysis, while the factual and content areas are important, the skills and techniques, or more simply the investigative know-how, are of paramount importance. Content can serve as the vehicle by which skills may be learned and not as an end in itself.

School and the Community

As teachers of children we must abolish the notion that the school is isolated from the influences of the surrounding community. The school must be an institution in and of the community it serves. The people living in a community have an interest and a right to take part in determining how their children are educated.

Educators for some time have maintained that the school's task is no longer to reshape students to fit the school but to reshape the school to respond to the requirements of the individual. Educational research is filled with data in support of the idea that children must be treated in the variety of ways their differences require.

The school system, as represented by administrators, teachers, and custodial personnel, cannot successfully meet the challenge of teaching children if it is isolated from the human and physical needs of the community it serves. As the teacher of a science unit, a social studies unit, or a mathematical game your sensitivity to community needs, human and physical, will in large part determine your effectiveness with the children you teach.

Observe, Hypothesize, Test

For many years the teaching method in science has been the following formula: observe, hypothesize, test. There is nothing wrong with this formula except that it is not enough. Consider a collection of blocks—all the same color but different shapes (cube, rectangle, diamond, sphere, etc.), sizes (large and small cubes, rectangles, diamonds, etc.), and made of varying materials according to shape and size. The primary child will observe this set of blocks but he may focus on some minor or insignificant property of the set; for example: he may observe that one or two of the blocks are dirty from handling. The intermediate-grade child will hypothesize but may choose the wrong variable for testing and end up not knowing what to do next; for example: he may hypothesize that all the blocks have different weights and choose size as the determining variable to test this hypothesis, only to be confused when some big blocks seem lighter than smaller blocks. He may choose the correct variable for testing, *obtain positive results*, and not know what to do with his results; for example: he may hypothesize that all the blocks have different weights, choose one shape to test

this hypothesis and arrange them according to weight (determining that some smaller blocks are heavier than some larger blocks), but not conclude that the blocks are made of different material. The middle-grade youngster can formulate propositions, based on his testing, but may not know how to systematically combine his propositions so as to test all possible combinations of the variables involved; for example: he may propose that the blocks are made of different material and all blocks of the same shape and size are made of the same material but find it difficult to set up the combinations (material, shape, and size) for meaningful testing procedures. The approach to science teaching can be synthesized out of the observe-hypothesize-test formula. This synthesis requires clever yet patient teacher guidance—not structured unimaginative teacher direction. There is room in this formula for minor or insignificant observations, testing of wrong variables, and unsystematic combinations of propositions. The teacher can synthesize from the formula meaningful student-centered science learning, provided this formula does not become an end in itself, but rather a vehicle to stimulate exciting individual patterns of observing, relating, and thinking.

This is what the American Association for the Advancement of Science has to say on the subject:

Science is more than a body of facts, a collection of principles, and a set of machines for measurement; it is a structured and directed way of asking and answering questions. It is no mean pedagogical feat to teach a child the facts of science and technology; it is a pedagogical triumph to teach him these facts in their situation to the procedures of scientific inquiry. And the intellectual gain is far greater than the child's ability to conduct a clinical experiment or to discover some of the characteristics of static electricity. The processes of scientific inquiry learned not as a set of rigid rules but as ways of finding answers can be applied without limit. The well-taught child will approach human behavior and social structure and the claims of authority with the same spirit of alert skepticism that he adopts toward scientific theories. It is here that the future citizen who will not become a scientist will learn that science is not memory or magic but rather a disciplined form of human curiosity. From the start the child is an active participant in the scientific tasks. He does, indeed, observe, classify, measure, predict. He has the chance to work as a scientist by carrying out the kinds of tasks which scientists perform.[1]

The Science Curriculum

Developing a unified and meaningful science curriculum is a difficult task. For many reasons, a science curriculum must be "tailor made" to meet the unique challenges of an individual school system.

The most frequently asked question in this development is—What topics do we teach at each grade level? It is generally agreed that there should be some form or sequence to the topics considered in the elementary schools in order to reduce unnecessary duplication of effort. It is im-

[1] American Association for the Advancement of Science, *Science—A Process Approach Description of the Program*, *Part A*, Washington, D.C., 1967.

portant for the fifth-grade teacher to have a good idea of what the fourth-grade teacher covered in science. It is important for the third-grade teacher to be aware of the depth and scope of coverage of science topics in the sixth grade. Furthermore, although our immediate interests are understandably focused on the children in our own school, we cannot, nor can a science curriculum, neglect to deal with the coordination of this curriculum among grades in different schools.

There is general agreement about the subject-matter content distribution in our elementary schools but there is no general agreement about the sequence of topics. It is not realistic to assign specific concepts and topics to specific grades, for our expanding accumulation of scientific knowledge soon makes grade placement for all time out of date. There is no doubt that most topics can be taught at any grade level, so long as the teacher accepts that the degree of understanding will be governed by the maturity of the children in the class. The grade placement of a science topic immediately sets certain limits on the degree and depth of understanding obtainable. In general, it is unreasonable to expect the same depth of understanding from a third-grader involved in an electricity and magnetism unit as you might expect from a sixth-grader. No topic or concept can be considered and really developed at only one level. Understanding must evolve from repeated learning experiences, and therefore there will be a degree of "grade placement" of various science topics in a science curriculum, but these topics should be treated at several different levels, not just one. This then becomes a sequential approach which will provide the degree of continuity desired. It is cautioned that this sequential approach should not prohibit the second- or third-grade youngster from exploring a topic just because it has been placed in a higher level of the program.

There is a great deal to teach. Obviously, attempting to teach every concept and every topic at each level is impossible. In general, the same topics should not be taught in succeeding years. Time must be allowed for experiences outside the school to be related to activities in the classroom, and frequently this time gap should be a year or more. It is tragic to note the number of children that have the same unit on weather during each grade in elementary school. This is unnecessary and certainly one sure way to destroy their interest in science.

The curriculum reformer is eager to supply the teacher with new materials—to get into the classroom and provide teacher training in their proper use. The result of this effort is hopefully an end to rote learning and boredom and the birth of excitement, discovery, and student experimentation. Unfortunately, materials alone will change very little in the classroom. More attention must be accorded the teacher and in particular an understanding of the pressures imposed on the teacher by parents and school administration to get the children to "know" the material prescribed for that grade. These pressures do not make life difficult for the teacher—on the contrary, rote learning and adherence to a strict curriculum schedule, while not exciting for either the children or teacher, do establish a pattern which is easily followed year after year. Breaking into this pattern is the difficult task of the curriculum reformer. The average teacher usually will pose the following question when confronted with a new approach: "Oh, no, do I have to teach the children something new in addition to the regular material we are supposed to cover?" This question is then followed by another such as "What is the new material they are supposed to know?" The average teacher is not ready to "waste" time on new approaches because there is not enough time to cover the required material. Teachers with this attitude, whatever the real cause, will not try new materials enthusiastically. When they do try new materials their attention will always be focused on getting the material completed (making sure the new material is "learned" so they can return to the work which must be covered). People constantly ask "Why don't they teach those kids what they are supposed to know?" "What's all this discovery nonsense?" Certainly, untestable learning—at least untestable by usual testing patterns—such as use of materials for free exploration and discovery "won't help these kids learn to spell, read, multiply, etc.," according to these skeptics.

The curriculum reformer must do more than supply new materials and train teachers in their use. He must also find ways to cope with the dilemma of balancing certain expected standards, imposed on schools by internal as well as external forces, with his new material, which stresses process rather than facts and by its very structure attacks the time-honored mode of teaching and learning. Unless he can effectively meet this challenge, the most resourceful and powerful materials he can produce will end up as nothing but fragments of information parceled out in rote "learning" exercises.

Contemporary Issues

By and large, public schools tend to avoid, skirt, or detour real-life problems and controversial issues involving race relations, alcoholism, drugs, materialism, religion, politics, consumer competency, sex education, population explosion implications, environmental pollution, and marriage and family life. When one eliminates all of these things, there is not much left and school becomes a pretty sterile and atypical place. The "beefing-up" of the curriculum is most often concerned with new science, mathematics, foreign language, English, or other subject programs, but it too often neglects involvement with real-life problems or controversial issues. Any one of them is apt to offend or encroach upon the prerogatives or beliefs of some group, so everyone must be penalized. We desperately need reappraisal of curriculum and inclusion of curricular experiences that represent modern knowledge, and new kinds of opportunities for problem-solving and decision-making in the changing milieu of social, political, and economic life of schools and communities.

Three controversial issues which surely deserve special attention in the latter part of this century are sex education, misuse of drugs, and environmental pollution. Interestingly enough, the solution to the problems associated with each of these issues will require much more than technological "breakthroughs" by scientists and engineers. Each issue will be resolved only if society chooses to make the sociological efforts required. Technology may assist but it will be powerless without the committed "social conscience" of all peoples to meet the challenges offered by these issues.

Sex Education

Parents have the primary responsibility for the education of their children. Ideally the home should be the child's primary source of sex education. In actuality the home has too often not provided adequately even the rudiments of sex education. Many parents have been raised in circumstances in which bodily functions were considered bad or taboo, and have themselves never learned acceptable terms for bodily functions or sex organs. They are often confused and ashamed and reticent to speak of sex in terms which are meaningful. They have not always succeeded in giving children standards of acceptable behavior, or a realization of the role of members of their sex in adult life. Frequently, and for various reasons, there is no effective communication between parents and children. Moreover, there is a significant number of homes deprived of one or both parents by death, divorce, or separation.

The vacuum often left by the parents' absence or abdication of their responsibility leads the child to turn more and more to other sources for sex information. As the pupil progresses through school, his increasing withdrawal from adults fosters his reliance on peers for this information.

The school cannot do the total job. But as an agency that touches the lives of children, it has an obligation to contribute to their preparation for their roles in society. The school's silence here will convey a value judgment. In addition, the school is the only agency that sees every child over a prolonged period of time and is expected to provide values or at least help the pupil develop the ability to make value judgments based on sound information. Furthermore, the school's sequential contact with the child permits the continuance over a long period of time of a process that other agencies deal with only intermittently. Finally, the school can approach sex education without the emotional overlay and personal reference which may be an obstacle in the family setting. Group teaching can permit greater objectivity.

Elementary school children are asking questions, questions about themselves and the people around them. All human beings go through a life cycle. During the early years of development growth changes are rapid. Babies triple their birth weight in the first year of life and by the late teens most youths reach their maximum height. Physical development is rapid and can reasonably be predicted. Physical growth in early adolescence involves tremendous changes in height, weight, body contour, and overall strength. These changes are frequently so rapid that the individual barely becomes accustomed to one stage before another arrives.

Children question the rapid changes that happen to them. They are naturally curious about their personal development and the teacher must be willing to accept the challenge of developing meaningful activities out of this *growth explosion*. The reality of growing cannot be set aside for a health course at a specific time of the classroom day. Growing bodies are a part of every curriculum. To think that this growth and the discussions it generates can be or should be regimented into a unique curriculum capsule is complete nonsense. Curriculum experts in all areas must seek a unified approach to deal with the individual and his physiological development. Proper beginnings in primary, intermediate, and middle school levels will develop the foundations for a free yet realistic approach to sex education.

Drug Abuse

The drug crisis today is one of the most urgent problems in our nation. More and more young adults and children are being victimized by drug abuse. The drug problem is no longer limited to

any one region of the country or to any one segment of society. A short-sighted approach to the problem is to talk only in terms of eliminating the illicit drug supply. What is more urgently needed is a long-range program that will eliminate demand as well.

Today the facts related to the dangers of drug abuse are readily available and they reveal tragic information. The most terrifying truth of all is that the age of introduction to drug use is getting lower in nearly every part of the country. Children are being exposed to drugs at age eleven, twelve, or even younger. Being exposed to drugs may not necessarily mean that they use them. But it does present another "alternative" during the crucial years of adolescence—probably the most mixed-up, shakiest period in a child's existence.

The schools, community agencies, and parents must share in a common effort to inform intermediate school youngsters about the danger of drug misuse or abuse. The form of this effort in the elementary school must include the development of student-oriented units of work on drug abuse, as well as general education of teachers to the seriousness of the problem.

Environmental Pollution

Daily we are being made aware of facts about the seriousness of environmental hazards which have resulted from man's neglect of his natural surroundings. The magnitude of this problem has made it difficult for individuals to think that they can cope with it in any meaningful fashion. It is almost too big and in a sense too remote for one man to seriously consider. It certainly is paradoxical that twentieth-century man should be reaching for the planets, or even the stars, while he is standing in polluted water and breathing a poisoned atmosphere.

The seriousness of environmental pollution dictates that causes rather than symptoms must be treated. This implies doing more than making the present adult population aware of the problem. It means educating today's school children, who will be the adult population of the future. It means developing the social conscience of these young children with regard to the present environmental crisis and to the consequences of continued neglect.

Textbooks

Science is a *doing activity.* It is not static. Current textbooks for science are attempting to present science as a doing activity, but for the most part they are not fully achieving this goal. The real problem with a textbook is that it does a magnificent job of *departmentalizing* learning. Dr. Elizabeth Wood, an eminent crystallographer, has this to say about science textbooks: "They

should be written like murder mysteries—instead they are written in quite the reverse manner. In most textbooks you are told who committed the murder on page one and then for two-hundred pages thereafter you are told how it was done." It is no wonder that the majority of these texts fall short of their objectives.

The textbook "partitions" the learning experiences for easier consumption by the learner. This approach—namely, dividing difficult phenomena into sections and investigating these sections on a less complex scale, has been used in all areas of human endeavor with great success. The important point is, Do we as teachers partition our teaching in ways similar to the presentations in textbooks? Possibly more effort should be exerted toward unifying what we learn and do in science classes with what is going on, for example, in social studies investigations. The use of "partitioned material"—textbooks—should be broadened. Is it unrealistic to consider the possibility of using a science textbook as "the" textbook for a social studies class? We think not. Maybe textbook publishers would do us a favor by *not* titling science textbooks as such with the result that these books would have the chance of becoming active agents in improving student understanding of arithmetic, history, and English.

Social change, national and international conflicts, disease, class struggles, military supremacy, and political power have always had a tremendous impact on our acquisition of scientific knowledge. In our attempts to better perceive nature and society as they really are, the teacher of science must constantly demonstrate his awareness of this impact by his actions in the classroom.

The increased desire of school districts to plan their own programs, coupled with moderate gains in teacher ability and desire to teach science, has reduced complete dependency on the use of conventional science textbook series. However effective the text material, the sole use of a text can force a structured program that limits the scope of topics in the science curriculum. Increasing numbers of schools and school districts are organizing their science programs without science textbooks and are investing their budgets in equipment and library materials which accommodate the versatility and individualization of their curricula [Non-basal, Multi-level Reading materials]. Totally new activities must be developed where the nature of the activity and the equipment utilized will permit full physical involvement of all students. Increased imagination of authors and publishers to provide other than conventional textbook material will be required to maintain and increase effectiveness in elementary science education.[2]

Inquiry, Observation, and Laboratory Experience

There is much being said about the *inquiry* or *discovery* method of science teaching. It is refreshing to note that this method is receiving such concentrated attention, although the implications resulting from this attention are rather disturbing. One implication is that science has suddenly changed from whatever it used to be to a discovery or inquiry kind of activity, and because of this change, we in the schools had better present science in the new form it has now assumed! The

[2] Paul F. Ploutz, "Trends in Elementary School Science," *Science and Children Magazine,* National Science Teachers Association, Washington, D.C., February 1965.

basic methods have not changed—individual discovery and inquiry have always been fundamental to science. This approach is new to the teaching of science in our schools, not to the scientists in their laboratories! It is fortunate that we are now attempting to teach in our schools the way science has always been, not the way it seems to have just suddenly become.

The teaching of science requires more understanding on the part of the teacher as to how children learn than dedication to the notion that a given number of facts and concepts must be mastered. This is not to say that facts and concepts are unimportant, but the methods and procedures followed in acquiring the beginnings of early understanding are more important.

Science education cannot assume, as it has up until now, that elementary school children have developed the beginnings of adult understanding and require only concentrated exposure to fundamental laws as embodied in current science curricula. Most elementary children, as well as many adults, do not have the ability to organize the understanding that they have arrived at from the raw materials of experience. This ability is not acquired through the memorization of many related or unrelated facts about nature. Nor is it acquired through science curricula that merely list

basic concepts the teacher is expected to convey at specific grade levels and that children are supposed to assimilate by some magical means.

In all child-oriented classroom activities the ingredients must be *equipment for each youngster, the statement of a problem to which individual responses and solutions are desired, and a patient yet competent teacher.* Within this structure new questions will arise, leading to further explorations and experiences from which other questions will be formed. *The laboratory should not be considered merely as the place where questions are answered, but rather as the place where most of the time questions are shaped.*

Contrary to common belief it is more difficult to teach a class in which equipment and materials are in abundance than one where materials are in short supply. In the latter case class control is relatively easy. All children see the same demonstrations. All react at the same time. All are simultaneously reacting to the same teacher questions. In a situation where materials are plentiful and children are permitted time to manipulate equipment independently, class control is much more difficult. All children now see the results of their own explorations. Each child now is free to react differently because of his individual ability to use the equipment. Responses are not simultaneous or in unison, the class noise level is greater, and class control obviously presents a special challenge, but the rewards are great. It is in this kind of classroom atmosphere that the child can experience the excitement of learning.

Children should be placed in situations which

require them to make decisions. Some of these decisions may or may not be meaningful. Is it important that all decisions be good or meaningful? Cannot the process of merely making a decision have a beneficial outcome? A child's ability to make decisions depends on his reaction to his present situation and his ability to organize meaning out of raw experience. This ability will improve when the child is allowed to practice making decisions based on raw experience.

Individual achievement or success should not be measured solely by how many "right answers" a youngster may write down, but by how he develops as an observer. Observational skill is not gained merely by telling a youngster he should become a better observer. It can be acquired only through situations where the student is given the opportunity to practice the art of individual inquiry and individual thinking.

Youngsters will improve their ability to think, relate, and observe if given time to practice thinking, relating, and observing.

Reading Problems?

How often have you heard the statement "Those kids can't do that—they can't read"? It seems that in classes where the general reading level is below grade level many activities and experiences are put aside until "we get them up to reading level." The attitude revealed by this statement appears to be related to the idea that the classroom day must be subdivided into special packages of time: a time for science, a time for

history, a time for spelling, a time for reading, a time for arithmetic.

Students who are reading at a low level and whose school day is fragmented into pieces of subject matter usually cannot relate learning experiences that have similar elements. How about using science as a vehicle to motivate youngsters to want to read, spell, multiply, and verbalize? Cannot reading, spelling, and mathematical skills be integral parts of science experiences? To improve reading is it always necessary to start with a reading book?

The poor reader—who is frequently the slow student—can deal with concepts and ideas. He can be motivated to be curious and enthusiastic and to develop a free questioning attitude. Science represents an avenue through which the stigma of "poor reader" may be overcome provided the school is willing to devote the time and patience to stimulate these children in other methods of individual achievement.

Can the goal of grade-level literacy be achieved by all students? Is this, in fact, ever a reasonable objective for all students? Possibly the high priority assigned and the subsequent energy devoted to reading problems might be better directed to a concern for overall education rather than just literacy. A child unable to develop efficiency in reading might be better served if he is instructed and educated by some other tool. A student unable to develop certain reading skills may have other talents which can be developed. Because a child is unable to read it does not mean he is unable to think and develop other talents and skills. The handicapped reader can experience success from the imaginative development of a science curriculum that finds ways of utilizing a multimedia, experience-oriented approach.

Have we placed too much emphasis on reading? Because of this emphasis are we insisting that before a student can achieve success in school he must develop literacy? We are willing to accept the idea of a normal distribution in other talents such as music, art, mathematics, etc., but unwilling to accept this idea for the area of reading skill. Certainly, we must make every effort to teach each child to read, but if unsuccessful we must be

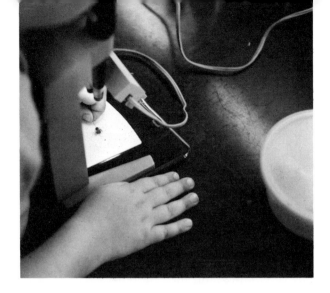

prepared to educate the child by some other means.

There are individual differences among children—individual differences in their ability to master various skills—and until we do more than pay lip service to this concept and develop alternative educational procedures, we will have done nothing more than make a mockery of the idea of equal education for all children and we will continue to fail children just because they are different from one another.

Academically Unsuccessful Children

The focal point of any curriculum is its ultimate effect on the development of the individual. A curriculum must be developed and implemented in a manner such that each individual can actively participate and identify his role in the successful completion of a classroom experience. It must be broad enough to span the entire student-ability spectrum yet personalized enough to permit children to understand their individual roles in its successful accomplishment. Present trends in curriculum development place greater emphasis on student involvement with materials. Children exposed to this emphasis may not react as expected or with enthusiasm. Most curriculums seem to be developed for the middle- and upper-middle-class child. The lower-class child from disadvantaged environments is frequently considered a risk—*a risk in the sense that he cannot be trusted to manipulate and/or care for equipment in an "acceptable" manner.* These are usually children that read well below grade level, are be-

havioral problems, and are difficult to interest in conventional activities.

Strict discipline has been the conventional way of handling the problems unique to these children. Certainly, freedom of physical activity and independent use of classroom materials have usually been considered unsatisfactory practices. Basically, children react in accordance with the methods employed during their early development. Teachers are quick to stereotype children. Once a youngster has established a "reputation," it is extremely difficult to change it or the effect it will have on other teachers. Therefore, a troublesome, uncooperative child (earlier labeled a "risk") remains as such in the eyes of most teachers. If he is given the opportunity to manipulate equipment, and subsequently breaks it, teachers usually respond, "I told you so, he just can't be trusted." Their predictions were not unfounded and there is general self-approval of their keen insight in judging children.

What did they expect? Such teachers get back exactly what their teaching methods produce: a youngster incapable of dealing constructively with materials because he has never been given the opportunity to practice using materials or equipment. Children are quick to know what behavioral patterns are expected of them. They are adept at discerning the teacher's feeling of their "place" in the structure of the class and usually respond accordingly.

Considerable attention is currently focused on the disadvantaged child. What curriculum materials should be used? Disadvantaged youngsters do not need a different substance for their education. They can learn concepts, manipulate materials and equipment, formulate ideas, and express opinions. They can be enthusiastic, curious, and practice creative thinking. All of the worthwhile student-centered activities of any learning situation can be just as real and meaningful to disadvantaged youngsters as they are to any other youngsters. *The substance need not be different but the approach must be different.* These youngsters need a great deal more encouragement, direct experience, and experience with success. Progress is slower and teacher patience must be unlimited.

Perhaps the term "disadvantaged" is not the best descriptive term and should be replaced by "academically unsuccessful." There are many classifications. No matter what the classification by different investigators, the one shared characteristic of all groups is lack of success in school activities. Recent research leads to new assumptions about these students and their role in the learning situation. The most important of all these assumptions is that everyone can learn, provided he is given the opportunity to develop confidence and self-respect.

Too many people in our educational system still operate on the premise that a child who is "different"—the disadvantaged—the youngster with interests and background unlike his peers—really can't learn very well or very much and furthermore it doesn't really matter whether he does or not. The data "locked up" in the educational literature cannot solve the problems of educating the disadvantaged. It is what is in the heads and hearts of educational personnel that can. The challenge is to train enough school people with the kinds of attitudes that can make a difference.

Nerve—Failure—Right Answers

The following true story about a fourth-grade class should stimulate some thoughtful consideration about the nature of our teaching methods and the school systems charged with this overwhelming responsibility.

A particular fourth-grade class was just starting the first lesson of a *Balancing Blocks Unit*.[3]

[3] John McGavack Jr. and Donald P. LaSalle, *Guppies, Bubbles, and Vibrating Objects* (New York, The John Day Company, 1969).

In this unit, each youngster is given a board two feet long, a fulcrum, and eight small blocks. Essentially, what each student does for approximately six weeks is to manipulate the blocks in different positions, while at the same time keeping the board balanced on the fulcrum. Raw experience is accumulated and in time the student tries to generalize from this raw experience, developing some qualitative and/or quantitative rule about the *balancing situation*. In this particular class the first lesson of the unit was just starting. The lesson sheet asks each youngster, "Can you balance the board on the fulcrum?"

All students except one successfully balanced the board on the fulcrum in several ways. This particular student had tried *once*, failed, and would not try again. The classroom teacher urged him to try again but he would not. During the teacher's conversations with this youngster, another boy walked over, abruptly picked up the board, quickly balanced it on the fulcrum, and disgustedly said, "*There, you dope, that's how you do it.*" This abrupt interjection apparently motivated the reluctant youngster to become actively engaged in the balancing activity, for he ultimately did very well in the unit. It was later learned that this boy was brilliant. The interesting point is that this youngster did not have the *nerve to fail.* In this classroom he had always been the *academic leader.* He had always gotten the *right answer.* He had seldom failed, and hence he did not have the "nerve to fail." As it turned out, his contemporary who offered him assistance was not labeled a bright student. He was accustomed to failure and consequently he did have the *nerve to fail.*

Do teachers have the *nerve to fail?* Do school systems have the *nerve to fail?* Are schoolteachers and hence the systems they represent apprehensive of change or new situations because they do not have this *nerve to fail?* Have external and internal pressures caused school systems to lose their *nerve to fail?* Have they abdicated this right to failure—because of community pressure, or because of the lack of imaginative and daring leadership at all levels? The truly great intellectuals and leaders of all ages have been able to cope with failure. Certainly the scientist in his laboratory,

28

the mathematician seeking new numerical patterns, or the historian piecing together fragments of events in years past all must have had *nerve to fail.* Thomas Edison is reputed to have tried at least one thousand different substances in his attempt to develop a filament for the first incandescent light bulb. An associate remarked that it was a pity they wasted so much time on materials that had failed, to which Edison replied, *"Nonsense, we didn't fail—instead we now know one thousand substances that won't work."* In the story about the youngster balancing the board, the sterile conditioning process of his previous school years had shaped a personality whose major concern was for *right answers* or *teacher approval.* Little time had been devoted to *experimenting in learning.*

Evaluation

Evaluation is an important part of the teaching procedure. Teachers must give more than casual concern to current testing techniques. In any curriculum, evaluation cannot be ignored. It does little good to design imaginative curriculum materials and to educate teachers in their productive use if classroom evaluation procedures virtually undermine the objectives and aims of the new curriculum programs. There is no point in talking about the acquisition of certain skills, and developing exciting approaches directed at learning the "process of science," if our examinations make no effort to deal with these objectives but instead insist on the regurgitation of detailed information upon command.

Teachers must concern themselves with the difficult task of writing evaluative questions which measure the aims and objectives of a curriculum. In a very real sense it makes little difference who writes the textbooks or educates the teachers, for in the final analysis those who control the evaluation procedures largely control the curriculum content. This is why it has become increasingly important for classroom teachers to place emphasis on a long-neglected area. Considerable time and energy must be devoted to learning how properly to construct test questions which adequately measure the aims and objectives of a curriculum. We must recognize that the material to be tested goes far beyond the routine memorization of facts. A new perspective is needed to permit the teacher to span the unimaginative chasm of most testing procedures and develop the willingness to experiment with the testing of "process and attitudes."

A few general questions about evaluation require consideration.

1. Can progress be evaluated without the use of a formalized written measuring instrument?
2. Can content and process be measured simultaneously? Can they be measured independently?
3. Are content and concept evaluations similar?
4. To what degree does form (organization) affect the ultimate results of evaluation?
5. How does past experience affect our approach to the evaluation process?
6. Is evaluation motivated largely by parental and/or school administration pressures?
7. Is evaluation a necessary final activity for all learning processes?

Every day as individuals we classify and evaluate "conditions" of our environment. We offer sweeping evaluations of our neighbors and business or social contacts. Frequently we hear statements such as "Jim is a good man"; "Oh, yes, he is a very responsible lad"; "He is a very successful businessman"; "She sews beautifully"; "A very competent person." The bases for remarks of this sort do not always stem from a large amount of personal "raw experience." Nevertheless they are the result of some experience and certainly support our willingness to accept "raw experience" as the foundation for evaluation. The classroom and its children form a "unique set" from which we daily collect and classify raw experience, which we knowingly or unknowingly evaluate without the use of a formalized written evaluative procedure!

It is possible to consider evaluation for content the simplest of all evaluative procedures. Evaluation for content does not always imply understanding of content. When understanding and content are linked together in one evaluative device, the evaluation procedure immediately becomes much more complex to devise. The strictly content-oriented evaluative device encountered in many classrooms today requires only the recall of certain memorized facts. The following is an example of this kind of "test":

1. Light travels in straight lines. True or False?
2. The closer one is to a light source the greater is the observed intensity. True or False?
3. What happens to light when it passes through a prism?
4. White light is composed of what basic colors?
5. What great scientist first observed the colors in white light?
6. Material which does not permit white light to pass through it is called _____.
7. Name some materials that are translucent.
8. How fast does light travel in a vacuum?
9. Can light travel faster in a substance than in a vacuum?
10. When light passes through a lens or a glass of water the light is "bent" and objects observed through the lens or water appear larger. True or False?

This test could be rewritten in the following form, in which understanding and content are more evenly balanced:

1. Below is a picture of a light source and a pencil. Draw the position of the shadow cast by the pencil.

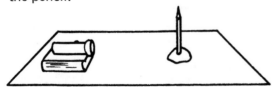

2. In which direction would you move the pencil to produce the darkest shadow?
3. In what position in the diagram must you be to observe red light? A, B, C, D, or E?

4. Glass plates are placed between a light source and an observer. Which graph best represents how the intensity of observed light changes as the number of glass plates added is increased? A, B, C, or D?

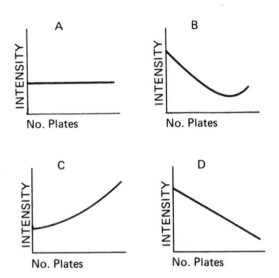

5. A light signal must be flashed over a distance of one mile. The person sending the signal has a choice of four paths to select in sending the signal. Over which path will the signal travel the fastest and arrive at the destination first? A, B, C, or D?

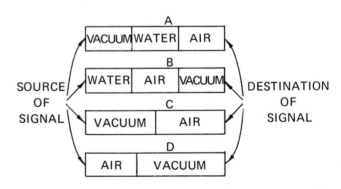

30

6. A magnifying glass (or lens) bends the light so that objects viewed appear to be larger. Which kind of lens bends the light more and hence makes objects appear even larger? (a) a thick lens or (b) a thin lens?

7. Sir Isaac Newton, using a prism, discovered that white light is composed of several different colors—red, green, blue, etc. After white light has been separated into its various colors is it possible to recombine these colors and make white light again?

Evaluation of any kind should lead to the formulation of searching questions which ultimately will provide considerable student-centered participation and stimulation. The evaluative procedure then becomes more of a class activity than a competitive exercise in which all that matters is checking the *right answer.*

Content and concepts can be measured simultaneously. It is preferable to design situations where they are considered together. In most classrooms, though, it is probable that content is measured independent of concept understanding.

Process need not be linked to content. The process employed by an intermediate-school youngster in classifying rock samples according to size, shape, or color is a result of independent action motivated by past experience or present impulse. The scheme or pattern developed is an indication of an *individualized process*, which the teacher wants to observe, encourage, and develop. *Process is not so much taught as it is learned.* Process implies confrontation—confrontation with situations which permit the practice and development of a youngster's ability to make raw experience meaningful.

Ideally, the most efficient as well as the most difficult evaluative device to develop is one in which there is a delicate balance between content, concepts, and process. Each one can be considered independently. It is the blend of all three which most school systems proclaim as their ultimate goal in the preparation of an "educated individual." Putting into classroom practice this blending of content, concepts, and process is a difficult task. Teachers with the *nerve* to practice this blending—realizing that *mistakes* are inevi-

table—will accept the responsibility of shaping the patterns of meaningful learning experiences for all youngsters in the educational establishment.

The routine mechanics of administering and organizing the form of an evaluative procedure requires more than casual concern. Evaluations should not be so crowded with directions and/or instructions as to cloud the objectives of the evaluative device. Certainly you have often heard the remark "It's good to practice learning how to take a test," or "One must get accustomed to the testing situation." Remarks of this sort seem to imply that it's the "testing situation" which is of greatest concern, not the content, concepts, and processes the test is designed to evaluate. Organizing an evaluative device in a simple straightforward manner and creating a relaxed classroom atmosphere will place more emphasis on the content, concepts, and processes in the test and less on the pressure of the "testing situation." The evaluative or testing situation need not be a pressure-packed traumatic period of the school day. Usually it is the teacher's organization of the evaluative device and the manner in which it is made a part of the daily classroom program which creates the fear, anxiety, or apprehension in the minds of youngsters. How often have classroom teachers offered the following response to an unattentive class: *"You better listen because I am going to test you on this next week"*? The evaluative device becomes the *club* that is used to motivate learning. The teacher who uses this procedure reinforces personal fears and fosters anxieties and apprehensions about the testing situation. Possibly the frequent use of the club will result in youngsters' becoming immune to its threat and the associated tensions. In either approach the true value of an evaluative procedure is completely destroyed. To be sure, questions are asked and questions are answered, but certainly very few new questions are shaped from such procedures.

Individuals generally react to situations in terms of their accumulated past experience. The teacher's past experience with evaluative procedures tends to shape present approaches to evaluation. College students preparing to be teachers are frequently confronted with the dilemma of reconciling how the professor actually handles the evaluative procedure in his own classes with how he says it should be considered in the elementary or high school situation. The old cliché "Do as I say, not as I do" frequently appears to be true. Past experience can be modified by present experience, but once a mold has been created from previous experiences, for some teachers the present is no longer powerful enough to effect any change.

To what degree do pressures external to the classroom motivate formal evaluation? Parental pressures regarding evaluation are a reality, but the degree of general parental concern varies among school districts. Rules for dealing with specific situations are impossible to devise. The teacher's evaluation of a child's progress ultimately must be a judgment decision. This judgment decision is substantiated by a collection of quantitative and qualitative information. For the beginning teacher the assignment of grades is one of the most trying experiences. There are many doubts—the adequacy of tests, the level and extent of emphasis in certain classroom work, the number of formalized evaluative periods, and more. The beginning teacher is inclined to be introspective in struggling with his first assignment of grades. The more experienced teacher seems to have fewer problems with the grading situation. Indeed, this is a result of more experience in collecting evaluative data and using it to carefully meet the grading situation. The more experienced teacher does run the risk of being less introspective about his procedures than the beginning teacher. Concern motivated by introspection must not be overlooked. Perhaps a beneficial result of parental concern about grades may be the rebirth of an introspective attitude.

Earlier it was stated that "evaluation is a necessary part of the teaching procedure" and that "teachers must give more than casual concern to current testing techniques." This is true, yet should all teaching procedure be followed by an evaluation? In fact, might not one of the testing techniques be no test, no evaluation? In many respects teachers attempt to overevaluate or to insure that most classroom situations are ones which easily lend themselves to some form of student progress evaluation. Does a particular science unit always have to end with an evaluation? In a sense, must we always "tie in the loose ends"— summarize the results? Why not let some of the loose ends dangle? Some activities may be good intrinsically. Are conclusions always necessary?

Probably the most important feature of a particular science experience is the change it produces in the children who have participated. These changes, other than straight knowledge of content, are in the category of new skills and attitudes. For example: Is curiosity stimulated? Are more questions asked? Can predictions be made? Is attitude more critical? Can new tests be designed? How is information correlated? Any effective evaluation must seriously consider these questions.

Conclusions, evaluations, or summaries should not always be thought of as the necessary final activity for all learning experiences.

Many teachers are reluctant to let pupils draw their own learnings from an experience. Instead, they feel they should summarize at the end of a period what has happened and what they intended the children to learn. This unfortunate tendency is so common among teachers that it has been given a name, lysiphobia—the fear of leaving "loose ends." Besides forcing on the children conclusions they are not capable of assimilating, this tying-up things in a neat package cuts off the gradual growth in understanding which comes when the children try out their glimmerings of new ideas or other experiences at school and at home. In fact, it is probably worthwhile to do the contrary, to stir up any conclusions the children have reached by reminding them of the incompleteness of their understanding—of unanswered questions or of ambiguous interpretations.[4]

Teachers attempting to teach science in the elementary school by the process approach or the laboratory method often ask the same question: "How can we evaluate the students' progress if some investigations are open-ended and we cannot insist on right answers?" Perhaps we should not be so concerned with right answers but rather with the interest, motivation, and outright zeal with which a youngster will attack a problem when he is allowed to draw conclusions based upon his own observations. The alert teacher can probably evaluate a student's progress more realistically by simply watching closely the way in which the child operates under these new conditions. It is not necessary to always have something concrete in the form of an objective evaluation.

The authors caution the teacher who is self-sufficient and in a "private world," apart from reality, when the door to the classroom is closed and the four walls form the physical boundaries for the learning experience. Objectivity is important. Teachers must regularly make an inventory of skills mastered. The community rightfully insists on performance and the present trend of increasing involvement by community people in the school will no longer permit the teacher to be the only judge of student performance. The teacher must work increasingly harder at developing better techniques for both objectively and subjectively measuring the progress of students.

In the final analysis, no one has ever discovered an infallible method of measuring the really important outcomes of a science program. Mere knowledge of content and facts that can be re-

gurgitated on a written quiz is of relatively small value. The most important outcomes are the attitudes that students develop, the skills they gain, and the ability to operate and function satisfactorily under a set of different circumstances while using these same acquired skills and attitudes.

Evaluating a science program's effectiveness is very subjective and depends primarily on one's personal judgment. However, there are many subtle but significant signposts to look for. One might be the level of general interest, discussed earlier in this section. Another might be the number of pupils that volunteered for additional activities. How many youngsters carried on further experimentation at home or after school? How many slow readers turned to books for additional information? How much noticeable improvement has there been in the quality of work accomplished by individual students?

Do not attempt to judge or evaluate all students by the same criteria. Accept the individual differences of the students in the class and look for evidence of increased interest, effort, growth, and achievement.

Leave the pupils mainly to their own spontaneous self-activities. The teacher may awaken and give direction to their curiosity by an occasional adroit question; but he

[4] Robert Karplus, *Elementary Science Study Newsletter*, October, 1965.

33

should chiefly rely upon the action of his pupils' own powers for the discovery of new facts. As a general rule, nothing should be told to pupils which they can discover for themselves. The zealous and impatient teacher will often fail here, and the failure will be a serious and fatal one.

It is so much easier to tell a child what we wish him to know, rather than wait for him to discover it for himself, that the inexperienced and careless can rarely resist the temptation but the babbling teacher will assuredly learn, in the long run, the truth of the maxim "The more haste, the worse speed."[5]

Maybe the message here is that we should "teach" less, evaluate carefully, and allow the children to learn more.

The Classroom

Classroom facilities and designs for teaching elementary school science vary greatly among school systems. With the present trend to include

[5] 26th Annual Report by the Superintendent of Public Instruction of the State of Michigan—for the year, believe it or not, of *1862.*

science as a major segment of the elementary school curriculum many schools have developed modern science rooms for this phase of the curriculum. Where these facilities are present they are usually found at the intermediate or the middle school level.

Most school systems are in the position of having to incorporate new science curricula within existing classroom space. Unfortunately, classroom design did not anticipate the degree of independent student involvement, with large amounts of material, now current in the new science curricula.

In general, schools have discovered that classroom size, limited storage facilities, and fixed classroom furniture now inhibit their progress in implementing new science curricula. To some degree it is difficult to understand how school planning (curriculum and building) permitted such a situation to develop. Schools have always maintained their interest in student involvement as well as independent and personalized development, yet fixed furniture and inadequate storage space seriously restrict attainment of these goals.

Each elementary school classroom should have certain basic services available. These services are water, electricity, and bottled gas. Student desks (preferably tables) should be flat and not permanently fixed in the room. Peripheral counters, with storage space below, and large cabinets are needed for storage and work areas. These are the basic ingredients necessary in planning any classroom, not one in which the emphasis is only on science. There are many ways to incorporate these services and facilities into a classroom scheme which will permit flexible and imaginative teaching.

Lacking any portion or all of these basic requirements does not prohibit successful teaching, but it does place a much greater burden on the classroom teacher.

With greater emphasis in science teaching on the independent use of materials by each child, the most important features of a classroom must be its storage facilities and numerous flat work surfaces available for independent activities. Usually any room can be modified to permit greater storage and an increased amount of flat work surface area. The special room facilities—for example, special student desks and elaborate demonstration tables—can be very expensive and in large measure quite wasteful.

The elementary school classroom should be viewed as the place where learning can proceed realistically. The realism of our world and its *people-to-people* interaction is a culture in which technology, science, and the humanities coexist. Why not this same coexistence in our elementary school classrooms? Is it unrealistic to have a classroom design which with its simplicity and flexibility does permit as well as encourage coexistence of technology, science, and the humanities? Do specialized rooms further the child's understanding and appreciation of the necessary links among these three areas? The elementary school classroom needs to be specialized only to the extent that it provides for *the specialization* to be learning itself—learning in an atmosphere which combines experiences from technology, science, and the humanities. The elementary school which provides separate rooms for each specialized activity will find it very difficult to implement such combined learning experiences. Certainly the complete absence of specialized facilities is as unreasonable as the presence of only specialized facilities. A balance between the two extremes is necessary.

Classrooms possessing the basic services (adequate storage and flat surface work areas) are ideally suited for all teaching. Science is not the only subject undergoing rapid changes in the classroom method of teaching. This is true in English, reading, mathematics, social studies, and foreign languages. The emphasis is on greater independent use of numerous materials. More lasting results may be obtained by making these materials available in all rooms rather than available only in a series of specialized rooms.

The present trend toward ungraded schools places greater emphasis on the development of the individual child. Since the administrative structure of such a school needs to be flexible, large numbers of specialized classrooms would interfere with this desired flexibility. What we need in classroom design, school building planning, and curriculum development is less specialization in

specific areas and greater specialization in our efforts to unify all learning experiences. The units described in this book lend themselves well to the ungraded school because they are composed of lessons in which students can progress at their own rate of speed.

Concerning Science Equipment

When children are placed in a science environment and are given the proper materials and direction, they can discover for themselves many of the fundamental concepts and principles which constitute the scientific process. This is science teaching by the inductive or laboratory method. It is one in which the child learns science in much the same manner that a scientist does, by actually doing.

Professor Jerome S. Bruner of Harvard cautions against arbitrary elimination of any scientific subject on the ground that it is unsuited to the elementary grades. In his book *The Process of Education* he says, "*Any subject can be taught effectively in some intellectually honest form to any child at any stage of development.*" His view is supported by Dr. Barbel Inhelder of the Rousseau Institute in Geneva, who on the basis of current experience with the learning process of children believes that basic notions in subjects such as physics are perfectly within the grasp of children of seven to ten years of age, provided that they are separated from mathematical expressions and studied through materials that the child can handle himself.

This in turn implies that at least in principle every student in a class should have his own equipment with which to work and experiment.

It is generally agreed that science in the elementary school should be based upon experience a child can gain by actively exploring with his senses. Obviously, then, equipment which a youngster can operate with his own hands is of prime importance.

Often science courses devote too much time in the laboratory absorbed in getting a right answer in the right blank on the right line—an answer that must agree with the one in the teacher's manual, all of which gives the student a false impression of the scientific endeavor. What we need are some experiments that have unexpected answers so the student will have an opportunity to develop some confidence in his own efforts and learn to account for his errors.

Max Planck, sometimes called the father of modern physics, when asked to name what he thought was the best laboratory manual, answered, "One hundred pages of blank paper." This is the spirit of the new laboratory approach where the student is given an opportunity to think, to organize his own ideas and to evaluate his findings in the light of known theory or thorough application. He will learn that the so-called conclusions only establish a basis for inquiry and as a mode of thinking provides the best means so far discovered to enable young people to participate in both the world of today and the world of tomorrow.[6]

The units in this book are built around relatively simple materials. Many of the supplies

[6] Paul De Hart Hurd, *Science Teaching for a Changing World*, Scott, Foresman, February, 1965.

needed are available in supermarkets, dime stores, and hardware establishments at modest prices. Another place that may prove to be a great resource for teachers in gathering the necessary materials in sufficient quantities is the Federal Surplus Warehouses, which are located in each state. This agency permits educational and eleemosynary institutions to buy large amounts of valuable and useful materials at extremely low cost. In addition, those curriculum development organizations that seem to be enjoying the most success have concentrated upon the wide use of simple and abundant materials. Commercial companies have also attempted to make large quantities of simple science apparatus marketable in economy packages. No longer, then, is it valid to exclude science from the elementary curriculum by complaining that equipment costs are prohibitive. The present emphasis on the use of equipment in the teaching of elementary school science assures the development of a wider choice of materials—games, puzzles, records, tapes, and single-concept film loops.

More significantly, the trend toward individualization of instruction and the need for classroom sets of certain items is causing: (1) simplification of present apparatus,

(2) cost reduction of expensive items, and (3) creation of new apparatus of simple design. An example of a significant breakthrough was the development of simple microscopes which could be made available to large numbers of students at a very low cost. Hopefully, suitable planetaria, or aquaria, transformers, meters, motors, and numerous other items, will experience the same cost reduction. The expanded NDEA funds and other federal assistance are also reducing financial difficulty for school districts in purchasing equipment, library books, and related material.[7]

There is still another approach to solving the problem of equipment. Recently there has been a trend toward the development of science kits.

Today, as never before, there is a national concern to discover and develop abilities in science. In the elementary and secondary schools, there is a movement toward a sequential instructional program which would involve the offering of a laboratory science each year from kindergarten to high school graduation. But in some schools teachers are still handicapped by restricted space, inadequate facilities and equipment, short class periods and heavy work loads. Many have turned to science kits as a partial solution of their problems and are using them for such diverse purposes as demonstration, loans to pupils for their experimentation, aids to TV teaching, or for special projects such as science fairs and clubs. For some schools, the kit is the laboratory. A wide variety of kits for most science subjects at every grade level is available from commercial suppliers. The selection of kits presents special problems to teachers and school administrators who must judge their suitability for the school program.[8]

[7] Paul F. Ploutz, "Trends in Elementary Science Education," *Science and Children Magazine,* National Science Teachers Association, Washington, D.C., February 1965.

[8] Albert Piltz and William Gruver, *Science Equipment and Materials; Science Kits*, Office of Education, Publication #29049.

Science kits in themselves are no panacea for all the problems involving school science equipment. Although packaged kits of many types are available for all grade levels and can prove very effective if utilized properly, their acceptance is by no means unanimous, nor should it go completely unchallenged. For every proponent of science kits there is probably at least one dissenter. The critics of kits say that they may be of limited use, or unsuited to the school science program. Occasionally, the names assigned to some kits can be misleading. They may consist of mere collections of unrelated scientific novelties which contribute little to the understanding of basic concepts. The instruction manuals which accompany them may encourage "cookbook science" rather than promoting any interest in discovery. Sometimes the cost of a kit is higher than the total cost of the individual component parts, while replacement of parts may be a further problem, since some kits are rendered useless if certain key pieces are lost or broken. Often the quality of their construction may not measure up to standards for science equipment and the teacher and class may waste valuable time in the routine of re-sorting items after use.

On the other hand, the proponents of science kits claim that where science facilities are limited, kits make possible greater student participation in laboratory-type activities. They provide for mak-

ing needed materials readily available in conveniently packaged form for teachers who generally have little time or training to prepare science demonstrations. Additionally, where storage space is at a premium, the compactness of kits is an asset. They can also provide an economical source of supplementary science material along with accessories at less cost than the same items purchased separately. On occasion, the wide use of kits may help the differing needs of pupils in the same class. Out of class, they can be used for data collecting by students during weekends and holidays. Interest in science may be stimulated by the use of kits and a poorly motivated student may become interested in experimenting by manipulation and assembling of materials in an investigation.

These two divergent views about science kits and their possible use in class are probably due to the vast differences to be found in the kits themselves. The kits vary widely in the range of their contents and their quality, value, aims, and degree of sophistication and adaptation to the rapidly changing demands of the science curriculum. The selection of kits is important and should be given careful consideration. The authors favor the wide use of simple materials, abundant and easily available locally.

Whatever a school's final decision is, if it results in more opportunities for the students to discover for themselves something about science, then the decision has been a wise one.

Nongraded Classes and Science

The organization of nongraded classes as a way of promoting individual child progress in school has been given considerable attention in recent years. A nongraded program in its simplest form is an administrative plan which removes rigid grade lines and divides the curriculum into a series of learning levels. The program is generally designed with children's growth and learning characteristics in mind. It is the consensus among educators that each child grows and learns at an individual rate and should be permitted to progress at his own rate of speed. Unfortunately, many schools have constructed a curriculum so rigid

that they delimit a student's progress in trying to make him conform to established and inflexible time schedules. Thus, questions such as how much time should be allocated for each subject area and what time of day shall it be given become more important than what is actually being taught.

In a nongraded curriculum an attempt is made to gear the instruction to the individual child according to his special needs and abilities. Children who learn at a more rapid rate are enabled to progress faster through the curriculum. Those who need a longer period of time to complete the curriculum are able to accomplish this without repeating any block of material. Dr. Robert T. Linstone, an authority in the field of nongraded education, states, "We learn primarily by our mistakes for it is difficult to tell if anything is wrong by analyzing only our successes."

In summary, a nongraded program is one which is geared to individual differences as closely as possible and where each child has an opportunity for continuous progress. "Failure" in the normal sense of the word does not exist in this type of program. Instead, a youngster realizes that learning from his mistakes and "failures" is a part of the total learning process.

Perhaps the following section, from Jack London's famous sea story *Martin Eden*, describes it more clearly from a different perspective.

Knowledge seems to me like a chart-room. . . . The part played by teachers is to teach the student the contents of the chart-room in a systematic way. The teachers are guides to the chart-room, that's all. It's not something that they have in their own heads. They don't make it up, don't create it. It's all in the chart-room and they know their way about in it, and it's their business to show the place to strangers who might else get lost.

Some persons need guides, most persons do; but I think I can get along without them. I've spent a lot of time in the chart-room now, and I'm on the edge of knowing my way about, what charts I want to refer to, what coasts I want to explore, and from the way I line it up, I'll explore a whole lot more quickly by myself. The speed of a fleet, you know, is the speed of the slowest ship, and the speed of the teacher is affected the same way. They can't go any faster than the ruck of their scholars, and I can set a faster pace for myself than they set for a whole school-room.

Jerrold R. Zacharias of M.I.T. has put it still another way:

There is an approach to education that treats it primarily as a kind of substance, as so much intellectual content, which is first in the teacher's head and then transmitted to the student's head. Now one does not have to be content with this kind of education. Instead of simply reading about or being told about some subject matter, one can develop an approach that enables children to learn things for themselves through being *involved directly*, being able to shape, change, manipulate, the subject matter they are studying. . . . from playing with blocks to playing with microscopes.

The first kind of learning tends to make walking encyclopedias of children for a brief period of time, while the second tends to foster creativeness and initiative which has been learned through involvement.

The science units in this book are designed along those guidelines described by the second premise. Children are given a chance to become involved along with their teachers and continuous progress can be achieved by learning from one's mistakes. This blend of learning science by direct contact and involvement coupled with the concept of continuous progress for every child, with an emphasis on profiting by one's mistakes, tends to create a healthy stimulating atmosphere conducive to learning for children.

Why Do It This Way?

Why Do It This Way?

Science Units and Curiosity

Designing a science unit at any level requires more attention to how children learn than dedication to how many facts can be conveyed. The intermediate school youngster can begin to deal concretely with objects although he may not yet express abstract hypotheses about objects. He has learned to use logic in fundamental operations such as classification, ordering, time, and space. He has not acquired the ability to systematically combine propositions, controlling variables and testing combinations of ideas.

Children free to function on an intellectual level display a natural drive to use their intellectual abilities. From birth and throughout an infant's earliest years there is a keen drive to explore the immediate environment. During a youngster's preschool and early primary school years there seems to be no end to questions related to the exploration of the environment. Curiosity is at its peak and teachers can either find ways of extending, nurturing, and enhancing that curiosity or completely extinguish it.

Children appear to lose some of this curiosity between the third- and fourth-grade years. Possibly, this may be due to the "system's" obsession with having children acquire knowledge as factual information. The challenge to the intermediate school teacher is to develop a teaching pattern which keeps this curiosity alive through continued emphasis on the development of cognitive abilities, utilizing the youngsters' natural curiosity as the basis for much of the classroom learning.

There seem to be two forms of curiosity displayed by children. One is that of finding answers to puzzling questions. Because an observed event

is puzzling and does not seem to agree with what the individual knows, he is disturbed at lacking an adequate explanation for the event. This stimulates a need to produce an explanation. Curiosity is directed toward a specific objective.

The other type of curiosity is not directed toward a specific event but rather is merely for wondering and finding excitement in dealing with new ideas. Youngsters take toys apart, investigate vacant garages, or stick their heads or hands into

open holes. These actions are not motivated by the search for a specific answer to a problem. The youngster simply finds pleasure in letting his natural curiosity lead him.

Both types of curiosity are worth developing and imaginative science activities can provide the needed stimulation.

The Senses and Autonomous Learning

All information is gained through our senses. The early beginnings of understanding about the surrounding environment should receive special attention through activities which will improve or develop:

1. Observation of objects with the senses
2. Observation of interaction of objects
3. Classification of observations—similarities, differences, and changes.

Professor Bruner has emphasized that there are two kinds of learning behavior. One is clear, meaningful, rational, deductive, purposeful, and straightforward, whereas the other is hypothetical, tentative, intuitive, playful, imaginative, and sometimes even wrong.

During the elementary years the latter behavior—playful, hypothetical, intuitive, tenta-

tive—ought to be emphasized, building a foundation for later years on which clear, meaningful, rational, deductive learning can proceed.

Young children are autonomous individuals. Unconsciously they explore and manipulate their surroundings. The role of the adult is to control or redirect some of these explorations so they do not endanger themselves or others.

Youngsters have experiences according to what interests them at the moment without thought for safety, rules of conventional use, or values which adults place on certain behaviors. Children react intuitively and instantaneously to things about them.

Most of a youngster's awareness of things about him is in terms of the concrete. He responds to feel, taste, location, and shape rather than abstract concepts and values attached to these things by adults. A youngster's encounters with ideas and interpersonal behavior follow the same pattern. He does not feel compelled to use conventional labels. Without knowing the "accepted social behavior" he easily joins in play with other children.

Unfortunately, this intuitive response on the part of youngsters is soon reduced in the public school setting. It is replaced by conventional responses, textbook-determined answers, and teacher-determined ways of doing things. Labels are given to objects and they become an end in themselves, something to be learned, rather than used as a means of communication. Given a specific event or object we condition youngsters to respond in the "expected way."

The result of this conditioning process is that children quickly lose their instantaneous curiosity about things around them and instead look for the "acceptable answer." Those youngsters lacking a good memory or "retrieval system," and also lacking experience with objects or events they are asked to recall, end up feeling inadequate and guilty because of failure. Having lost intuitive power, these youngsters in turn lose autonomy and failure becomes defeat.

It is not difficult to survey a classroom to determine the degree to which youngsters lack autonomy. Try counting the number of times students answer a teacher's question with a reply which is a question itself. For example: Teacher: "Why does a crystal stop growing?" Student: "Is it because there is no more growing solution?" The students that dare risk giving their own answers are frequently few in number.

Certainly, as teachers we need to control a youngster's encounters with his environment, for physical as well as psychological reasons. But possibly we have exerted too much control. We may have controlled to the point where a youngster's intuitive power and autonomy are given over to authority—authority which is external to the youngster. This in turn then exposes the educational system to a major inconsistency between what goes on in the classroom and what is deemed essential to the development of autonomous, sensitive, and creative human beings.

Early learning experiences in science need not be complicated. In fact these experiences should not be labeled "science experiences," for they require the youngsters to develop and practice skills basic to the total development of a child—not just unique to one field of learning. Units the teacher will develop must take advantage of existing materials and in most instances these materials should be available in large numbers. Frequently, teacher-designed or commercially designed units are undertaken using insufficient quantities of the required materials. The major key to the successful completion of a child-centered activity is the presence of adequate quantities of the necessary materials—there can be no shortcuts on materials. If units call for clay, soap, microscopes, chemicals, magnifying glasses, seeds, soil, light sources, etc., be sure they are available in sufficient quantity before the unit is begun. Remember, there is a vast assortment of common household materials which can serve as the equipment and supplies necessary for the development of a science unit.

Testing a Unit

Evaluation is an integral part of science teaching. It may be built into some units, while others do not lend themselves to direct evaluation. There is no fixed requirement for direct evaluation. Most of the learning activities at the intermediate level are basic to all learning, and it is possible to evalu-

ate progress not only by the amount of information retained but by the manner of acceptance and the approach to new situations in other fields. Probably the best evaluation of a particular activity is an interested class, for an interested class is a successful one.

All children want to be successful or at least adequate to a task. A child's view of his own adequacy changes continually, the changes being directly related to his own day-to-day attitudes and the behavior of others toward him. To help him cope with this continually changing viewpoint of his inherent adequacy it is important to show him that he is capable of learning through experience. Furthermore, he needs to recognize that he has learned, that he has really made progress.

Of course, some problems children may confront will not be solvable. Some problems turn out to be too difficult. Yet failure to solve them does not mean a child is inadequate. Creating situations in which children are encouraged to express their own ideas—many of which may be wrong—and then continually correcting them may lead them to think that all their ideas are wrong. Even though their ideas may be incorrect, children should be encouraged to think and find out that they are able to do so. Not all their misconceptions can be corrected without impeding the child's desire or search for adequacy.

In order to strengthen the child's viewpoint of his own adequacy we must permit him to do those things he does well for longer periods of time. Is it wrong for a child to enjoy his own ability at a specific task? Why must he quickly move to another immediately after achieving a success?

Realization that he can learn through experience, recognition of his own progress, acceptance of the notion that some problems will be insolvable, and knowledge that he is free to express his ideas—these are some of the major attitudes we want every child to develop.

In traditional ways of teaching, evaluation focuses on student performance. The student has the role of responding to the required learning task, such as a test, provided by the teacher. In a truly inquiry-oriented situation evaluation is a shared responsibility. The student still has the responsibility to perform certain processes but he is now more aware of these processes as he uses them. Therefore, he is in a better position to assess his own growth in inquiry processes. In this situation the teacher's role is to generate the strategies, develop the techniques, and create the atmosphere in which learners can exhibit, practice, and identify desired processes. Evaluation directed in this manner will result in the emphasis being placed on learning rather than on teaching.

Content versus Process

Nothing can be gained by encouraging conflict between content and process. The effective teacher will create a classroom environment which will encourage students to study subject matter, and at the same time exert an increased effort in understanding how they learn. They can learn how ideas are formulated and tested. An inquiry-centered class has no reason to consider the existence of a conflict between content and process, for in this setting teachers and students alike recognize the need for data and how that data is processed.

The seeming conflict between content and process vanishes when educators begin to really see, as well as understand, the relationship between what children learn and how they learn.

Individuality and the "System"

Not all individuals have the same quality of concepts or ideas available for retrieval. There are radical differences between individuals. The degree and kind of past experience individuals bring to a learning situation has a profound effect on the individual's ability and willingness to encounter new learning.

Certainly all students of a given age or grade level do not have a backlog of common experiences. Students who have had opportunities to explore ideas autonomously will display a varied and active "warehouse" of concepts and ideas. Students reacting to assigned individual, autonomous learning situations will permit the teacher to more effectively diagnose pupil differences and consequently shape more meaningful individualized learning experiences.

Motivation in the classroom is largely the result of positive or negative stimuli by the teacher. Reward or threat of punishment is expressed through remarks such as "Well done, Mary"; "Good job, John"; "Keep up the good work, Charlie"; "If you don't do your work, John, I'll give you a bad grade"; "Why can't you work like the other good students?" Some youngsters respond favorably to positive remarks, others to negative remarks, while still others fail to respond to either. In order to be in a position to know what motivational needs exist we must place students in autonomous learning situations whereby they are able to respond to external rewards and pressures. Stimulating the individual is the challenge of creative teaching.

Most educators agree that there is a need to develop creative individuals and that creativity is a highly prized objective in this society. Furthermore, it is generally accepted that the creative act is a highly autonomous act and that creation results from students being placed in autonomous learning situations. Autonomy breeds creation. Therefore, unless we give pupils autonomy—individualize their instruction—we have no way of perceiving creative acts.

For too many students school has become a game of following rules, many of which are intuitively and quickly grasped. For those that stick to the rules and agree to "play the game," success is usually assured. Those that refuse to play the game or attempt to alter its rules are usually doomed to failure. In any event the result is energy devoted to conformity or to hostility rather than the pursuit of personalized learning.

Primary and intermediate school children are ready to try anything. They have the right blend of curiosity, imagination, physical stamina, and spontaneous motivation to make learning effective. This period in a youngster's life passes by quickly. If our classroom materials and our classroom teachers are not ready for the challenges these characteristics present, the most impressionable years of childhood have been lost.

How to Do It

How to Do It

Teaching is not synonymous with telling. The teacher is not primarily a guardian of the archives; he is first a guide to children, assuring them of their right to full development of their gifts. He knows this development is not always easy to assure; for children do not choose their parents, nor their society.[9]

The teacher creates the atmosphere in which children react with their environment in a personalized manner. The method of science is not one but many, for different people possess different ways of approaching problems. Science assumes an open mind and a readiness to question or modify beliefs on the basis of evidence. Therefore, the successful teacher must possess certain unique qualities. He is a person who listens to ideas, helps children find exciting things to do, encourages students to work independently, doesn't tell all the answers but **permits** mistakes, is excited about student ideas, stimulates question formation, and helps students realize that they have learned. Essentially, the teacher should realize that it is through a youngster's school experiences that he comes to view himself as an able person—able to think, to work cooperatively with others, and to learn new things.

During the elementary school years, the school system is attempting to set its mold for each inquisitive, active, noisy, and frequently annoying little creature. Youngsters are told when to talk, when to be quiet, when to take out their work

[9] Paul F. Brandwein, *Elements in a Strategy for Teaching Science in the Elementary Schools*, Harcourt, Brace & World, 1961.

materials, when to put them away, when to go to the lavatory, when it is time for a drink, when to say "good morning" if the principal or another visitor enters the room, and so it goes with each phase of the school day becoming a regimented pattern forming the parts which make up what we adults designate the **system**. The important thing seems to be the system and conformity to its rules of accepted behavior. Schools have become very successful at teaching children conventional responses.

Unknowingly, teachers, in their efforts to meet the standards established by the system, permit the regimentation of the system to flavor their classroom activities. We do an excellent job of taking a heterogeneous group of youngsters as they enter school and over a period of years blending them into one large homogenized mass and proudly acclaim them educated. All we need to do next is to figure out some way of pasteurizing the resultant product and the process would be completed. Youngsters are individuals and we must make every effort to treat them as such if true learning is to be fostered.

51

The following units represent **doing** activities which will enable the teacher to facilitate learning. The materials required are simple and should be available in sufficient quantity before starting. Not all of the units require the same period of time. They are all open-ended and require considerable teacher planning. Some of the units are much longer than others and may at first appear to be too lengthy for intermediate children. For some classes this may be true and therefore it may be possible to complete only a portion of a particular unit. A unit may be ended prematurely and continued later in the year or possibly not at all. These units are designed to permit maximum flexibility by the teacher in planning classroom activities. The major considerations are student interest and active involvement. Provided a particular unit continues to generate interest, enthusiasm, and active involvement, it would seem appropriate to continue it, possibly expanding its scope. Certainly it is imperative that the teacher generate personal interest and enthusiasm for the type of student-centered activities advocated by these units. The teacher must indicate by his actions his interest and enthusiasm in each one of the activities. The units provide the teacher with concepts, activities, and necessary background material; imagination, initiative, patience, and understanding must be provided by the teacher. None of these units should be considered strictly science units but rather experiences which will permit youngsters to react with their environment and by so doing gain practice in thinking, relating, observing, expressing, and cooperating.

Hopefully some of the experiences in these units will motivate the classroom teacher to develop additional units. Remember, the primary objective of teaching is not merely the imparting of facts and laws to children. We should want our children to improve in the skills of thinking, observing, relating, and working independently. In order for children to acquire these skills time must be devoted to the practice of them. Science can be used as a **vehicle** to encourage and carry on these activities, probably at the expense of not covering all the **must areas**, but with the possible reward being youngsters better prepared to read, talk, and think with understanding. This, then, is the prime responsibility of a teacher.

Children require confrontation with real things and real problems, not solely to increase their storehouse of factual information but to have frequent opportunity to exercise and improve their skills in observing, relating, expressing, and thinking. Dedication to the teaching of science implies dedication to the task of helping children to learn—and the learning experience should encompass **all** experiences interrelated into a unique **oneness**. The techniques employed in making science exciting and meaningful to young children are the same techniques needed to make reading, spelling, mathematics, history, and art exciting and meaningful. As teachers, our efforts should be aimed at creating the classroom atmosphere in which this **oneness** becomes a reality.

AEROSPACE

How to Begin

Imagine an intelligent race of fish that for a long time have been dimly aware—through distorted images glimpsed overhead and by means of objects which occasionally fell into their watery element—that there was another world above the surface of the sea. They have speculated about it for ages, constructing endless theories, and formulating philosophies, even theologies. But their real knowledge about the weird realm of dry land is utterly lacking.

Then suddenly, they invent a periscope and thrust it through the barrier overhead. At once, a new universe is opened up—a universe full of strange creatures and phenomena that it will take them centuries just to record, much less to understand.

A few years after the development of their periscope, these fish take the next step; they build a special vehicle and escape from the sea into the hostile new element of air. Here, for the first time, they discover fire, electricity, extremes of heat and cold, the behavior of gases—all the things that can never be studied in the sea, and which are the very foundation of science and technology, as we land dwellers know them.

All men until this age have been deep-sea dwellers, unable to see the universe as it really is. Now the time has come to emerge from the ocean of air, to exploit the limitless—and still unimaginable—possibilities of space.*

*Reprinted from *Man and Space* by permission of Time-Life Books, © 1964 Time, Inc.

Why Do It This Way?

Everyone on the planet earth is influenced by man's achievements in air and space. As remarkable and spectacular as these achievements may be they are merely the beginning of much more to come. Undreamed-of adventures await man's creative thinking. Each aviation and space success started as an idea of man. Robert Goddard, considered by many to be the father of modern space flight, once stated it rather succinctly, "There is one thing stronger than all the armies in the world; and that is an idea whose time has come."

One out of every fifteen adults employed in manufacturing today earns his livelihood either directly or indirectly from aerospace. Our environment has taken on a new dimension. New in the sense that we are now capable of viewing it from a new perspective, a different vantage point. These new and open dimensions challenge our thinking regarding possibilities for new learning tasks, new concepts of vocation, new elements of communication and transportation.

New concerns are arising because of legal and international problems, mind exploring concepts

as to the best ways of managing the envelope of air that surrounds us, and the new and creative ways of reaching for the distant lands and the more distant stars.

It can probably be safely said that most intermediate school students are more knowledgeable about aerospace than most elementary school teachers. With this in mind perhaps the intermediate grade teacher will find this unit particularly enlightening.

This unit is a simulation exercise through a problem-solving approach involving actual experiments and decision-making processes centered around an imaginary space flight. In most role-playing situations of a similar nature the students tend to make decisions based upon emotion and conjecture and very little on experience or real investigation. Thus, this activity encourages students to find out by actually attempting to solve a few of the problems they might be confronted with if this were a real adventure rather than an imaginary one.

A crisis occurs during the flight by way of an accident causing a crash-landing on an alien planet. The students are faced with the immediate problem of survival or of a possible return trip at a later time, providing they adequately solve the first dilemma. The activities suggested represent a

"hands on" approach to solving the most critical problems facing our young space voyagers.

The teacher is encouraged to go beyond, using his own unique talents and imagination and not limit horizons to what merely can be perceived, but rather to what might be aspired.

How to Do It

This how-to-do-it section is something of a departure from the format followed in the other units in this book. The primary reason for this is that there are many more activities open to investigation in the total environment of this "alien planet" and its nearby space. It is anticipated that the class will get right into the swing of things and want to design many of their own experiments. In addition, the teacher may wish to introduce other areas for the students to consider, such as social structure of the marooned colony, legal and educational concerns if the group decides to stay on the new planet, leadership questions in terms of who shall run things, religion, languages, hospitals, city planning, and so on. There is no real limit except time and imagination as to the number of other areas which may be explored in this

unit. It can easily serve as a bridge to other subject matter areas and immerse the class in a total project involving many diciplines and fields of human endeavor. The science period may prove to be just one small part of the larger exercise. If this unit is tried in a departmentalized school, an excellent opportunity exists for cooperation between teachers with articulation and integration of subject matter, possible on a team teaching basis.

The **micro-investigations** in this unit are designed to get the intermediate student actively involved in solving specific problems related to the main problem of survival. Some are short and can be accomplished in one or two class periods, others may take some weeks to complete. They are not an attempt to be a panacea for all the problems facing our marooned space travelers; however, they should serve as a springboard from which the big questions can be further explored. **Micro-investigation** is the authors' term to denote an investigation simulated in the lab or field which deals with a larger, or **macro, problem** but on a smaller scale. It also denotes the use of small quantities of materials (for safety and economic purposes). This approach allows each youngster to be involved in a number of experiments. For each of the major criteria decided upon by the class as the topics which need immediate attention, at least one activity has been included and delineated in detail. Where the writers discovered existing investigations and materials already well developed dealing with the major criteria, they were either adapted and modified or referred to for suggested use.

These activities are not to be considered the end but rather the beginning of a series of open-ended investigations geared toward solving specific problems. While this may sound like a paradox, it is hoped that as the students endeavor to answer one question, they may, in fact, raise many new ones.

The investigation activities chosen for this unit were gleaned from a number of sources. An attitude of "eclectic pragmaticism" governed the selection and inclusion of activities represented. They were picked for their proven success either through the writers' personal classroom experi-

ences or from large-scale use by the National Aeronautics and Space Administration (NASA).

Suggested Teacher Procedure

1. Present each student with the Student Introduction sheet.

2. Give each student the Lost on the Moon problem sheet for practice in decision-making. Individual scores should be compared with group score results.

3. After completing Item 2, let the class try the decision-making sheet on the list of Priority Things to Find Out for Survival on an Alien Planet.

4. Now present students with the problem about Crash of an Interstellar Spacecraft on the Earth.

5. Suggest that students work on some micro-investigations in order to gain information about topics related to Priority Things to Find Out for Survival on an Alien Planet (Item 3).

Student Introduction Sheet

Imagine that you are a member of a group of marooned space travelers from an alien planet. Your craft crashed on earth, a planet quite similar to your own world. It is now a challenge for you and your group to survive for approximately three months. Although this environment is similar to your home planet, little previous knowledge

can be assumed but must be acquired through your own investigations. You will be dealing with principles of chemistry, physics, geometry, geology, meteorology, astronomy, and perhaps cross into other disciplines during the investigations.

You will receive two lists designed to assist you in the decision-making process of selecting which areas of importance to begin your investigations in. The first one, titled Lost on the Moon, is a practice lesson to test your powers of assigning priorities to problems. Since you are relatively familiar with some of the characteristics of your native satellite, the moon, this shouldn't prove too difficult. However, be careful and try not to make snap judgments as to what is vital and what is not. Then try the second list for the Priority Things to Find Out to Survive on an Alien Planet and don't hesitate to add some of your own ideas to the list. Try these tests individually and as a class or small group. Compare your results. Now you are ready to start. Bon Voyage!

Lost on the Moon: A Decision-Making Problem

You are in a space crew originally scheduled to rendezvous with a mother ship on the lighted surface of the moon. Mechanical difficulties, however, have forced your ship to crash-land at a spot some 200 miles from the rendezvous point. The rough landing damaged much of the equipment aboard. Since survival depends on reaching the mother ship, the most critical items available must be chosen for the 200-mile trip. Below are listed the 15 items left intact after landing. Your task is to rank them in terms of their importance to your crew in its attempt to reach the rendezvous point. Place number 1 by the most important item, number 2 by the second most important, and so on.

a. _____ box of matches
b. _____ food concentrate
c. _____ 50 feet of nylon rope
d. _____ parachute silk
e. _____ portable heating units
f. _____ two .45 caliber pistols
g. _____ one case dehydrated milk
h. _____ two 100-pound tanks of oxygen
i. _____ stellar map (of the moon's constellations)
j. _____ life raft
k. _____ magnetic compass
l. _____ 5 gallons of water
m. _____ signal flares
n. _____ first-aid kit with injection needles
o. _____ solar-powered FM receiver-transmitter

Lost on the Moon: Scoring Key*

Lost on the Moon items, along with the reasons for the ranking.

(15) box of matches . . . little or no use on moon

(4) food concentrate . . . . supply daily food required

(6) 50 feet of nylon rope . . . . . . useful in tying injured, help in climbing

(8) parachute silk . . . . shelter against sun's rays

(13) portable heating unit . . . . useful only if party landed on dark side

(11) two .45 caliber pistols . . . . . self-propulsion devices

(12) one case dehydrated milk . . . . food, mixed with water for drinking

(1) two 100-pound tanks of oxygen . . . . . . fills respiration requirement

(3) stellar map (of the moon's constellations) . . . . one of the principal means of finding directions

(9) life raft . . . . CO_2 bottles for self-propulsion across chasms, etc.

(14) magnetic compass . . . . probably no magnetized poles; thus of no use

(2) 5 gallons of water . . . . replenishes loss by sweating, etc.

(10) signal flares . . . . distress call within line of sight

(7) first-aid kit . . . . oral pills or injection medicine valuable

(5) solar-powered FM receiver-transmitter . . . . . distress signal transmitter, possible communication with mother ship

*Your score can be determined by the difference between the number you assigned an item and the suggested numbers assigned above. *Low score wins.*

56

Priority Things to Find Out
for Survival on an Alien Planet

Rank in order of importance those items you think need to be determined first. Add any additional items you think should be explored.

A. oxygen supply (determining availability of immediate and future needs)

B. radiation (solar-electromagnetic, etc.)

C. determination of type of star around which alien planet revolves

D. repair of spaceship

E. gravitational effects (size and density of planet)

F. orbital characteristics

G. effect of lone satellite upon primary body (tides, etc.)

H. communications—repair of radio, instruments

I. extending available food supply

J. meteorological and geological conditions of alien planet

K. _____

L. _____

M. _____

N. _____

Crash of an Interstellar
Spacecraft on the Earth

You are all in an interstellar spaceship which has crash-landed on the earth. Do you stay on earth or return to your home planet?

CONDITIONS AT OUTSET

1. You are oxygen-breathing beings and there is oxygen on this planet, but you don't know how much is available.

2. You have sufficient O_2, H_2O, and food on board to support your crew for three months.

3. The radio equipment in the ship was damaged on landing but is repairable. The radio electronics expert on board was killed in the crash.

4. The spaceship was damaged but is repairable. On board the ship is an adequate supply of meteorological, astronomical, geological, and other laboratory instruments which were not damaged in the crash. It will take approximately three months to repair the ship for a return flight to your home planet. You will have to design and construct any additional equipment needed from existing supplies and materials.

A Word to the Teacher

As the teacher you are to function primarily as a resource person capable of directing pupils and facilitating learning. Refrain from giving away answers; try to "teach" by not "teaching" so much. It is important to allow the students to make their own decisions whether you agree with them or not, for they must see the need for being responsible for their decisions since *their* survival depends on it. Guide them in the explorations suggested by the various micro-investigations. The following table provides a résumé of formal micro-investigations suggested in this unit.

Proposed List of Criteria and Allied Micro-Investigations

Priority List	Micro-Investigations
1. Oxygen supply (determining availability of immediate and future needs)	1.1, 1.2
2. Radiation (solar-electromagnetic, etc.)	2.1, 2.2, 2.3, 2.4, 2.5, 2.6
3. Determination of type of star around which alien planet revolves	3.1, 3.2
4. Repair of spaceship, launching tests, and navigation	4.1, 4.2, 4.3, 4.4, 4.5, 4.6, 4.7, 4.8
5. Gravitational effects (size and density of planet)	5.1
6. Orbital characteristics a) Rotational period b) Revolution c) Inclination of axis	6.1, 6.2, 6.3, 6.4, 6.5, 6.6, 6.7, 6.8

d) Latitude and
   longitude
e) Celestial coordi-
   nates
f) Seasonal changes
7. Effect of lone satel-   7.1, 7.2
   lite upon primary
   body
8. Communications   8.1, 8.2
   (repair of radio,
   instruments)
9. Extending available   9.1
   food supply
10. Meteorological and   10.1 (Try "Measuring
    geological conditions   Raindrops" and
    of alien planet   "Snowflake Replicas"
                            units)

The teacher is encouraged to develop additional micro-investigations using the pattern developed in this unit. Some of the youngsters may
make excellent suggestions for the development
of interesting, additional micro-investigations.

Micro-Investigation 1.1

Topic Ecological Systems

Problem Must astronauts traveling in space take a
similar environment with them?

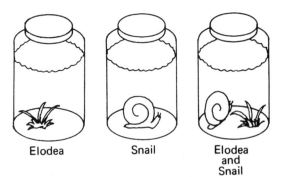

Elodea   Snail   Elodea
                           and
                           Snail

Materials

3 bottles or jars with tight covers
aquarium plants
aquarium snails
aquarium water

Procedure

1. Fill the 3 bottles with aquarium water.
2. Into each jar place the following:
   Jar A—aquarium plants
   Jar B—aquarium snails
   Jar C—plant and snails
3. Add more aquarium water so that each
   jar overflows.
4. Cover each jar tightly and allow them
   to stand at room temperature in an
   average-lighted room for a few days.
5. Observe periodically.

Related Questions

A. What is the condition of the living organism in each jar after approximately
   3-5 days?
B. Considering the basic environmental
   needs of a living organism—food, oxygen, temperature, light, etc.—explain
   the cause of the resulting conditions in
   each jar.
C. Relate each jar to possible conditions
   in a manned space capsule.
D. Discuss reasonable conditions you believe should exist in a manned space
   capsule and explain the reason for including each.
E. Discuss what is meant by a "closed
   ecological system" and what is actually done in a manned spacecraft.

58

Micro-Investigation 1.2

Topic Cabin Atmosphere—Oxygen

Problem Is it necessary to know amount and rate of oxygen usage in manned spacecraft in order to properly regulate the cabin atmosphere?

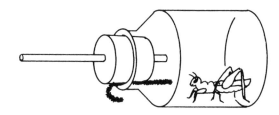

Materials

> ½ pint milk bottle
> pipe cleaners
> glass tube
> ink
> 1-hole rubber stopper
> calcium hydroxide (CaOH)
> small animals (mouse, cockroaches, crickets, grasshoppers, salamanders, etc.)

Procedure

1. Place animal(s) in bottle.
2. Place a pipe cleaner soaked in calcium hydroxide down into the bottle (CaOH absorbs CO_2).
3. Insert glass tubing into stopper allowing approximately 2/3 to extend beyond the stopper.
4. Now stopper bottle tightly in such a manner that the pipe cleaner still remains suspended.
5. Apply minute amount of ink to tip of glass tube—wipe off excess.
6. Observe movement of this ink marker.

Related Questions

A. What causes the ink marker to move?
B. Is it possible to determine the amount of O_2 used by the animal?

C. How can we improve our indicator tube to show rate of consumption?
D. Are there other factors which could affect our results using this apparatus? List them.
E. Manipulate the bottle in such a manner as to cause a change in rate and amount of O_2 usage. List other influences you can use on bottle to cause these changes.
F. Relate your answers to the above questions to problems in maintaining proper cabin atmosphere in manned spacecraft.

Micro-Investigation 2.1

Topic Eye Protection

Problem Does the extreme intensity of visible light in space often require the use of mechanical aids to enable astronauts to see?

Materials

> flashlight (2-cell only)
> mirror
> cellophane in various colors
> felt-tip marker

Related Questions

A. Discuss reasons for reaction of eye pupils when subjected to the bright light.

B. Which cellophane color(s) reduces the pupil reaction most? Why does this happen?

C. What possible methods might be used to provide protection for astronauts' eyes and still allow for greatest visibility?

Micro-Investigation 2.2

Topic Space Hazards—Micrometeoroids

Problem Is meteoric material in outer space a hazard?

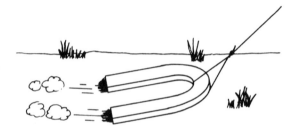

Materials

string (3 feet to 4 feet)
strong U-magnet
microscope

Procedure

1. Attach string to magnet.
2. Have student drag magnet across lawn or field, allowing the magnet to collect any material that might be attracted to it.
3. Observe material collected—about 5%-10% might be meteoric.
4. Observe some of the particles under a microscope. Note the kinds of structure.

Related Questions

A. How can we identify the particles from outer space?

Procedure

1. Look at the pupils of your eyes in the mirror.
2. Cover one eye while observing the pupil of the other eye.
3. Move the flashlight so that it shines into one eye at an angle—move it away quickly; observe action of pupil.
4. Repeat, moving the light back and forth quickly. Try this on another person and observe the reaction of his pupils.
5. Now try using the different colors of cellophane and make a filter for the flashlight. Repeat the above procedures for shining the light into the eye.
6. Print a word on the lens of the flashlight with the felt-tip marker. Determine the cellophane color which when used as "sunglasses" allows you to read the word most easily.

B. Why would you not drag the magnet along a roadway curb?

Micro-Investigation 2.3

Topic Detecting Radiation

Problem How do you build equipment to detect radiation?

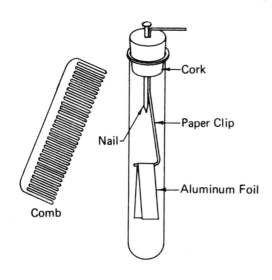

Part A—Electroscope

Materials

test tube	aluminum foil strips
small cork	alcohol
small nail	glue
paper clip	

Procedure

1. Push nail and paper clip through cork together.
2. Take aluminum gum wrapper and cut in half lengthwise: ½" X 3"
3. Soak strips in alcohol to dissolve glue and peel off paper backing.
4. Assemble as illustrated: nail, cork, paper clip touching nail, test tube, aluminum foil glued onto paper clip.
5. Carefully assemble and proceed.
6. Take a comb and rub it on some wool and touch it to the nail sticking out of the test tube.
7. Note what happens to the foil halves.

Explanation Rubbing a comb on wool generates static electricity, covering the comb with extra electrons. Touching the nail transfers the electrons down the nail to the foil halves. Because equal charges repel (negative and negative), the foil halves push away from each other and spread apart. Rubbing a glass rod on a polyethylene plastic bag will remove electrons and charge the rod positive. Touching the nail with the rod will also spread the foil halves.

Over a period of time the halves will collapse. This is a result, in part, of cosmic rays streaming through the jar, ionizing some of the air, discharging the foil. The collapse speed is a measure of the number of cosmic rays entering the jar. Other forms of radiation which normally aren't present will cause the same result. Hold up a radium dial wristwatch to the glass bottle. The watch radiation will collapse the foil halves also.

This type of instrument is included on many satellites that study radiation.

Related Questions

A. Because some strong types of radiation are very harmful, why is it necessary to explore space with unmanned satellites before sending up our astronauts?
B. What results would you expect if a solar storm were to erupt on the sun? Is it necessary to constantly watch the sun when planning future manned space flights?
C. What is a cosmic ray?
D. What is ionization?

Micro-Investigation 2.4

Topic Space Hazards—Micrometeoroids

Problem Are small particles traveling through space at tremendous speeds able to penetrate a spacecraft?

Materials

paper straw
plastic straws of different sizes
raw potato

Procedure

1. Hold the potato in your hand (between thumb and index finger). Do not hold it in the palm of your hand.
2. With the straw in the other hand, try to drive the straw through the potato.
3. If after a few trys you have no success, try covering the end of the straw with your thumb in order to trap an air column.
4. Just before you attempt to pierce the potato with the straw, bring the potato quickly toward the straw.
5. Repeat, using different sizes of straws.

Related Questions

A. Relate this activity to particles traveling in space. How do size and speed affect the ability of the straw to penetrate the potato?

B. Devise methods by which spacecraft might be protected from meteoroids traveling in space.

Micro-Investigation 2.5

Topic Solar Storms

Problem Are solar storms a hazard?

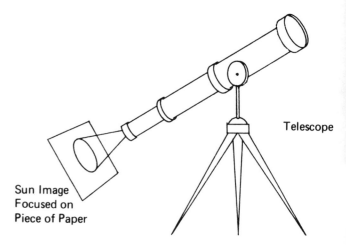

Sun Image
Focused on
Piece of Paper

Telescope

Materials

telescope and stand (reflector-type)
sheet of paper (white)

Procedure

1. DO NOT LOOK AT THE SUN DIRECTLY WITH A TELESCOPE! Just as you could burn a hole in a piece of paper, you can burn the retina in your eyes and become blind.
2. Focus the telescope on the most distant object visible, such as the horizon, the moon, BUT NOT THE SUN.
3. Once it has been focused, point the telescope at the sun by watching its shadow on the ground, NOT BY LOOKING THROUGH IT AT THE SUN.
4. Now, hold a piece of paper a few inches from the eyepiece and reposition the telescope until a 2-inch or 3-inch image of the sun appears on the

Topic Light Reflection

Problem Do reflective qualities of a body in space indicate the nature of its surface texture?

Materials

source of light (gooseneck lamp)
paper in different colors
footcandle meter (preferred) or light meter
sandpaper in different grades, fine to coarse

Procedure

1. Shine light at an angle on paper.
2. Use sandpaper and notice the amount of illumination that the light meter records.
3. Experiment with different colors and establish a scale of reflected light.
4. Tear papers and place combinations on another paper.

Related Questions

A. Using your results as a guide, discuss the nature of the moon's surface and the amount of light it might reflect.
B. Relate the same for the earth.
C. Why do some areas on the moon appear darker than others?
D. What types of problems, due to light

paper. Don't make the image smaller—it becomes too bright.

5. Finally, focus the eyepiece so that a sharp, clear image is formed.
6. Examine the image on the paper. Small black dots may appear on the image which are sunspots on the surface of the sun. Some large spots measure up to tens of thousands of miles in diameter.

Explanation These are violent eruptions on the sun. Because they are cooler than the surrounding areas, they appear darker. These eruptions send out deadly radiation which reaches the earth in 8½ minutes and streams of particles which arrive a day later. We observe the effects of large spots as northern lights and communication disruption.

Related Questions

A. Why shouldn't you look at the sun directly or with a telescope?
B. What is one purpose of our sun-studying satellites in relation to man in space?
C. How could you determine rotational speed of the sun?

reflection, might our astronauts experience while on the moon? How can these be corrected?

Micro-Investigation 3.1

Topic The Sun's Motion and Rate of Motion

Problem How do you make indirect observations?

Materials

shirt cardboards	paper punch
scissors	clock or watch
graph paper	with a second hand
cellophane tape	

Procedure

The sun is an ideal object to study because it costs nothing to observe and creates drama as it changes size, color, and position throughout the day, month, and year.

We can see the sun on any clear day, yet we are advised not to look directly at it. The main reason is the painless but irrep-

arable damage the sun's intense ultraviolet rays can do to our eyes.

How do you observe an object that cannot be looked at directly? The following investigation is one way to answer this question. You may well come up with others.

Fold a shirt cardboard along the dotted line, as shown in step 1 below. Using a paper punch, make a circular hole in the center of a 3 X 5 card. Tape the card over a small rectangular hole cut in the center of the sun shield, as in step 2. Tape a strip of graph paper on the backstop and fold the shirt board to form an angle of about 45° between the backstop and the sun shield, as in step 3. Place the device in sunlight. A small spot of light should fall on the graph paper. You are now ready to make observations.

As the earth rotates, the sun apparently travels in a westerly direction. As a result, the spot of light will move as the sunlight coming through the hole changes. Mark the progress of the moving dot of light by making a neat pencil mark on its advancing side each minute. After five or ten minutes of observation connect the dots made on the graph paper. The line formed by connecting the dots can be referred to as a "time line."

Is the line straight or does it curve? How long is the time line? Did the spot move from east to west or west to east? How far did the spot move in one minute? Did it move five times as far in five minutes? Ten times as far in ten minutes? Does the spot change its size or shape during the course of the observation?

If you fix one box permanently in one spot, you can make observations weekly over the course of the school year. It is suggested that the observations be made at the same time each week. In this way, you readily see the seasonal changes in the sun's position.

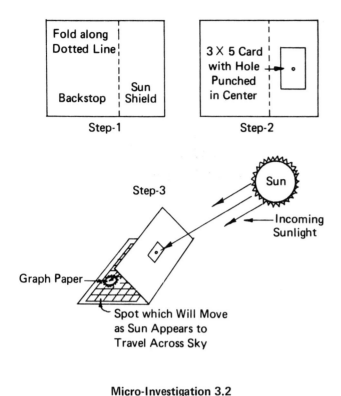

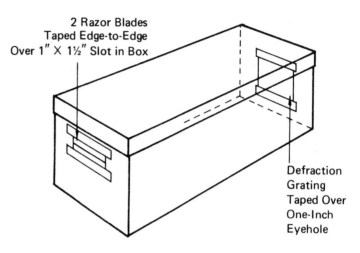

4. Look at the flame of the candle through the spectroscope.
5. If you have difficulty seeing the spectrum, try rotating the box as you look through the flame.
6. Check encyclopedia on "spectrums" for more details.
7. Pour onto candle flame sparingly—sugar, salt, baking soda.

2 Razor Blades Taped Edge-to-Edge Over 1" X 1½" Slot in Box

Defraction Grating Taped Over One-Inch Eyehole

Micro-Investigation 4.1

Topic Constellations

Problem Does the appearance of constellations in space depend upon the position they are viewed from?

Materials

thread or string
stars cut from paper
tape or tacks
shoe box

Procedure

1. Suspend threads from the top of the box. Hang paper stars on the thread. Hang in such a way as to take on the shape of the Big Dipper.
2. Look at the Big Dipper from one observation hole in the side of box.
3. Now move to a different position (hole) and observe. The Big Dipper will probably no longer have its familiar shape.

Micro-Investigation 3.2

Topic The Components of Light

Problem What is a spectroscope? How can you construct one?

Materials

shoe box
2 razor blades (single edge)
transmission-defraction grating
platinum wire
baking soda
table salt
sugar
candle

Procedure

1. Cut a thin slit in one end of shoe box.
2. Cut a hole smaller than defraction grating in other end of box, being careful to avoid touching the grating's surface. Tape grating over large hole.
3. Tape the razor blades over small slit—make sure that only a small slit exists when completed.

Related Questions

A. Explain and discuss how (when we travel in space) the appearance of constellations will be different. This will affect an astronaut's bearing on direction when flights to the stars become a reality.

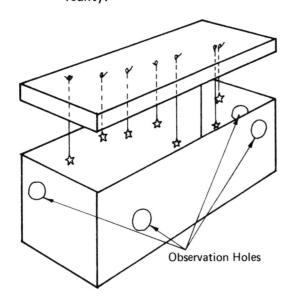

Observation Holes

B. List different ways of identifying stars, constellations, etc.

Micro-Investigation 4.2

Topic Rocket Fuel Combustion

Problem By increasing the surface area, do you increase ignition and burning rate?

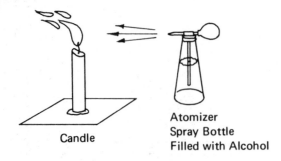

Candle

Atomizer
Spray Bottle
Filled with Alcohol

Materials

beaker with alcohol
spray bottle
candle mounted
    on card

alcohol
evaporating dish
wood splinters

Procedure

CAUTION—To be demonstrated by teacher only.

1. Plunge a burning splinter into a beaker of alcohol.
2. Light an evaporating dish of alcohol and observe burning rate.
3. Light the candle and let the wax drop on the card.
4. Mount the candle in the wax before it cools.
5. Holding the spray bottle parallel to the flame, spray the alcohol across the flame. Keep the spray back from the flame two or three feet.
6. Note the reaction.

Related Questions

A. By spraying the alcohol, why did you get such instant combustion?
B. How might this concept affect the design of a rocket motor?
C. If your clothing were on fire and the only liquid nearby was an open vat of gasoline, would you jump into the vat? Why or why not?

Micro-Investigation 4.3

Topic Oxidizers

Problem Is a high concentration of oxygen necessary to support efficient combustion in rocket engines on earth and in space?

Materials

hydrogen peroxide
manganese dioxide (the black powder from the inside of a new flashlight cell)
drinking glass
broom straw
wood splinters

Procedure

1. Pour about one inch of hydrogen peroxide into a drinking glass and add a small amount of manganese dioxide.
2. Place a piece of cardboard over the top and notice the bubbles that escape from the peroxide. These are bubbles of oxygen gas.
3. Light a broom straw or wooden splinter and blow it out. Put the glowing straw or splinter into the gas and notice how the oxygen affects the action.

Related Questions

A. Why do we use pure oxygen in rockets instead of air?
B. Why do we use pure oxygen in liquid form at –297°F rather than gaseous oxygen at room temperature?
C. Consider volume versus temperature.

Micro-Investigation 4.4

Topic Weather in the Space Age

Problem Do pressure systems affect our weather?

Materials

gallon jug
rubber stopper
rubber tubing
alcohol
4-inch to 6-inch glass tubing to fit one-hole stopper
bottle of soda (the bigger the better; better still would be one bottle and one opener for each participant)

Procedure

1. Add a little chalk dust to the air inside jug.
2. Pour a few inches of warm alcohol into gallon jug.
3. Close the jug with a one-hole stopper fitted with rubber tubing.
4. Blow into tube—increase pressure.
5. Immediately squeeze tube so that no air escapes.
6. Release hold on tube.
7. Notice what happens inside of cloud bottle.
8. With a bottle opener, the participant should flip the cap from his bottle of soda. Note the cloud formed by the reduction of pressure.

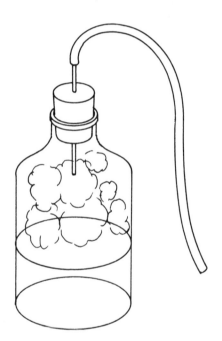

Micro-Investigation 4.5

Topic Simulated Repair of Rocket or Spacecraft, Launching Trials, Fuel Mixtures, etc.

Problem Can you simulate repairing a damaged spacecraft and then launch it?

Materials

model rockets
glue
xacto knives
model spray paints

commercial model rocket engines
balloons
CO_2 cartridges
string or monofilament fishing line
soda straws
baking powder
vinegar
electrical launching mechanism (available commercially)

Procedure

1. Assume that initially the only fuel mixtures available are vinegar and baking soda. Try mixing approximately equal quantities inside a toy balloon. The chemical reaction should produce sufficient gas to inflate the balloon.
2. What happens when the gas-inflated balloon is released? Why is it propelled? Could this fuel mixture be used to propel a model rocket?
3. Tack a piece of string or fishing line from one end of the classroom to the other.
4. Blow up a balloon or better still use your vinegar-baking soda mixture. Tape a section of soda straw to the balloon to serve as a guide.

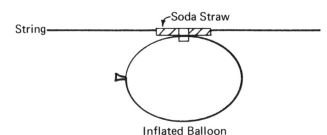

String — Soda Straw

Inflated Balloon

5. Slip the soda straw guide over the string. Make certain the balloon is fully inflated. Hold the open end securely with thumb and forefinger. Release balloon. What happens?
6. Try similar experiments, possibly using commercial CO_2 cartridges for propellants.
7. In small groups, construct various rocket models, use commercial model rocket engines. Have launching contests. Attempt to measure altitude by triangulation methods learned in other micro-investigations (6.2, 6.3).
8. As a culminating activity try constructing a large Saturn V (Apollo moon rocket) as a class project.

Micro-Investigation 4.6

Topic Visual Activity—Field of Vision

Problem Are the location and operation of instrumentation in spacecraft partially dependent upon the astronaut's field of vision?

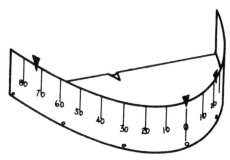

Materials

strip of cardboard, 45 inches × 4 inches
metal or wire clips
felt-tip marker or ball point pen
3/4-inch wooden base cut in half-circle, 18-inch radius
black paint
ruler
thumbtacks

Procedure

1. Prepare a scale of degrees on the cardboard as shown in the diagram. Paint one side black.
2. Thumbtack to wooden base so scale is facing out.
3. Identify 0 by use of a metal marker or piece of tape.
4. Fashion two more markers which can be moved along top edge of cardboard.
5. Person being tested should sit so that nose is in groove on baseboard and should look directly at 0 marker while markers are moved along scale until they just disappear from view. (Do not look at moving markers, only 0 markers.)
6. Read number of degrees as field of view for each eye. Prepare chart of your group.

Related Questions

A. Are both eyes usually the same?

B. What effect does wearing glasses have?
C. At what point in your field of vision can you detect the slightest movement?
D. Relate astronaut activities which might be dependent upon field of vision.

Micro-Investigation 4.7

Topic Visual Activity—Depth Perception

Problem Does depth perception help in the maneuvering of spacecraft?

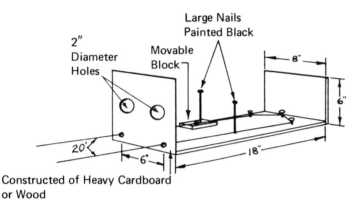

2" Diameter Holes

Movable Block

Large Nails Painted Black

8"

6"

20'

6"

18"

Constructed of Heavy Cardboard or Wood

Materials

wood (one piece = 18" × 6" × 3/4"; second piece = 8" × 6" × 3/4")
4 wood screws approximately 1 1/4 inches long

string 45 feet long
2 nails
small wooden block
carpet tacks
drill—2-inch diameter
black paint

Procedure

1. Prepare and assemble apparatus as shown in the diagram.
2. Clamp to edge of table and extend strings to approximately 20 feet.
3. Use a chair which allows person being tested to sit so his eyes are at the same level as holes in apparatus.
4. Using a ruler, add a scale to center of baseboard as shown in diagram.
5. Sitting on the chair and holding one string in each hand, attempt to line up nails as quickly as possible.

Related Questions

A. Prepare a chart of the performance of each individual in your group using the following headings:

Trial 1	Trial 2	Trial 3	Trial 4
Error			

B. Can depth perception be improved by repetition of the activity?
C. Describe types of activities in which astronauts would need good depth perception.

Micro-Investigation 4.8

Topic Tracking Stations for Space Flights

Problem Are global systems of tracking stations and communications networks essential safety systems?

Materials

large wall map of the world, 36" × 27"
large sheet of clear plastic, 36" × 27"
scissors

yardstick
French curve
grease pencils (black, white, red)
rubber cement and thinner
paintbrush, 2-inch
paper cup, 2 1/2 inches to 3 inches in diameter
12 feet of clear cellophane tape, 1 inch wide

Procedure

1. Locate tracking stations on world map with 1/8-inch dots. (These are approximate locations.)

   a. 27°N; 128°W; RXV—ship at sea
   b. 34-½°N; 120°W; CAL—near Los Angeles, Calif.
   c. 28°N; 110-½°W; GYM—Guaymas, Mexico
   d. 33°N; 106°W; WHS—near El Paso, Texas
   e. 28°N; 97°W; TEX—near Galveston, Texas
   f. 30-½°N; 86-½°W; EGL—near Pensacola, Fla.
   g. 28-½°N; 80°W; CNV—Cape Kennedy, Fla.
   h. 32°N; 64-½°W; BOA—Bermuda
   i. 27-½°N; 15-½°W; CYI—Canary Islands
   j. 7°S; 14°W: ASC—Ascension Islands
   k. 12°N; 9-½°E; KNO—Kano, Nigeria
   l. 19°S; 48°E; TAN—Tananarive, Malagasy Republic
   m. 30°S; 80°E; SCQ—ship at sea
   n. 25°S; 115°E; CRO—Carnarvon, Australia
   o. 31°S; 137°E; WOM—Woomera, Australia
   p. 3°S; 171-½°W; CTN—near Canion in Phoenix Islands
   q. 21-½°N; 159°W; HAW—Hawaii
   r. 26°N; 145°W; RTK—ship at sea
   s. Syncom satellite near India—coordinates unknown

2. Draw to scale a 1,500-mile-diameter circle around the dots to indicate communication coverage.

3. Cut plastic to fit map and cover map with properly thinned rubber cement. Place plastic sheet over the map immediately and smooth out all air bubbles.

4. Place tape around all four edges, bending tape to have 1/2" on each side.

5. Using French curve, sketch orbital path of space flights. Use different color grease pencil for each. (In class, this could be done while watching TV reports or radio reports.)

6. Locate point of impact.

7. Locate and mark points of orbital maneuvers.

Related Questions

A. How many days passed during the orbiting? (day and night)

B. How much time actually passed? (hours)

C. How many times did they cross the International Date Line, and what happens when they do?

D. Why were the ships at sea located where they are?

E. Why was recovery planned where it was? (Consider also location of retro fire.)

F. What types of survival training are necessary for the astronauts? Why?

G. What visual aids are there for aiding navigation?

H. How many times does the sun rise and set during the trip? Why?

I. How many times would the astronauts cross the equator?

J. Why were the Syncom satellites placed where they were?

K. How would we use Tiros photos in preparation for the flight?

L. Where do you think Soviet orbits might be? Why?

M. Would there be any advantage to manned polar flights? What disadvantages would there be?

N. Why is it necessary to keep track of orbits of all satellites?

O. Could your students use the following day's newspaper reports to evaluate launch day's classwork and improve it? Suggest oral reports on their reading, written compositions, etc.

P. Would the Van Allen Radiation Belt be of concern while planning orbits?

Q. Approximately how much time and in what geographic locations are the astronauts out of contact with a tracking station?

R. Notice changes in time zones during the flight.

S. What other experiences would you hope for or guide your class toward while doing this exercise?

Micro-Investigation 5.1

Topic Weight on the Moon and the Planets

Problem Does the size of an object (planet, moon, etc.) affect your weight?

Materials

    pails (same size)
    7 pounds of sand
    2 shopping bags

Procedure

1. Fill one pail with 6 pounds of sand. Surround with bag.

2. Fill another pail with 1 pound of sand. Surround with bag.

3. Feel the difference in weight. The 6-pound pail represents 6 pounds on the earth. The 1-pound pail represents 6 pounds on the moon.

4. Fill other pails with other planet proportions; for example: Jupiter's gravity is 2.6 times that of the earth's. Therefore, the Jupiter pail would contain 15 pounds of sand.

Related Questions

A. How will differences in gravity affect man's ability to do work on the surface of the moon?

B. How will this affect the design of moon-roving vehicles?

C. What statements can you make regarding rocket lift-off from the moon as compared to earth's lift-off (thrust)?

D. Will construction design and materials be different depending upon which solar body is being explored? Explain.

E. What is mass? What is weight? Does a weightless object have mass?

Micro-Investigation 6.1

Topic Orbits

Problem Is the spacecraft's orbit and its control important for your safe recovery?

Longitude

Fig. 1

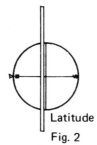

Latitude

Fig. 2

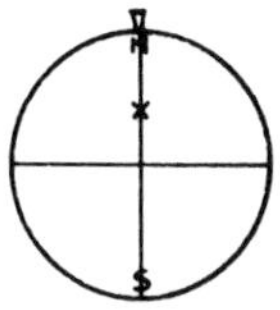

Launch
Site

Fig. 3

Flight
Path

Fig. 4

Materials

yardstick

2 large balloons (light green or yellow in color)—should inflate to at least 15" in diameter or larger and should be a circular shape

2 rubber bands

2 felt-tip markers (black and red)

large wall map of the world

Procedure

1. Inflate one balloon; bend over nozzle and tie off with a rubber band.

2. With a black marker, mark the North Pole (N) at the nozzle and the South Pole (S) directly opposite and in proper position. (Fig. 1)

3. Lay the yardstick on the table and line up N and S Poles. Your partner will then support the balloon while you draw a straight line of longitude from N to S Pole with a black marker. (Fig. 1)

4. Turn the line of longitude perpendicular to the yardstick. Now you support the balloon while your partner draws a line of latitude around the exact center of the balloon with a black marker. Which line of latitude does this represent? (Fig. 2)

5. Refer to the world map and locate 80°W longitude and 29°N latitude. Where is this geographically? Mark an X on the line of longitude to represent point of rocket launching. Mark with a red marker. (Fig. 3)

6. What is the tilt of the earth's axis?

7. Approximate this tilt using the yardstick as a guide.

8. One person now holds the red marker on the red X while the other person rotates the balloon to form a complete circle, keeping the proper degree of inclination by using the yardstick below this line of flight. (Fig. 4)

Related Questions

A. What does the balloon represent?

B. What does the line of latitude represent?

C. What is the name of the point of rocket launch (geographically)?

D. How many times does the orbital path cross the line of latitude?

E. What would be the land mass crossed south of the line? Roughly, make a sketch of that land mass on the balloon.

F. What other land masses would be crossed by the orbital path? Sketch those land masses.

G. Where would be good locations for tracking stations? Place dots to represent them on the balloon. What things must be considered?

H. Where should we try orbital maneuvers? Why?

Micro-Investigation 6.2

Topic The Clinometer

Problem Using geometrical triangulation, can you determine the altitude of any visible object?

Materials

protractor

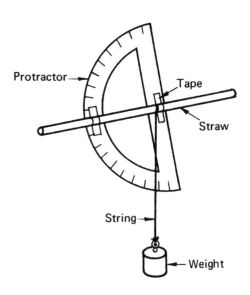

Related Questions

A. How can we account for error in altitude calculation?

B. How can we reduce error in altitude calculation?

C. How could the altitude be calculated mathematically?

Micro-Investigation 6.3

Topic Parallax

paper or plastic straw
tape, string, or thread
small weight
graph paper

Procedure

1. Attach straw with tape to straight edge of protractor.

2. Attach string and weight at middle of protractor and allow them to hang freely.

3. Sight the North Star (Polaris) and note the angle measured. This angle should correspond to the line of latitude where you live.

4. An astronaut, by sighting a fixed object (star, sun, satellite), can determine position the same way with calculations in geometry.

5. The height a model rocket reaches can be determined by using a sextant. Measure the distance from the clinometer to the rocket, then measure the angle at the highest point of the rocket's ascent. The height can be determined by using the geometrical triangulation formula or by plotting on graph paper.

Problem Using geometrical triangulation, can you determine the distance from earth to other celestial objects?

Materials

oak tag disk (6-inch diameter)
2 straws
tape and glue
2 thread spools
heavy cardboard
nail

Procedure

1. Set up apparatus as illustrated:

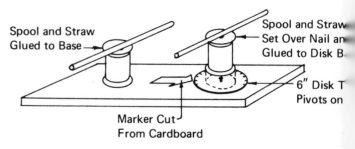

Spool and Straw Glued to Base

Spool and Straw Set Over Nail and Glued to Disk B

6" Disk That Pivots on

Marker Cut From Cardboard

2. Place small object 1 inch in front of first spool and sight it in through straw (A).
3. Turn disk until object is visible through straw (B).
4. Mark position of pointer on disk.
5. Repeat with object 2 inches away, then 3 inches, etc., until disk is calibrated.
6. Use this instrument to determine unknown distances from first spool.

Related Questions

A. Can distance be determined with an instrument like this, even though it is impossible to measure this distance directly?
B. What happens to the calibrations on the disk as the object gets farther away? How could the instrument be changed to measure more distant objects?
C. How can the earth be used as an instrument of this sort; first using the earth's daily rotation, then using its annual travel around the sun?

3. Observe what happens at varying velocities.
4. Determine what forces work on a satellite and what keeps it in orbit.

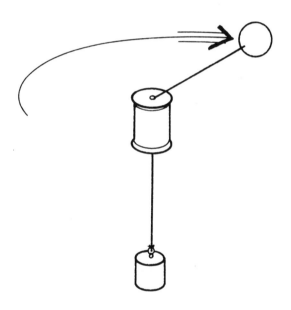

Micro-Investigation 6.4

Topic Orbit Velocity

Problem What other forces act upon a spacecraft as it is orbiting our earth?

Materials

3-foot piece of heavy cord
sponge baseball
heavy weight (1 lb.)
metal sleeve or wooden spool
wire cutters

Procedure

1. Attach string to ball. Run a weighted cord through the sleeve and attach to the eye hook.
2. Swing ball around until velocity of the ball counterbalances the weight.

Related Questions

A. If you cut the string, what would happen to the ball? What would this represent?
B. What do the varying velocities show?
C. How would you show an elliptical orbit using this device?
D. What forces are acting upon the orbiting object?

Micro-Investigation 6.5

Topic Scale of Other Planet Sizes in This New Solar System

Problem Can you construct a model to demonstrate the relative sizes of the planets?

Materials

ruler	pencils
facts about sizes	oak tag

Procedure

Before you can start, you need the following figures: (all of these relate to the earth as if it were 2 inches in diameter).

Mercury =   .36 (about 4/5 inch)
Venus   =   .95 (about 2 inches)
Earth   = 1.00 (about 2 inches)
Mars   =   .53 (about 1 inch)
Jupiter = 10.96 (about 22 inches)
Saturn   = 9.03 (about 18 inches)
Uranus   = 3.70 (about 7 inches)
Neptune = 3.50 (about 7 inches)
Pluto   =   .45 (about 1 inch)

Using the pencil, ruler, and oak tag, make nine circles representing each of the nine planets. The diameters of the circles will be the same as the measurements given above. If you are interested in comparing these with the sun, the sun would be 240 inches in diameter.

Micro-Investigation 6.6

Topic Scale of Planet Distances

Problem How can you make a model of the solar system?

Materials

string
ruler
planets made from the preceding table

Procedure

Before you begin, you will need the following measurements:

If the earth is 2 inches from the sun
Mercury will be 4/5 of an inch from the sun
Venus will be 1 2/5 inches
Mars will be 3 inches
Jupiter will be 10 3/5 inches
Saturn will be 19 inches
Uranus will be 38 and 2/5 inches
Neptune will be 66 inches
Pluto will be 79 inches from the sun

1. Cut a piece of string about 90 inches long.
2. Tie a short string to each of your planets.
3. Let one end of the string represent the sun and measure the various distances given above along the string.
4. Tie each planet on the long string at its proper distance.
5. When you have tied all the planets on the long string, you will have a small model of our solar system which can be used in the classroom.

Micro-Investigation 6.7

Topic Planetary Motions

Problem Can you make a "model" for predicting planetary motion?

Procedure

1. The planets revolve around the sun in circular orbits.
2. The orbital speed of a planet is constant (does not change).
3. The orbital speeds of the planets decrease as the distance from the sun increases. For example, Mercury has the fastest orbital speed and Saturn has the slowest. (Uranus, Neptune, and Pluto were unknown to Copernicus so we will forget them for now.)

Questions

1. What are the orbital periods of the planets? (orbital period-sidereal period)
2. What are the distances from the sun to the different planets? Is that the same

as asking, What are the radii of the planets' orbits?

In order to fully understand these questions and to understand the observations necessary to answer them, construct a picture of the system on your playground. Make observations of this make-believe planetary system. Your observations will be similar to those made of the real solar system by astronomers.

You will have a total of four labs. After working with these labs, you will be given observations of the real solar system. Using procedures learned during these labs, you will then be able to answer the two questions above.

Definitions

1. *Inferior planet:* A planet whose orbit is inside the earth's orbit. Mercury and Venus are inferior planets.
2. *Superior planet:* A planet whose orbit is outside the earth's orbit. Mars, Jupiter, and Saturn are superior planets.
3. *Conjunction:* When the sun is directly between a planet and the earth and on the same straight line joining the two.
4. *Opposition:* When the earth is directly between the sun and a planet and on the same straight line joining the two.

Are there any inferior planets not named above? If so, what are they?

Are there any superior planets not named above? If so, what are they?

To answer the above questions remember the solar system is currently known to have nine planets. (In the past not all nine were known.)

Duties of team members:

1. *Superior Planet:* The Superior Planet will *walk* around the Sun in an orbit determined by the length of his string. He will walk at a rate *less* than that of the Earth. He will do his best to walk at a constant rate.
2. *Earth:* The Earth will *walk* around the Sun in an orbit determined by the length of his string and at a constant rate of speed which is *greater* than that of the Superior Planet. The Earth will start the motion (by saying "go") after everyone is ready and the Superior Planet is seen in conjunction with the Sun (Sun directly between planet and Earth). Earth will stop the motion (by saying "stop") when he sees the Superior Planet in conjunction again.
3. *Earth Timer #1:* Earth Timer #1 will measure the time between the two conjunctions of the Superior Planet (the synodic period of the superior planet). That is, he will measure the time between "go" and "stop."
4. *Earth Timer #2:* Earth Timer #2 will count the number of times the Earth returned to his start marker between "go" and "stop" (number of complete revolutions). 1 revolution = 1 sidereal period, which for the Earth is called one year.
5. *Superior Planet Timer:* The Superior Planet Timer will count the number of times the Superior Planet returns to his start marker. (He may or may not return!) If the Superior Planet makes a complete revolution, the Superior Planet Timer must time it.

OBSERVATIONS

1. Time recorded by Earth Timer #1 for synodic period of Superior Planet:

2. Number of complete revolutions of Earth recorded by Earth Timer #2:

3. Time of one complete Earth revolution recorded by Earth Timer #2:

4. Number of complete revolutions of Superior Planet recorded by Superior Planet Timer (if any):

5. Time of one complete revolution of

Superior Planet (if any) recorded by Superior Planet Timer:

Suggestions

Practice before attempting to actually obtain times. Cooperate with one another. Try to have fun and learn something at the same time.

Repeat This Lab

Start and stop the motion when the Superior Planet is seen at opposition (Earth directly between Sun and planet) instead of conjunction. You will find different times because no two people walk at exactly the same rate.

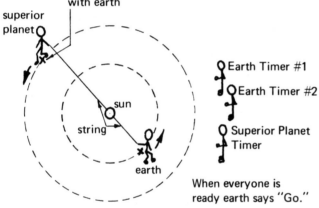

Place a marker at superior planet's feet at start. Likewise with earth

superior planet

sun

string

earth

Earth Timer #1

Earth Timer #2

Superior Planet Timer

When everyone is ready earth says "Go."

Stop: Next conjunction of superior planet

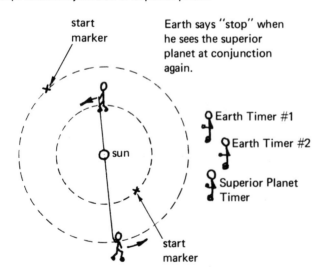

start marker

Earth says "stop" when he sees the superior planet at conjunction again.

sun

start marker

Earth Timer #1

Earth Timer #2

Superior Planet Timer

CAUTION: Earth may have to duck under the superior planet's string

Micro-Investigation 6.8

Topic The Moon's Elevation Above the Horizon

Problem Contrary to popular notions, the moon is often visible in the daytime or early evening sky. Can you measure the moon's elevation and predict its motions through the heavens?

Materials

paper
pencils or crayons
compasses

Procedure

1. Learn direction-finding by using a simple compass and trying to identify landmarks around the school or at home.

2. Measure angles by using your fist. Stand and extend your left arm parallel to the ground and clench your fist. In much the same way that one would climb a rope, place your right fist upon the left and so on, fist over fist successively, as shown in the diagram, until you have reached directly over your head.

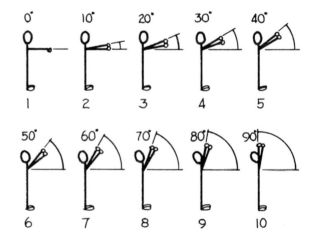

3. From position 1, where both fists are directly in front of the body and parallel to the ground, to position 10, where the "top" fist is directly overhead and perpendicular to the ground, your fist traverses 90 degrees of arc. It

The drawing should show the approximate position and shape of the moon
for the first half of the lunar month.
Observation must be done in the same
place and at the same time each evening about 6 p.m. EST. You will soon
begin to predict where the moon
should be, even in inclement weather
when the moon is not visible. You will
develop a concept of the moon's motion and will anticipate its varied
shapes as the sun's light illuminates its
surface from different angles.

5. It is suggested that you discuss your
observations and drawings with class-
mates. If time permits, continue the
activity for at least three months, since
observing three complete lunar cycles
will give you a chance to apply your
new-found knowledge a second and
third time.

follows that each closed fist approximates 10 degrees and each finger 2 degrees. With this fundamental and readily available measuring device you can
locate the moon and estimate its altitude above the horizon.

Count the number of fists required to
reach the 90° position. The average
number of fists needed after a few
trials should be nine.

4. Start the investigation at the beginning
of a new lunar cycle and conduct it as
a combined home and school activity.
Before starting, consult the local newspaper for times of moonrise, moonset,
and phases.

Go outside shortly after sunset on a
clear evening and try to find the moon.
Measure the number of degrees the
moon lies above the horizon. Follow
up at school whenever the moon is visible. Keep a record book of drawings
depicting the moon's position, shape,
and relative size on successive days or

Micro-Investigation 7.1

Topic Lunar Origins

Problem How can you investigate the theory that
the moon originally came from the earth?

Materials
globe

Procedure
The geologist in your crew feels that the
moon was once a part of the earth, bil-

lions of years ago when the earth was in a molten state. He theorizes that a blob was pulled off which eventually became the moon.

Take a globe and investigate the following:
1. What is the general shape of the Pacific Ocean?
2. What type of terrain surrounds the Pacific?
3. Examine the other half of the globe. Do the continents seem to be huge jig-saw-puzzle pieces that would fit together?

If the moon was formed from the earth's crust, its composition will be roughly constant throughout. If, on the other hand, the moon and earth were formed from adjacent but separate gas clouds, the interior of the moon will be similar to that of the earth, just proportionally smaller. The earth is known to consist of several distinct regions or zones, each characterized by its own properties of hardness, composition, etc.

The interior of the earth can be studied with a seismometer, an instrument that records sound waves generated by quakes and tremors. The different regions of the earth will transmit and reflect sound waves in separate, distinct, characteristic ways. These waves can be generated by artificial means with high explosive charges.

Explanation

This theory holds that the moon was once a blob that was pulled off the earth by centrifugal force, leaving the Pacific as a scar.

There are some drawbacks to this theory. The most significant is the fact that, at present, it is impossible to account for a rotational speed necessary to throw the moon up, away from the earth. Further studies of the earth's magnetic field, by near-orbiting scientific satellites, may show that this also played a role significant enough to provide the additional force required.

Micro-Investigation 7.2

Topic The Seismometer

Problem How can you build equipment to detect earth vibrations?

Materials

2 yardsticks	board
ballpoint pen	string
paper	screw eye
spring wire	clay
nail	

Procedure

1. Wrap spring wire around one end of the yardstick.
2. Attach string approximately 9 inches from other end of yardstick.
3. Attach other end of string to screw eye on the other yardstick (3 inches from one end).
4. Insert nail through first vertical yardstick and into second horizontal yardstick.
5. Place clay in front of string.
6. Attach pen to wire.
7. Place yardstick, clay, and pen on board on a table just touching nail of other yardstick. Tighten string.
8. Place paper under pen; jar table. Notice wavy lines.

Related Questions

A. What does the length of the waves tell us?
B. Why would you need more than one to pinpoint an earthquake?
C. Could there be moonquakes?

Micro-Investigation 8.1

Topic Crystal Receiver

Problem How can you build a "penny detector" radio receiver?

Materials

tape
paper clip or safety pin
penny or other coin
piece of 1" × 2" wood about 5 inches long or 5-inch-long cardboard tube
tube from paper towels or bathroom tissue
piece of board to mount parts on
wood screws and washers
magnet wire (any size from #24 to #32 will do)
hook-up wire (bell wire will do)
earphones

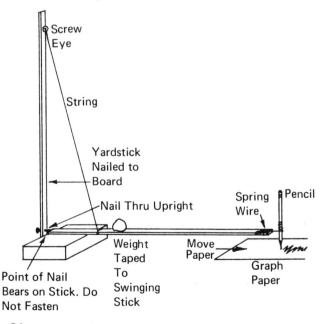

Screw Eye

String

Yardstick Nailed to Board

Nail Thru Upright

Point of Nail Bears on Stick. Do Not Fasten

Weight Taped To Swinging Stick

Move Paper

Spring Wire

Pencil

Graph Paper

Topic Heat Detectors

Problem How are temperatures accurately measured on spacecraft?

Materials

    small compass or galvanometer
    steel wire
    copper wire
    candle or preferably a Bunsen burner

Procedure

1. If a galvanometer is not available, take a small compass and wrap some copper wire around it to form a coil.
2. Set up as follows:

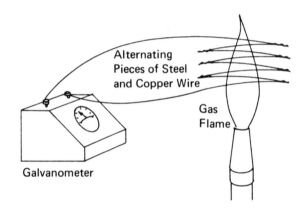

3. If a compass is to be used, hook the two wire ends of the coil up in place of the galvanometer.
4. With the compass case only, align the compass needle with the coil.

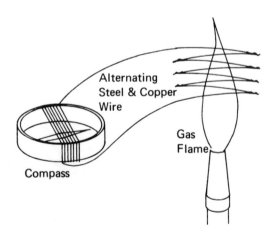

Procedure

1. Wind coil on 1″ × 2″ wood block or 5-inch-long cardboard tube. Start about one inch in from end leaving about 12 inches of wire hanging free for making connections later. Neatly wind wire in one smooth layer with no space between turns for 3 inches along coil form. This will take patience but a neat job will work best. Leave 12 inches of wire at end. Use tape to hold at each end.
2. Mount parts, as in diagram below, onto board, bending safety pin or paper clip so that it barely touches the surface of the coin. If a paper clip is used it must be sharpened to a point on the end that touches the coin.

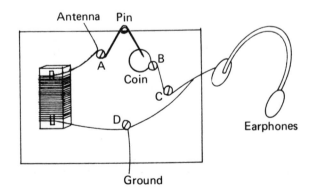

5. Heat one set of junction ends. Notice what happens to the needle, either the galvanometer or the compass.

When the junction is heated, a voltage develops between the two different metals. The voltage registers on the galvanometer or sends a small current through the compass coil, generating a magnetic field to deflect the needle.

Related Questions

A. If a far more delicate device of this sort could be built and calibrated, how could it be used to measure temperature?

This type of instrument is called a thermocouple and is capable of measuring temperature to hundredths of a degree.

B. List some of the applications of the thermocouple in space science studies.

Micro-Investigation 9.1

Topic Comparative Ecology

Problem What effects will "local" terrain and ecological factors have upon your survival?

Procedure

Lay out 50-square-foot tracts of land using string. Once your boundaries have been established, walk over the area enclosed, observing the amount and type of plant life. This tour should not take more than a few minutes. Now you are ready to observe and record.

OBSERVATIONS

1. Evidence of water:
2. Altitude:
3. Approximation of slope:
4. Light conditions:
5. Type of forest litter:
6. Description of ground cover:
7. Tree count: Count only those trees that are older than one year. How can you tell? Once you have counted all of the trees, use your tree finder to identify them. A single glance will tell you if the tree is deciduous or coniferous. Use these two categories for the major division of tree types and set up a chart of tree names and how many of each tree you find. What is your total number of trees?

The observations below are going to be made by estimating the abundance of some factor compared to the total 2,500-square-foot tract.

1. Estimate the percent of exposed bedrock:
2. Estimate the number of mosses:
3. Estimate the number of lichens:
4. Estimate the number of ferns:
5. List any special observations, such as bracket fungi, animal life, food sources, etc.

Micro-Investigation 10.1

Topic Atmosphere

Problem Do surface temperatures of the moon

undergo extreme variations due to the lack of a dense atmosphere?

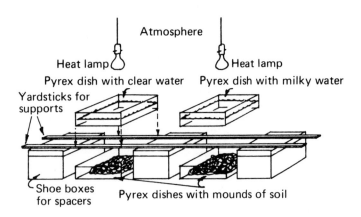

Atmosphere

Heat lamp — Pyrex dish with clear water — Heat lamp — Pyrex dish with milky water

Yardsticks for supports

Shoe boxes for spacers — Pyrex dishes with mounds of soil

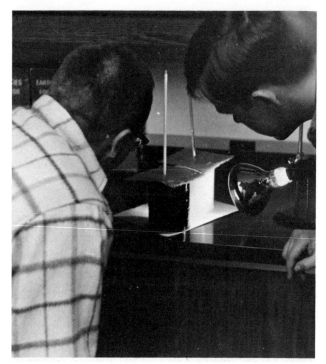

Materials

2 infrared heat lamps with clamp-type holders

2 thermometers

4 clear glass, Pyrex-type, baking dishes (square)

1/2 pail of sand or dirt

1/2 pint milk or white ink

2 ring stands

3 shoe boxes

2 yardsticks

Procedure

1. Assemble apparatus as shown in diagram.
2. Form mound of dirt in bottom dishes.
3. Fill one of upper dishes half full of clear water and fill other dish half full of milky water.
4. Insert thermometers so that bulb tips are approximately 3/4 inch below surface of dirt.
5. Turn on both heat lamps.
6. Record temperature readings of both thermometers every 15 seconds for approximately 5 minutes or until temperatures stabilize.

Evaluation

In evaluating the success or failure of the students in this unit, the teacher will be faced with a variety of things to consider. We do not feel that the actual results are too important. What is really important is how the students conduct their in-

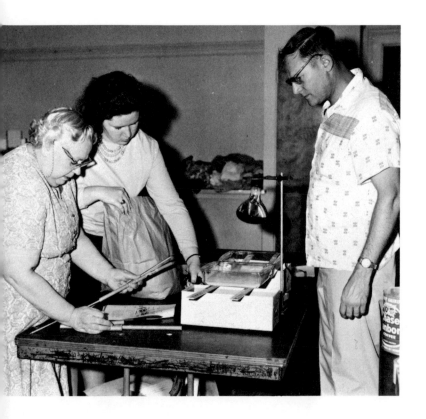

quiry after decisions are made. If there is one constant that might be evaluated, it would be the consistency of action they take toward achieving a chosen goal. They may be serendipitous during an individual activity but shouldn't lose sight of the overall problem. This decision-making process becomes of paramount importance, for once the student decides to act, all subsequent activities should build toward this goal.

If at the conclusion of the unit the desired behavior is not attained, the results should be evaluated liberally. However, any radical deviations from the initial decision without adequate justification could prove disastrous if this were a real situation and not simulated. For example, if the students choose to leave the planet at the end of the three months, or for the period selected, and then find that they have not adequately prepared for this conclusion, the results may prove catastrophic and the evaluation should reflect this. In their new plan to leave, they would still have had to explore and prepare for an extended stay on the planet in order to repair the ship.

A good deal of subjective evaluation on the part of the teacher, based upon direct observations of the students' activities, consistency of purpose, and student feedback is necessary, but the students should be allowed to express their feelings about their actions and be responsible for their outcomes.

AIR POLLUTION

How to Begin

Over 100 million tons of pollution settle on this country every year, or about 1,000 pounds for every man, woman, and child. Some authorities claim that breathing in New York City for one day is equivalent to smoking three packages of cigarettes. Man dies at the rate of hundreds per day when the air stagnates, thickens, and darkens with pollution. The extent to which this "normal pollution" condition impairs our health is unknown.

This unit will deal with the serious problem of air pollution, using meteorology as the vehicle for the investigation of the effects of air pollution.

Why Do It This Way?

Air pollution is certainly not the only environmental hazard man must conquer. It is relatively easy to deal with and will serve as an example of how other environmental hazards can be considered in the daily classroom work. Always remember that all forms of environmental pollution have a major impact on health and ecological systems and it is undeniably related to economics.

How to Do It

The transparent nature of air is subject to varying degrees of visibility. Changes in visibility represent a way of gauging the degrees of air pollution. Materials necessary for Activity 1 are: tissues, coffee cans, strips of white flannel, microscope, microscope slides, and oil.

Activity 1

1. Introduce the word **visibility** by discussing its source from the word **visible** meaning **to see**. The class can be taken outside where some distant features are visible, such as downtown buildings, a church steeple, a water tower, a hill, or some other familiar landmark. Ask the class how far away these landmarks are (exact measurements can be taken from a town map procurable from the town office or a topographic map of the area which the high school earth science teacher generally has on hand).

2. After approximate distances of each landmark have been determined, ask the students to write down their estimates of the visibility. Some will say they can see the sky or perhaps a cloud or the moon. At this

point it should be stressed that the term **visibility** refers exclusively to the horizontal plane, or the distance you can see parallel to the ground. Eventually a student will suggest that the visibility is at least as great as the distance to the most distant visible landmark. Ask each student to keep a record of the visibility for several days. If possible, an examination should be made at the beginning of the school day and again during the afternoon. To add to their observations the class might clip "city pictures" and "country pictures" from magazines and notice the difference in visibility.

3. After several days, the teacher should ask the class to give reasons which might explain the changes in visibility from day to day and morning to afternoon. Some students will suggest fog, dirt, or smoke as factors which affect visibility. These suspended particles are distributed in a fairly even manner along the student's line of sight. When this is discovered, the students may react with surprise as some imagine these particles to be more numerous as distance increases. That is, the class should not be allowed to formulate the notion that a visibility of five miles, for example, means that

there is a wall of fog, dirt, or smoke which immediately restricts visibility to zero at a distance of five miles. A bit of role-playing would be profitable at this point. The students might think of themselves as being on some distant hill looking at their own school. How would this role reversal alter what they see?

4. To distinguish fog from dust and artificial air pollutants, the class should be asked to describe the quality of the air when the class is out estimating visibility on a foggy morning. Most students will at least note the relative "wetness" of the air and they may even be able to see individual fog droplets in the air or resting on hair or garments. The descriptive aspects of the term "humidity" and the related words "muggy" and "sultry" may be introduced. It may be pointed out that when fog is present the relative humidity is 100%, but when the humidity is between 70% and 100% water vapor begins to condense around dust particles, forming haze which may reduce visibility to as little as four miles even in the complete absence of man-made pollutants.

5. Dust and smoke particles may be demonstrated by noting their accumulation on a

coffee can cover, for example, after one week or even one day of exposure out of doors. Pieces of white flannel placed near the school's chimney may indicate the presence of particulate matter. When a calm day occurs, the pieces of cloth might be placed at varying distances from the chimney. Do the sizes of the trapped particles indicate anything? What conclusion can the students draw?

6. A hydrocarbon is a complex organic compound generally used as a fuel. Hydrocarbon pollution may be demonstrated by fastening a tissue or napkin with a rubber band to the exhaust of an automobile, or better, a school bus or truck. After the motor of the vehicle has run for sixty seconds remove the heavy black deposit, which is mostly hydrocarbon and unburned gasoline. Caution: to be demonstrated by the teacher.

7. The class should be asked to notice, perhaps while riding the school bus, the gray hydrocarbon deposit on vegetation or snow along either side of heavily traveled highways. Hydrocarbons also escape while gas is being pumped into autos at service stations. The resultant odor usually appeals to people. Unfortunately, lead, a component of the gas, is inhaled simultaneously, and lead is a poison which accumulates in the body.

8. Dust, smoke particles, and hydrocarbons are the only varieties of air pollution that restrict visibility, even though sulfur dioxide and more notably carbon monoxide contribute greatly to health hazards. At each visibility estimation an attempt should be made by the class to distinguish the primary visibility restricter(s): water vapor (in the form of fog or haze), airborne dust, particulate matter, or hydrocarbon. This can be done by placing an oil-coated slide outdoors for a time and then subjecting it to microscopic examination. If microscopes are not available, a microprojector or bioscope may be used. Low visibility in the presence of visible water droplets of high humidity, of course, suggests fog or haze, while high winds and prolonged dryness suggest airborne dust. Of the man-made pollutants, particulate matter is more likely to be found near industrial centers than hydrocarbons, which are likely to be diffused over

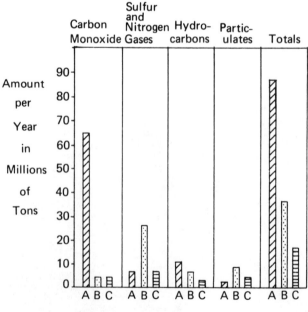

Major Sources of Air Pollution in U.S.A.

A Autos
B Factories, Power Plants
C Space Heaters, Refuse Disposal

the entire area of study. The question of how much hydrocarbon and particulate matter falls on the United States during an average year may now be posed to the class. Most estimates will be very small. The true amounts shown in the bar graph are in the millions of tons.

Activity 2

Materials necessary for this activity are: compass, coffee can cover, town map, unlined paper, facial tissue, cheesecloth or white cotton cloth, thermometers, and nylon string.

In this activity the teacher will refine some of the general notions expressed about visibility in Activity 1. The first step is to prepare a quantitative scale for determining visibility.

1. Provide each student with a sheet of unlined paper. Have each student indicate the position of the school by placing a dot in the center of the paper. Using a compass, mark the sheet with a series of concentric circles (the school at the center) which should be separated from each other by one inch. The students are now provided with a scaled map on which they can mark the position of the more obvious landmarks. These land-

marks can be found on a town map (which can be obtained from the town clerk or a topographic map which is normally kept by the high school earth science teacher). It may be necessary to go out of doors a few times to be sure that the landmarks selected are in view from the school grounds. With this scaled map students can make daily estimates of visibility from the schoolyard. Of course, this scaled map can be constructed with any convenient landmark in the center.

2. At this point the teacher should again generate discussion concerning the cause of changes in visibility by asking the class to list the kinds of material they believe are suspended in the air. Smoke, dust, and ashes may be some of the first pollutants named. Further questioning may be required to draw out the important effects of water vapor on visibility. Relative humidity may be obtained by a student calling the local weather bureau, airport, or radio station. Normally, the weather bureau is many miles from the school and the relative humidity at the school and the weather station may differ by as much as 5% or 10%. A solution for this problem involves making measurements of temperatures at the school.

Relative humidity is simply the amount of water vapor in the air compared to the maximum amount of water vapor that the air can hold at that temperature. If the air contains a maximum amount of water vapor, then the air is said to be saturated. Days on which the air is saturated, or nearly so, are said to be muggy, humid, and sticky. Clothes hung out to dry under these conditions remain sodden and perspiration clings to the skin causing skin temperatures to rise. Thus, the relative humidity appears to be directly related to the evaporation process. When the relative humidity is low, evaporation takes place readily. The sodden clothes dry quickly and the moist skin cools as it dries. Since temperature changes result from evaporation, the degree of cooling should reflect the relative humidity.

3. A wet piece of cloth may be attached with

string or a rubber band to the bulb of an ordinary mercurial thermometer. The so-called wet-bulb thermometer is now waved rapidly through the air until evaporation from the wet bulb ceases to lower the temperature. This reading may now be compared with the ordinary (dry-bulb) temperature of the air. With these two readings you can look in tables, normally available in intermediate level earth science texts, and obtain the relative humidity.

Many interesting questions can be generated about the term **humidity**. Some of the following questions and accompanying remarks may stimulate interesting classroom work.

1. *What is humidity?* The term **humidity** is used to describe water vapor or moisture present in the atmosphere.
2. *Is humidity visible?* Ordinarily, no, but under certain conditions of temperature and saturation excess water vapor is condensed as dew, mist, or fog at the earth's surface, and as clouds in the free air.
3. *What are the terms of measurement used?* Relative humidity, in percentages, when describing the condition of saturation, and absolute humidity, in weight per unit of volume, when describing the actual amount of water vapor present.
4. *What is relative humidity?* The amount of water vapor in a unit volume of space compared to the total amount that could be contained in the same space under the same conditions of atmospheric pressure and temperature is the relative humidity and is expressed in a percentage. For example, we know that under normal conditions of pressure at 70°F a cubic foot of space can hold 8 grains of water vapor. Therefore, air, with only 2 grains, has only one-quarter of its maximum capacity—that is, the relative humidity is 25%.
5. *What is absolute humidity?* The actual amount of water vapor present and usually expressed in grains per cubic foot.
6. *How much is a grain?* 1/7000ths of a pound of water.
7. *Will air always hold the same amount of moisture?* The total amount of water vapor that air can hold is dependent upon its pressure and temperature. At a pressure of 30 inches, air at 0°F will hold about one-half grain of water vapor per cubic foot; at 32°F, about 2 grains; at 70°F, about 8 grains; and at 100°F, about 20 grains.
8. *What happens if you try to force more water vapor into the atmosphere than it will hold?* Moisture will be deposited on objects and surfaces that are at the same temperature or cooler than the air. Beyond the point of saturation, a molecule of water vapor will be deposited from the air for every molecule of water vapor evaporated in the air.
9. *From what sources does the water vapor of the atmosphere come?* Lakes, rivers, and oceans are the chief sources of supply, although a considerable amount is obtained from plant, animal, and human life as well as from the surface of the earth itself. Any matter containing water will evaporate its content proportionately.
10. *From what source does air in homes and other buildings get its moisture content?* By evaporation from everything containing water—cooking foods, hot water, filled bathtubs, all evaporate water into the air. Dry air absorbs the moisture present in furniture and woodwork, so that it shrinks. The natural moisture of the human skin will also be absorbed by dry air.
11. *Is the rate of evaporation of water vapor into the atmosphere constant?* No. The rate is governed by the temperature of the air and its humidity. It is also influenced by the velocity of the air. Laundry exposed outdoors will dry more rapidly on clear, dry days than on damp, cloudy days.
12. *If, as you say, air in homes, offices, and*

buildings draws moisture from other objects that contain it, why does not the air become saturated and stay so?* Because the air in the average house is changed from 10 to 24 times each twenty-four hours by infiltration around windows, doors, and through walls that are not entirely insulated. Outside air during winter has a lower absolute humidity than the inside air that it replaces, so that a condition of complete saturation does not occur.

13. *If outside air is constantly replacing air in the house, why does it not bring in humidity with it?* It does, but outside air at a temperature of 32°F and 100% humidity can hold only 2 grains of moisture per cubic foot. When heated to 70°F, as would happen when drawn inside the house, it would still contain only 2 grains of moisture per cubic foot. The relative humidity would be only 25% since air at 70°F can hold about 8 grains per cubic foot when saturated.

14. *Why is it that the air in a newly built house is usually of a high relative humidity?* Because the new woodwork, plastering, and other materials are moist and the air in the house will absorb this moisture until the materials have dried out.

15. *What should the relative humidity in homes or offices be?* Authorities seem to agree that from 40% to 50% relative humidity with a temperature from 68 to 70°F is very desirable.

16. *How can the humidity in homes be increased?* By installing humidifiers or air conditioners which will enable the moisture content and temperature of the air to be controlled.

17. *Why does one feel colder in a room at 70°F and 25% humidity than at the same temperature with 40% or 50% relative humidity?* The human body is constantly giving off moisture which evaporates into the air at a rate governed by the dryness of the air. The drier the air, the more rapid the evaporation. All evaporation re-

quires heat, and this heat can be taken only from the film of moisture in contact with the surface of the body. It is easy, therefore, to understand that one will feel colder in dry air, where evaporation is rapid, than in conditions of higher relative humidity, when evaporation is retarded.

18. *Why does the process of evaporation require heat?* Evaporation is the release or transfer of vapor particles from wet surfaces due to the increased activity in some of the molecules. This speed is proportionate to temperature. Every particle that escapes from the surface takes with it an amount of heat greater than that in each of the remaining particles, with the result that the main body loses some of its heat or becomes cooler.

19. *Why do moisture and frost form on the inside of windows and doors in severely cold weather?* As the air comes in contact with the windowglass, the temperature of which is lower than that of the air in the room, it is cooled. Although the air was only partly saturated at the room temperature, when cooled to the temperature of the window the water vapor content is greater than is required to saturate the air, and the excess water vapor is therefore condensed on the glass. If the temperature is low enough, the condensed moisture will be frozen into a film of ice.

4. The list of pollutants suggested by the class should be expanded and added to, if necessary, by the teacher. The list might include carbon monoxide from autos, sulfur and nitrogen gases from factories, and particulates (smoke, dust, fly-ash) from factories, and refuse burning. Of these, only particulates and hydrocarbons restrict visibility. Using the scaled map, visibility may now be estimated to an accuracy of one-half mile by noting the most distant landmarks for at least one school week, once at the beginning of the school day and once during the afternoon. A posted log, which should include the relative humidity and the approximate

wind speed, will display visibility changes from morning to afternoon and from day to day.

5. After several days of visibility estimates the class should inspect the log. One trend identifiable by the students may be the increase of visibility from the morning estimation to the afternoon estimation. The class, very likely, will be unable to explain this trend since factory and automobile pollution reach a peak during the afternoon. As in the case of fog, a meteorological explanation must be drawn from the class. Begin by asking whether cold air or warm air is heavier. Then ask which condition is more likely to persist: cold air over warm air or warm air over cold air.

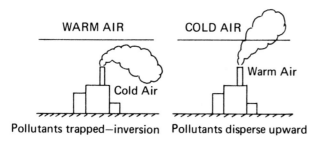

WARM AIR   COLD AIR

Cold Air   Warm Air

Pollutants trapped—inversion   Pollutants disperse upward

The above diagrams (which may be presented by an overhead projector or simply reproduced on the blackboard) should be sufficient to instruct the class that air pollution is most likely to intensify when cold air is overlaid by warm air. This condition is known as an **inversion** because it is the inverse of the usual condition where temperature decreases with height. The reason for the increase of visibility from morning to afternoon should now be evident in spite of increasing pollutant input during the day. The warming influence of the sun at the ground disrupts the inversion which formed as the earth cooled the air in contact with it the night before. A second reason for the visibility increase from morning to afternoon may be drawn from the class by having them inspect the log for relative humidity changes. The usual decrease of relative humidity from morning to afternoon results in an increase in visibility.

6. The day-to-day changes in visibility are, to a small extent, affected by changes in pollution input. These changes may be lower on weekends and holidays than on a business day. The effects of variable pollution input are often masked by changing meteorological conditions. Have the class inspect the log again to determine whether or not wind speed has anything to do with changes in visibility. The wind speed information can be obtained from the local weather bureau. A sufficient number of observations should lead the class to infer that brisk winds transport pollutants from their source and create a tumbling and mixing action which brings cleaner air down to the ground, leading to improved visibility. The same type of investigation of the log should now be conducted by the class with respect to humidity. For reasons already explained, visibility is inversely proportioned to humidity. Thus, the higher the humidity, the lower the visibility. The influence of high and low pressure areas on the degree of air pollution can be discussed at this time. Unless the elementary properties of pressure areas have been covered the teacher should ask the students which type of area has the stronger winds: low pressure or high pressure? Some members of the class will associate high pressure with "good" weather and hence with relatively light winds which, in turn, lead to an increase in air pollution. Since clear skies at night cause rapid cooling of the layer of air near the ground, this "good" weather, normally associated with high pressure areas, should also lead the class to associate high pressure areas with inversions. Further, high pressure areas normally produce clear nights, which allow rapid cooling of the ground. The air in contact with the cool ground gives up its energy, making the air cooler than air at a greater height. Therefore, high pressure areas which stagnate result in inversions. If you feel that the class would benefit from a continuing investigation in this area, you may wish to employ the "inversion box" which is described in the next lesson.

Activity 3

It is important to realize that weather conditions are not the cause of air pollution. Air is polluted when man-made sources contaminate the air with foreign particles.

Once contaminants are in the air, however, weather conditions affect the degree of danger these pollutants represent. Although we cannot control these weather conditions, it is important to know something of their effects on pollutants. A given source of pollution may be harmless or lethal, depending upon the prevailing weather. These dramatic contrasts suggest that the atmosphere is acting fundamentally differently at different times. Such is indeed the case, and this is the reason that studying meteorological aspects of air pollution is an excellent way toward understanding many atmospheric processes. Pollution in air may be thought of as a tracer, which may be easily followed, to reveal the nature of air.

Experimentation with an "inversion box," described below, exemplifies this sort of meteorological study. An inversion box is very simple and inexpensive to construct; a few minutes invested in its construction will reap great profits in seeing and understanding air's fluid properties.

What Is an Inversion Box?

An inversion box is a device designed to study air's behavior under different conditions. In its simplest form (see figure) it consists of a cardboard box one or more feet on a side. On one side the cardboard is removed and replaced with any transparent material (glass, Plexiglas, Saran Wrap, or more simply a plastic bag from the dry cleaners), through which students may observe the progress of the experiment. A slit is made across the back of the box, in a horizontal manner, midway between the top and bottom, and wide enough so that a piece of cardboard can be inserted horizontally into the box, thus dividing it into an upper and a lower chamber. Cardboard runners, taped or stapled along the inside walls, will keep the divider in place.

Holes cut into the sides of the upper and lower chambers allow air of different temperatures, as well as pollutants, to be injected into the box. A

small thermometer placed in each chamber is helpful, to give a check on actual temperature conditions.

Cigarette smoke serves as an excellent pollutant, as it is easily seen and inexpensive to obtain.

Warm air may be blown into either chamber by means of a hand-held hair dryer. By comparison with this warmed air, the room air will be cool. To exaggerate temperature contrasts, a tray of ice may be placed in the cooler chamber.

Normally, air is well mixed vertically, and temperature changes slowly upward. Sometimes, however, a layer of warm air will overlie colder surface air. This condition is known as an inversion.

Materials

cardboard box, a foot or more to a side
clear plastic laundry wrapper, large enough to cover the open side of the inversion box
tape (masking or cellophane)
knife, for making slits and holes
2 thermometers
cigarettes and matches
hair dryer
ice (optional)
black tempera paint—painting the inside of the inversion box makes the smoke easily visible
flashlight

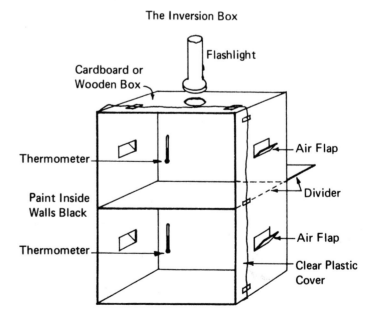

The Inversion Box

It is not necessary for every class member to construct his own inversion box, one for each six or so students is enough. This number will allow every student to become involved in the experiment. Groups of students can construct the boxes in class, an activity which takes half an hour or so.

There are several ways to introduce the experiment, one of which is described below. If the class has completed a unit on weather recently, it is especially helpful.

Start by asking what sort of **diurnal** changes in weather elements they can think of. Remind them, if necessary, that a diurnal change is one which takes place during each day, such as morning low temperatures and afternoon high ones. If the students have been taking weather observations at different times during the day, they may be aware of many daily variations. The most obvious ones are:

(1) The diurnal temperature variations: lowest around sunrise, highest in midafternoon.
(2) Lighter winds at night than during the day. The old saying "a west wind drops with the sun" is often true.

(3) Poorer visibility in the early morning than later in the day. Fog, haze, and dust are especially to blame.

The class may come up with many other, less commonly observed facts. Some may be contrary to those listed above. Although dropping a hint aimed at one of the above observations may be helpful to get the students thinking, there is no need to prod them into agreeing to, or even recognizing the validity of the three observations above. They may wish to reconsider their list later, in the light of their findings in this experiment.

Since the changes listed all take place within one day, the class is likely to guess that the position of the sun may be an influential factor. Probably they are well aware that diurnal temperature changes result from the presence or absence of solar heating. Since atmospheric heating and cooling take place "from the ground up," the coldest early morning temperatures and warmest afternoon temperatures both occur near the ground, rather than 100 or 1,000 feet up. This makes a good point of entry to the experiment.

Suggest that the class simulate conditions at different times of day, by injecting air of differing characteristics (temperature) into the inversion box. To follow the motions of the air, suggest they pollute the air with smoke and watch the action of the smoke.

Students probably will discover for themselves the most effective ways to use the inversion box. Here are some suggestions for the best results:

When creating a temperature difference between top and bottom sections, open the plugs for only the section into which the warm air is to be injected. Leaving other plugs closed helps to inhibit circulation of air between the divided sections, allowing a greater temperature contrast to develop.

Blow smoke gently into the lower (or upper) section. Inserting the lit cigarette itself will cause intense local heating and disturb the thermal pattern created by the hair dryer heating. Later, it is well to study *specifically* the effect of a "heat source," by injecting the cigarette and watching the results.

Darkening the classroom and illuminating the inside of the box by flashlight, through the top hole, makes the smoke most easily visible.

Be sure that the class studies at least two situations: hotter air on top, and then hotter air on the bottom. Students should then experiment with many other possibilities, such as turning the inversion box upon its side, thus creating a horizontal temperature contrast, or experimenting with an internal heat source.

Each group should take careful notes describing the behavior of the smoke under different conditions. Observations should include a record of temperature changes in each section of the box; this can be the job of one or two students. Another pair of students should record descriptions of the smoke as it appears every half-minute. The teacher should inject the smoke, or control the heating by the cigarette. A team effort like this allows more complete and efficient collection of data. It is also helpful to have one or two stand-by observers to watch the developments taking place. Team members should change observational stations after each experiment run, so that all become familiar with the total effort.

To emphasize the results of their experiments, it is convenient to introduce to the class the words **stability** and **instability**. The air is said to be stable when it is colder near the ground than aloft; it is unstable when the surface air is hotter. Under stable conditions, as the students saw, little happens; air remains static. Unstable conditions, however, indicate great mixing and turbulence.

It is an interesting fact that simply by heating air, it will move in certain directions. Be sure that the students ponder the curiosity of this fact. "Hot air rises" summarizes the situation, although it does not explain it. To study *why* hot air rises leads to discussions of buoyancy, specific gravity, and gravitation—an interesting digression for the more advanced class. Normally, however, a discussion along the following lines is sufficient:

If the class has no idea why the hot air rises, ask why it thinks the cooler air sinks. Why does anything sink? Because gravity pulls it, and it is denser than the substance (air, water) it is sinking through. Cold air is heavier than hot air; therefore it sinks to the bottom of the inversion box.

The class may watch a much more violent example of the same principle, using a glass half filled with water. Cover the top with a hand and invert the glass. As the students watch the less dense air struggle to the top of the water, amid great turbulence, they should see the similarity to the unstable inversion box situation.

By now, the class will be able to see some basis for the diurnal changes listed above. In the morning, stable conditions are the rule, as solar heating has been absent for many hours and cold, dense air lies on the surface. An inversion layer exists. Ask the class what kinds of pollutants enter the air at this time of day (6 to 9 A.M., say). What happens to these pollutants? The students saw the answer in the inversion box: the smoke and pollution hang close to the ground, with little dissipation upward. Ask the class what happens to this temperature pattern by afternoon. The sun has warmed the earth so that the lowest air is the hottest. Instability is the rule, the air becomes mixed to great heights, and visibility improves as the pollution is dissipated. Thus the third item of the diurnal change list is explained.

Diurnal changes in wind speed are a good example of the fact that inversions prevent air above from sinking, as well as surface air from rising. The class probably is aware that surface winds blow less strongly than winds high above the ground, and that the reason is surface friction. On a breezy afternoon, the surface wind may be 20 mph, while the wind aloft is 30. This suggests that the constant supply of strong winds from above, which occasionally drop down to the surface, keeps the surface wind at 20; otherwise it would slow down more and more due to friction, and finally stop. Now the class should see that during an inversion just this sort of thing happens. Surface wind becomes isolated from its "wind bank" aloft and loses much of its speed to friction. Thus the lack of mixing under stable conditions, illustrated by the inversion box, explains the diurnal variations of wind speed.

It should be explained that inversions do not form every night and dissipate each day. This is the usual pattern, but occasionally, under certain weather conditions, an inversion will linger for days. In such cases, the inversion may become a lethal item, as it prohibits the pollutants from being dissipated. In London in 1952, an inversion persisted for several days; the resultant pollution is estimated to have caused 4,000 deaths! In Donora, Pennsylvania, in 1948, twenty people died from air pollution during an inversion period.

A student might ask what happens after the pollution is spread farther upward into the atmosphere. Why doesn't it eventually pollute all of the air? The question is a good one. Indeed, *all* of the air would have become unbreatheable long ago if all pollution remained in the air. *Rain* is the great cleanser. Each tiny rain droplet forms around an impurity in the air—dust, salt, carbon, dirt, or whatever. As the drop grows it falls, and as it falls it sweeps other particles from the air. We have the rain to thank that our air is as clean as it is!

Additional Activities—Air Pollution

1. Make a collection of pictures showing various forms of air pollution.
2. Write to your state agency on air pollution and to the National Center for Air Pollution (U. S. Public Health Service, Dept. of HEW, Washington D. C. 20201) to obtain current literature or visual aids.
3. Identify the major sources of air pollution in your community. Classify the kind of air pollution, *i.e.* exhaust gases, dust, smoke—and the level of pollution.
4. Investigate the problems associated with intense smog in many of our cities.
5. Investigate some of the devices currently being used by power plants and other industries to limit the level of air pollution.
6. Contact state agencies to determine local and federal laws concerning the control of air pollution.
7. Discuss the relationship between population growth in the United States and control of air pollution.
8. Obtain information on such diseases as: emphysema, bronchial asthma, and lung cancer. Determine how air pollution is related to these diseases.
9. Our environment is being changed because of air pollution. Investigate how environmental changes in the past have caused some organisms to become extinct.
10. Investigate some of the characteristics of major chemical compounds such as carbon monoxide, sulfur dioxide, nitrogen oxide contributing to air pollution.
11. Invite an ecologist and safety engineer to your class to discuss the effects and problems of air pollution.

COMMONPLACE "THINGS"

How to Begin

There are many simple phenomena we spend little time exploring, primarily because they may be so commonplace. This is unfortunate, because in our efforts to deal with greater sophistication we may forfeit the opportunity to develop situations which lead to an understanding of fundamental truths. In this unit emphasis is placed on commonplace physical concepts using readily available materials.

Why Do It This Way?

Commonplace physical events can be investigated at any location—in school or at home. This unit attempts to stimulate student interest in commonplace events in the hope that individual home experimentation will be encouraged and greater skill developed in problem-solving situations related to real events in the immediate environment.

How to Do It

One of the most commonplace motions is a to-and-fro motion. We see examples of this motion in swings, jigsaws, clocks, rocking chairs, pistons in engines, and vibrations of strings in musical instruments. These motions have some interesting characteristics. Some of these activities were derived and adapted from the Cornell Science Leaflet *Round and Round* by Verne N. Rockcastle.

Activity 1

Materials needed:
  string   washers
  fish sinkers   ruler

1. Observe the simple to-and-fro motion of a pendulum. Attach a fish sinker or several washers to the end of a string about three feet long. Insert the end of the string between the cover and the last page of a large book (see photo).

The length of the pendulum can be changed by pulling the string into or out of the book.

lum and once again match its swing to that of the demonstration pendulum.

Measure the length of your pendulum and measure the length of the demonstration pendulum. How do the two measurements compare?

7. You can adjust your pendulum to make one swing every second. To do this, count the number of complete swings your pendulum makes in one minute. How many complete swings should there be in one minute so that each complete swing is one second long?

Adjust your pendulum until you get exactly this number in one minute. Measure its length.

Does adding more weight affect the period of the pendulum?

Is there one particular length for a pendulum that has a period of one second?

Permit students to have many different experiences with the pendulum. The questions suggested above for this activity can provoke excellent classroom discussions. Students should compare their findings in the open forum of a class discussion.

The period of a pendulum is determined by its length. This is true provided the amplitude of swing is not large—not more than 10 or 15 degrees. Adding or subtracting weights will not alter the period. Large weights added to the pendulum may affect the period because of air resistance during the swing. This should not be noticeable unless the weights have a large surface area.

Activity 2

Some to-and-fro motions are labeled vibrations. Musical instruments utilize the to-and-fro motion (vibration) of air columns or strings to produce various sounds. Materials needed: string, paper clips, rubber tubing, scissors, assortment of rubber bands, baby food jars, rulers, and plastic straws (1/4 inch diameter preferable).

1. Place a rubber band around a ruler (lengthwise) and place a pencil between the rubber band and the ruler—see photo.

2. Compare your pendulum with your neighbor's. Adjust yours to match the to-and-fro motion of his. What did you do?

3. When you make your pendulum longer, what does that do to the to-and-fro motion?

What does making it shorter do?

Your teacher will set up a demonstration pendulum in the front of the room.

4. Adjust your pendulum swing to match that of the demonstration pendulum.

Measure the length of your pendulum.

Measure the length of the demonstration pendulum. How do they compare?

5. When the pendulum makes one complete to-and-fro motion this is called a "period"—the time it takes to go through one complete to-and-fro motion.

What do you think will happen to the period of the pendulum if you double the weight? Write down your decision.

What will happen to the period if you triple the weight? Write down your decision.

Once again your teacher will start the demonstration pendulum in the front of the class.

6. Double or triple the weight on your pendu-

Strike the rubber band and you will hear a sound—try it.

What must you do to make the sound higher?

Try experimenting with different size rubber bands—short in length, long in length, thick ones, thin ones. Make a chart of your observations.

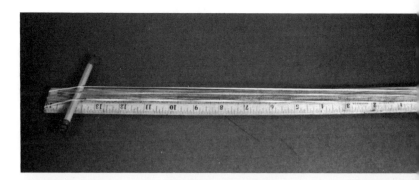

2. Fill a jar with water. About two or three inches from one end of a straw cut the straw halfway through with the scissors. Attach a paper clip to the short piece of the straw and right next to the cut (see photo).

Place the long end of the straw in the jar of water and blow *softly* through the shorter end. What do you observe?

Raise and lower the long end of the straw in the water while you blow. What do you observe?

Try experimenting with different size straws—small in diameter, large in diameter, short or long in length—make a chart of your results.

3. Go back and look at your findings for questions (1) and (2).

What was it that was vibrating in question 1?

What was it that was vibrating in question 2?

In both cases how did you change the sounds produced by the vibrations?

4. Cut a straw to make a reed. Place your lips about one inch over the straw and blow. What happens?

Try cutting the end of the straw off as you blow. How does the sound change?

The vibrations (to-and-fro motions) of strings and air columns are the source of all sounds produced by musical instruments. The length of the rubber band controls the pitch of the sound. Long lengths produce low pitches and short lengths produce high pitches. The violinist changes the pitch of a vibrating string by shortening its length with his fingers. The length of the air column controls the pitch of the sound. Long air columns produce low pitches and short air columns produce high pitches.

View the inside of a piano or observe the pipes of an organ. The long, heavy strings of the piano

Tap each with a wooden mallet or stick. You will produce clear notes—the short lengths producing high notes and the longer lengths producing lower notes.

Vibrations can be affected by the weight of the vibrating object. This can also be demonstrated. To control the pitch of a vibrating object sometimes weight is added to the object. Strike a tuning fork against your rubber heel and listen to its note. Now tightly wrap one or two rubber bands around one of the prongs. Strike the tuning fork again and the pitch will be lower.

Observe that the low notes in a piano come from strings that have been wrapped with coils of wire to make them heavier. The lowest notes on a bass violin or a cello are coils of wire (tightly wound) instead of strings. Inside each coil is a single taut wire. The coil of wire on the outside

and the long, large-diameter pipes of the organ produce the low-pitched sounds. The short, "thin" strings of the piano and the short, small-diameter pipes of the organ produce the high-pitched sounds.

Tuning forks (if available) can be used for demonstrations. A tuning fork is made to vibrate at a constant rate. It is constructed this way at the factory. If you strike a tuning fork (preferably against a rubber object like a heel of your shoe) and hold it near your ear you can hear its tone. Most tuning forks vibrate so fast you cannot see them move. To demonstrate its rapid vibrations touch a vibrating fork to the water surface of a glass of water. The fork will spatter the water. Hang a Ping-Pong ball by a thread (glue the thread to the ball) and carefully touch the ball with a vibrating tuning fork. The ball will jump aside.

Sounds from air columns of varying length can be demonstrated by making a "pop bottle" xylophone. Arrange a series of soda bottles on a table and fill each with enough water to make a musical note when you blow across the top of the bottle.

A "wooden" xylophone can be constructed very easily. Cut strips of wood (about ½" × 1") in varying lengths from 6 inches to 20 inches. Arrange them on two tubes of rolled-up newspaper.

is added weight to make the string vibrate at a slower rate than it would without the coil and hence produce a lower note.

The soda bottles can be used for another demonstration related to the weight of vibrating objects. Fill a bottle partway with water. Strike the side with a pencil and listen to the pitch. Add some more water, strike the bottle, and listen again. Note that the pitch goes down as more water is added. The added water slows down the rate of vibration and the pitch lowers. Using several bottles filled to varying amounts you can make a scale and possibly play tunes. It is important to note that the "tapping scale" (bottles filled with water and struck on the sides with a pencil) and the "blowing scale" (bottles filled with water and air blown over the tops) have different arrangements. In the "tapping scale" the fullest bottle (heaviest bottle) has the lowest note, yet in the "blowing scale" the fullest bottle (shortest air column) has the highest note. The arrangement of bottles for blowing to produce notes is just the opposite of those arranged for tapping to produce notes.

You can demonstrate how changing the density of a fluid will change the pitch of a note. Fill two *identical* glasses to the same level with water. Stir both glasses with a spoon striking the sides of the glass as you stir. The pitch of the note from each glass should be the same. While stirring one glass, add one rounded teaspoonful of sugar. Notice how the pitch lowers when the sugar is added. Compare the pitch of the two glasses. The one containing a water-sugar mixture will be lower than the other one containing only water.

Certainly, there are many other interesting demonstrations. Possibly you can make some of the suggested demonstrations, as well as others you are familiar with, into general student activities.

This activity has not attempted to deal with the propagation of sound. It has emphasized some interesting characteristics related to the production of sound—namely, sound sources and their vibrating characteristics. The teacher may find it worthwhile to use this activity as an introduction to the mechanism of sound transmission. It is possible that individual student reading and interest will naturally cause this to happen.

Activity 3

Another motion as interesting as to-and-fro motion is circular motion. Sometimes this motion is so rapid it is difficult to observe what is happening.

This activity will be somewhat different from the preceding ones. Instead of starting out with direct experiences for students, this activity first asks some questions related to experiences already a part of the students' background.

1. Wheels are very common things. Look at the following pictures and see if you can determine how the cart will travel when given a push.

101

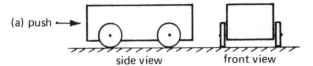

(a) push →

side view   front view

1. straight   2. curved to left   3. curved to right

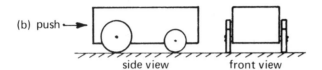

(b) push →

side view   front view

1. curved left   2. straight   3. curved right

2. Check which wheel travels farthest in one revolution.

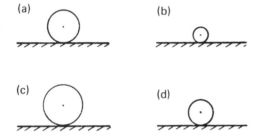

(a)   (b)

(c)   (d)

3. Label the circumference and diameter of each wheel in question 2.

Which wheel in question 2 has the longest circumference?

4. The diagram shows a train wheel resting on a rail.

Can you explain why the outside rim is slightly tapered?

What does the flange do?

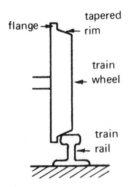

flange —

tapered rim

train wheel

train rail

5. When an automobile travels around a curve do all the wheels travel the same distance?

Look at the diagram and then answer the questions below it.

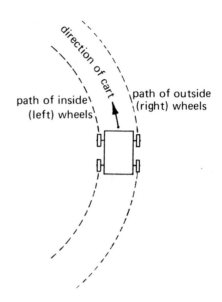

direction of cart

path of inside (left) wheels

path of outside (right) wheels

If the wheels were runners in a race, would the outside runner have to run faster to win the race?

Check which is correct:

(a) The outside wheels (right) travel farthest in going around the curve.

(b) The inside wheels (left) travel farthest in going around the curve.

(c) Both outside and inside wheels travel the same distance going around the curve.

6. When you have looked at cars parked in the school parking lot or on the street did you notice the "bump" underneath the car in the middle of the rear axle? Is there a similar "bump" underneath the car on the front axle? Look at some parked cars and see if you can find the "bump" in the rear, front, or in both places. You do not have to climb under the car.

The first part of this activity should stimulate many questions. Let the students work or even struggle with the suggested activity sheet questions before you enter into a general class discussion on any one of the topics. The level of understanding in your class will determine where to best start your discussions. Basically the two thoughts being considered in this lesson are how differences in wheel size (diameter) affect direction of travel and what relationship exists between diameter and circumference or distance traveled in one revolution.

Do your students understand that a small wheel makes more turns than a large wheel when moving the same distance? Do they understand that when a wagon or car goes around a curve the outside wheels travel farther than the inside wheels?

The wheels on either side of wagons or cars must be independent of one another so they can go around curves. As vehicles go around curves the wheels on one side turn differently from those on the opposite side. The axle between wheels cannot be solid. If it were, the wheels would skid. The answer to this is the **differential**, located in the middle of the rear axle of most cars. It is the "bump" you see in the middle of the axle. For most students at this age it is only necessary to explain that this differential allows for a difference in the number of turns of the car's wheels as the car goes around a curve. The details of a differential are too difficult for most intermediate grade youngsters, although a student that is really interested may be encouraged to find out more about the mechanics involved.

Some students may notice that a few cars have this "bump" (differential) on the front axle. These cars have front-wheel drive. Other cars have this "bump" (differential) on both the front and rear axles. These are called four-wheel-drive vehicles. The axle with the differential is the one that receives direct power from the engine.

Train wheels are interesting to study, for the wheels on one side of a railroad train *are* connected solidly to those on the other side (no differential), yet the train still goes around curves without the wheels skidding.

The question in the activity on train wheels is a difficult one for most students to explain. It can be used as a starting point for explaining the wheels' curious construction.

A train wheel has a slight taper. The diameter of the wheel next to the flange is greater than the diameter of the wheel at the outer edge. The flange on the wheel keeps the wheel from sliding off the track. Now imagine a train rounding a curve to the right. The track would curve to the right, but the train would tend to go straight ahead (inertia). This makes the train crowd to the

left as it goes around the curve. As the train pushes to the left, the left wheel touches the track next to the flange. The wheel is large in diameter next to the flange. The right wheel, however, rides on its smallest diameter because the whole train is pushing to the left. Therefore, the left wheel goes a little farther with each turn of the axle than the right wheel. This makes up for the difference in distance that each wheel must cover to go around the curve. If the train wheels did not have this taper they would skid going around curves, causing excessive wear on the wheels.

Circular motion plays tricks with us in the movies and on television. This may be a good time to do some demonstrations.

Set up a motion picture projector and operate it without a film threaded. Project the light onto a screen or a wall of the classroom. Stand near the screen or wall and wave a ruler or pencil back and forth sideways. You will observe a series of shadows on the screen or wall. The beam of light from the projector will flash on and off intermittently because of the shutter that flickers inside the projector. Every time the light flashes you produce another shadow on the screen (or wall) and hence you see a whole "bunch" of rulers.

Now construct a cardboard wheel as shown in the diagram (8 to 10 inches in diameter).

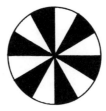

Put six equally spaced black spokes on the wheel. Through the center of the wheel put a small bolt. Secure the end of the bolt in a hand drill.

Hold the wheel facing the class, but in the beam of the projector, and spin it at various speeds. You can turn the wheel so that the spokes seem to stand still, go clockwise, or go counterclockwise.

When movies are taken of a rotating object, such as a wheel with spokes, strange things result.

In the camera a shutter opens to let the camera take a picture; it closes, and a split second later it opens again to take another picture. Although the camera takes intermittent pictures (24 each second), the wheel moves constantly. Suppose the wheel has twelve spokes in the same positions as the numbers on a clock. Suppose the first picture is taken when a spoke is at twelve—the other spokes being at the other clock numbers. If the spoke moves almost to one, but not quite, when the next picture is taken, this means the spoke that was at eleven moves almost, but not quite, to twelve. When you view the projected picture it appears that the spoke at twelve has moved backward slightly. If the spoke at twelve moves past one when the next picture is taken, then the spoke at eleven would move a little past twelve. When you view this projected picture the spoke at twelve has moved only slightly but in the right direction. The picture-taking rate and the projection rate of the film remains constant. The rotating motion varies and because of this rotational motion it will intermittently appear as stopped, as clockwise motion, or as counterclockwise motion. By playing with the cardboard wheel in front of the projected beam of light, you and your students can answer some of the questions about why wheels seem to do strange things in the movies or on television.

Activity 4

We frequently observe the swirling of fluids. Some examples are the swirling motion of water as it enters the drain in the washbowl, similar swirling motions in streams, or the whirling of papers and leaves on a windy fall afternoon. These motions are sometimes referred to as small whirlpools.

Materials needed: large mayonnaise or peanut butter jar, rice, food coloring (two colors), ruler, newspaper, ball, string.

1. Fill a wide-mouth jar about halfway with water. Place it on your desk after you have covered the desk with newspaper.

   With a ruler or pencil stir the water until you cannot make it go any faster. What do you observe?

   How far up the sides of the jar does the water climb?

   How low does the water get in the center?

   The "hole" that forms when the water spins is called a **vortex**. This is like a little whirlpool. Have you ever seen this in streams or while rowing a boat?

2. Now consider a thought question. Suppose you whirl a ball around your head on the end of a string. If you let the ball go while you are whirling it, does it continue to travel in a circle?

3. Go out to the play yard or into the gym and try it—what do you observe?

   Did the ball fly directly away from the center?

   Did the ball go off in a straight line in a particular direction?

   Draw a picture of how the ball seemed to travel after it was released.

4. If the ball is whirled in a larger circle and then released, will its path differ from the path followed by the ball whirled in a small circle and then released?

5. Is it harder to whirl a heavy ball than it is to whirl a light ball?

   Does the weight of the ball determine its path after being released?

Draw a picture of how you think a heavy ball seems to travel after being released.

6. When you were stirring the water in the wide-mouth jar, what caused the water to move in a circle?

   What caused the ball to move in a circle?

7. With a ruler or a pencil stir the water in your jar until it will not go any faster. Remove the stirrer and place a small drop of food coloring in the water.

   What do you observe?

   View the swirling water from the top and from underneath—the under surface of the water is an interesting view.

   Stir the water again and then drop a small piece of paper on the surface of the water. What do you observe?

   Does it make any difference where you drop the piece of paper—in the middle, halfway out, along the side of the jar?

8. Do you know what a "centrifuge" is?

   If you connected one line to a Ping-Pong ball and another line to a baseball and then whirled them about your head, both at the same speed, which one would try to pull harder away from you?

   If the lines connected to the Ping-Pong ball and the baseball were made of elastic, which line would stretch farther—the one connected to the Ping-Pong ball or the one connected to the baseball?

9. A "centrifuge" is a machine that spins materials at high speed and separates things of different weight. In a hospital, blood samples are placed in a centrifuge to separate the corpuscles from the plasma. The corpuscles are heavier than the plasma, so they move to the outside of the centrifuge.

   If you were using a centrifuge to separate heavy cream from milk, would the heavy cream go to the outside of the centrifuge or the inside?

10. Fill your jar halfway with clean water. Add one or two tablespoons of rice to the water.

    What do you think will happen to the rice when the water is stirred? (Answer this question before you try it.)

    Now stir the water. Does the rice move to the outside while you are stirring the water?

Considerable classroom discussion should result from this lesson. The following information should be helpful in stimulating classroom discussion or individual student projects related to some of the topics investigated in this activity.

The stirring of the water in the wide-mouth jar creates a **vortex**—a motion like a whirlpool. A tornado is a very strong vortex in the atmosphere. When this vortex is hundreds of miles in diameter it is called a hurricane. Hurricanes are like the vortex in a washbowl. As long as the swirl is strong, the vortex will not fill up (notice how the vortex in a washbowl builds up and diminishes). Whenever the vortex swirling motion is interfered with the hurricane "fills up" rapidly and loses its strength. Hurricanes which remain relatively stationary over the ocean surface and "lash" the coastline are very destructive. When the central portion, the vortex, of the hurricane remains over the ocean surface the mountain ranges or extensive hilly areas of the land masses cannot slow

down the spinning giant. The hilly land mass affects the hurricane's vortex motion in the same way your hand slows the spinning water in a washbowl.

An understanding of "swirling motion" in a jar is directly related to an understanding of the term **inertia**. The law of inertia states that things *tend* to remain unchanged in their motion even though the constraints around them try to change this motion. A package on the seat of a moving automobile tumbles forward when the car brakes are suddenly applied. A car passenger is "thrown" forward against the dashboard when the automobile suddenly stops. In both instances, the package and the passenger tended to remain in a state of forward motion. It was the constraint imposed by the car seat, as the car slowed down, which tried to change the motion of the package and the passenger. The inertia of the package and passenger tried to keep them moving forward.

Place a water cup on a sheet of paper. If you pull the paper slowly, the cup of water will move with it. If you snatch the paper quickly enough from under the water cup, the water will not spill, and the cup will remain in place. The inertia of the water cup tried to keep it stationary in spite of the constraint imposed by the movement of the paper under the cup.

Water whirling around in a jar or objects whirling around on the end of a string are constrained to move in specific directions by the jar and the attached string. The inertia of segments of water or the objects on the end of the string tend to make the water and objects, at each instant, move in a straight line tangent to the whirling motion. The sides of the jar and the string overcome this inertia and cause the change in motion from instant to instant. When the string holding the whirling object is released the object moves off in a straight line—tangent to the circle at the instant of release. Note that the object does *not* move directly away from the center. Although you feel a pull of the object directly away from you as it is whirled in a circle this is not the direction of some force acting on the object. If it were, the object would move directly away from you upon release. The pull you feel is exactly that force *you* must continuously exert to keep (constrain)

the object moving in a circular path overcoming its inertia—overcoming the object's instantaneous "desire" to move off on a tangential path at every point in its travel. The size of the object or the length of the string will not affect the results. The heavier object or longer string will only cause you to supply more effort to maintain a circular path (to overcome inertia).

The water in the jar would have moved out from its whirled path if the jar had not prevented it. Instead the water piled up against the sides of the jar as more water moved out from the whirled path. This piling up along the sides left the center with a "hole"—a vortex.

Just as the side of the jar constrained the water and the string constrained the object to move in a circular path, a satellite is constrained to move in its orbit about the earth by a constraint—gravity. Gravity keeps pulling the satellite toward the earth. There is no centrifugal force to balance the pull of gravity. If it were not for gravity, the satellite would move off in a straight line tangent to its circular path. The inertia of the satellite, the tendency of the satellite to move instantaneously in a tangential direction, is continuously overcome by the constraint (pull) of gravity toward the center. There is no force pulling the satellite away from the center of the orbit, only the tendency for it to move in a straight line unless something pulls it out of line. This pull is gravity and it is toward the center.

The spinning of a centrifuge separates things of different weight. The heavy objects move to the outside of the centrifuge because the surrounding fluid cannot constrain them to move in a circular path, overcoming their tendency (inertia) to move off in a tangential path. When the heavy objects hit the outside of the whirling container they are then constrained to move in a circular path. The lighter objects are found toward the center of the whirling fluid where the surrounding fluid is sufficient to constrain the particles to move in a circular path.

The experience with the rice (#10 above) is somewhat perplexing to students and does not have an immediate explanation understandable to intermediate school youngsters.

When the water and rice are continuously

stirred the rice does move to the outside of the jar and remain close to the sides. This is the "centrifuge action" you would expect—the heavier particles moving to the outside as the whirling continues. When the stirring is stopped and the whirling motion slows down, the rice does *not* collect around the outside, but rather collects at the center of the jar. The rice particles actually move in toward the center, as the whirling fluid slows down, and they settle in the center! There are many everyday examples of this, for example—sugar in the bottom of a glass of iced tea collects in the center after stirring.

The fundamental law explaining this phenomenon is the conservation of angular momentum. The experiment with the rice is a demonstration of this law. The change in spinning rate of an ice skater standing in one spot is another everyday example. The rate of spinning of the ice skater seems to change as he moves his arms in and out (fast, arms in—slow, arms out).

Not all questions or experiences have understandable answers or explanations. This experience may be one of the big questions neither the class nor teacher can at this time understand or explain.

Science is not fun because we know all the answers—what makes it fun is the exploration of the unknown and the combining of all our ingenuity, curiosity, and perseverance to discover explanations and truths.

Additional Activities—Commonplace "Things"

1. Show the effects of air pressure. Pour a cup of water into a gallon can. Heat the water until it boils. Place the cap on the can and allow it to cool. As it cools the can will cave in from external pressure.
2. Show the effects of air pressure. Obtain a piece of wood similar in size to a yardstick. Place it on a table with six inches of its length extending over the edge. Cover the other end with four or five unfolded sections of newspaper. Now strike the stick a sharp blow and it will break. The newspaper will hold the other end with sufficient force such that there will be a clean break at the edge of the table.
3. Consider ways to construct a molecular model of matter using marbles, Ping-Pong balls, beebees, or styrofoam balls. Random motion and its average effect are what you are seeking to demonstrate.
4. Consider the properties of carbon dioxide and oxygen. Show that air is needed for combustion (place a glass over a burning candle). Produce carbon dioxide by adding several drops of vinegar to a couple tablespoons of baking soda, mixed in half a can of water (do not use a glass). Collect the carbon dioxide released by placing the small can in a larger container. Carbon dioxide is heavier than air. It will accumulate in the bottom of the large container. Light some candles and "pour" the carbon dioxide over the candles.
5. Construct a homemade barometer, rain gauge, anemometer, and sling psychrometer. Chart the variations of a barometer for a period of time.
6. Collect information on the behavior of different animals during a change in the prevailing weather conditions.
7. Warm air rises and is less dense than cold air. Balance two inverted paper cups on the ends of a yardstick. The yardstick is supported in the middle. Place a burning candle below one cup. The stick will no longer remain in balance. The warm air has caused an air current to push up on the cup.
8. Keep a daily chart of cloud coverage, temperature, and pressure. After a period of time see if this information can be used to predict local weather conditions.
9. Display pictures of the harmful effects of tornadoes, hurricanes, and snowstorms.
10. Lime water can be used to detect the presence of carbon dioxide. Insert a rubber tube in a jar of lime water and blow into the tube. The lime water will turn milky white, indicating the presence of carbon dioxide.
11. Experiment with the evaporation of water from two different containers, one with a small surface area and one with a large surface area. Place the same amount of water in

each. Which one evaporates faster? (The large surface area container.) The earth is covered with water—this is the storehouse of the atmosphere's water vapor.

12. Discuss how large water masses affect local weather conditions. Keep records of temperatures recorded in your town and in a nearby town. Interesting results are observable during autumn, spring, and summer.

13. Water exerts pressure. Drill three holes at different heights in the side of a quart can. Place a small cork stopper in each hole. Fill the can with water and remove the stoppers. The effects of varying heights of water will be apparent.

14. Attach a string to a rubber stopper and whirl it around over your head. The stopper will travel in a circle. The pull of the string on the stopper represents the gravitational pull that the sun exerts on a planet. The stopper represents a planet. This pull alters the path of the stopper from instant to instant, causing it to move in a circle.

15. Discuss the Law of Inertia using examples common to everyday experiences. Some of these are: people traveling in a car which suddenly comes to an abrupt stop and the people continue moving forward; people in a car just starting up from rest feel themselves pushed back against the seat—trying to oppose a change in their state of motion (from no motion to motion straight ahead); people traveling in a car going around a sharp curve feel a sideways push exerted by the door of the car or by a person next to them—this push is changing their state of motion in a straight line to one in a curved line.

16. Contact an amateur astronomy club in your area. Maybe a night under the stars can be arranged. The moons of Jupiter can be observed with only a pair of field binoculars.

17. Distances can be measured by finding the angle subtended by a certain body and knowledge of some base line. Some students may become interested in finding out how this is accomplished. Make a graphical solution and more difficult mathematics becomes unnecessary.

18. Collect recent articles on space exploration and discuss their scientific as well as social impact on peoples of the world. The term **weightlessness** is one which should be explored. It is commonly misunderstood.

19. What are some of the environmental problems of living in outer space? What effects does space travel have on the human body and its systems?

20. Motions of certain planets in our solar system can be dramatized. Let the sun be represented by a basketball in the center of the playground or gymnasium floor. Make circles with the sun as a center using a long cord and chalk. The circles will represent the orbits of Mercury, Venus, Earth, and Mars. The radii of these circles should be in the following proportion 6 : 11 : 16 : 24. Children will represent each of the planets. Timing must be worked out carefully; for example, Mercury should make about four trips around the sun to every one of the Earth. The moon goes around the Earth twelve times while the Earth is making one trip. This could be worked out elaborately for presentation to other classes.

21. Study the location and some of the astrology connected with certain constellations. Project on the ceiling constellations children have made with pinpricks on black paper.

22. Have children collect information about the earliest astronomers—Copernicus, Galileo, Hershel, Brahe, etc.

23. The unit of distance for space travel is the light-year. Emphasize the magnitude of this unit and explain what it means. For example, the nebula Andromeda is estimated to be 2,500,000 light-years away, an almost incomprehensible distance.

24. Make star maps of circumpolar and seasonal constellations.

25. Observe the grooves in a phonograph record. How are these grooves made into sound?

26. Stretch a "slinky" across the room. Transmit a longitudinal pulse in the slinky. This is how sound travels through space.

27. Observe sound energy. Obtain a table model radio with the speaker exposed. Warm up the

radio with the volume all the way down. Hang a small piece of tissue paper over the speaker. Turn the volume up rapidly and note the deflection of the tissue paper. It is being bombarded by molecules.

28. Collect information on how temperature affects the speed of sound in air. It increases with temperature. Does this seem reasonable?

29. A common event in this day and age is the "sonic boom." What is the cause of this phenomenon?

30. With candle wax place a needle on the end of a tuning fork. Smoke a glass plate with a candle flame. Strike the fork and draw it across the glass in such a way that the needle draws a wavy line over the surface of the smoked glass. Use this to help explain wavelength, period, frequency, and amplitude.

31. Use a simplified picture of the ear to explain how it functions.

32. Have children note the difference in radio and television reception during the daytime and at night. Signals are reflected off the layers in the ionosphere and these layers change altitude during the course of a 24-hour period. They gain altitude in the daytime and decrease in altitude, or some may even disappear, at night.

33. Construct a complete weather station using home-made devices. Encourage the accurate and periodic recording of weather information. Records should be maintained for an extended period of time.

34. Air exerts pressure. Fill a milk bottle with water, place a piece of paper over its mouth, and then carefully invert the bottle. Air pressure will prevent the water from coming out. Really it is a total force over the surface of the paper, which results from a certain air pressure per unit area on the paper, acting to hold the water in the bottle.

35. Bring to bear knowledge of heat, temperature, and pressure to discuss the motion of air masses. High and low pressure areas result from a unique interplay of all these factors. Have children bring in weather maps from the newspaper. Discuss possible predictions made from these maps. Learn to read and understand the symbols.

36. Plan a trip to the local weather station as a way of culminating work in this area.

37. Consider some of the experiments now in process to control weather conditions such as snow, fog, rain, and hurricanes. For example, dry ice has been used to seed clouds in an attempt to cause moisture in the clouds to condense as rain or snow depending on the temperature. Not all efforts have been successful but there are indications the future may hold some interesting advances.

38. Demonstrate air pressure with a hard-boiled egg. Set fire to a small piece of paper, place it in a milk bottle, and quickly cover the top with a peeled hard-boiled egg. In a moment the egg will drop into the bottle. The heat of the burning paper forced some of the air in the bottle out past the egg. As the remaining air in the bottle cools, it contracts, but additional air cannot enter the bottle from outside. The pressure outside the bottle is greater than that inside and the egg is forced into the milk bottle.

39. Construct a simple barometer from a milk bottle. It won't indicate air pressure but will indicate changes in air pressure. Stretch a piece of balloon tightly over the top of the milk bottle. Glue a straw to the surface of the rubber balloon. Increases and decreases in air pressure will be indicated by the change in the tilt of the straw.

40. Construct a hair hygrometer for indicating the moisture in the air. Human hair gets longer when it is moist, and shorter as it dries.

41. Investigate some of the major weather disturbances in the Pacific and in India—the monsoons of India and the typhoons of the Pacific.

CURRENTS AND CHARGES

How to Begin

It was during the Renaissance, in the fourteenth to sixteenth centuries, that a systematic study of electricity and magnetism developed, and it was not until the end of the past century that physicists had gained a clear understanding of the relation between these two areas. Hardly ever did a scientific achievement have such profound and far-reaching consequences. The harnessing of electrical power and the development of electrical communications have changed our whole way of life. We have learned that electric forces control the structure of atoms and molecules. Electricity is associated with many biological processes—for instance, with the actions of our nervous systems and brains.

Intermediate school youngsters are fully aware of the presence of electrical "things" in their environment. Some youngsters may have had experiences with commercially prepared "electricity sets." Your goal in this unit is to emphasize certain fundamental characteristics of electricity through student independent work with very simple materials.

Why Do It This Way?

This unit is subdivided into activities. Each activity does not necessarily represent one class period for science. This unit is **not** a teacher-centered activity. Youngsters respond to experiments they perform using questions from the various activities as starting points for individual or small group activities.

Students at the middle and secondary school levels often demonstrate a lack of fundamental information about electricity and magnetism, primarily because earlier experiences with these phe-

nomena have been superficial or extremely limited.

Many elementary school teachers are not "comfortable" when working with electricity and magnetism, this area therefore receiving considerably less attention from them than other segments of science.

Using the suggested approach in this unit will reduce considerably the anxiety of teachers inexperienced in electricity and permit all teachers to be more creative in their classroom experiences with electricity and magnetism.

How to Do It

The activities for this unit can center around

written question sheets developed by the teacher or verbal questions periodically stated by the teacher. The youngsters should be encouraged to keep permanent records of their experiences. Any scheme meaningful to the child should be acceptable. Given an opportunity, youngsters will compare their techniques and findings, from which will develop interesting changes in individual activities. Always encourage the youngsters to give written and verbal descriptions of their results.

Activity 1

For this first activity each child should have a bar magnet and a collection of iron washers or paper clips. One can of iron filings is also necessary. The following questions will permit individual expression.

1. You have been given one magnet. Move this magnet closer to the one your neighbor has. What happens?
2. How long a chain of paper clips or washers will your magnet pick up?
   Why do you think the washers or clips hold together?
3. Does magnetism affect all materials? Will magnetism go through anything? Make some tests on different materials. Think of a way to record your results.

4. Can you see magnetism? Sprinkle some iron filings on a paper which is covering a magnet. What happens to the filings? Are you seeing magnetism? What are you seeing?

Let this activity start with "play time" with the magnets. Do not be too eager to direct the class to formalized written or verbal questions about the magnets. When you do use the suggested questions permit adequate time for every student to make a specific decision. The development of an activity sheet is suggested.

The experiences in this activity can serve as the focal point for some meaningful classroom discussions. This will not be the first time the children have done something with a magnet. They probably already know about the "north" and "south" poles of a magnet. Knowledge of these designations, however, does not contribute to a greater understanding of magnetism. "North" and "south" are arbitrary designations which have no bearing on the real nature of magnetism. The fact that there are circumstances when magnets attract or repel one another is significant. The labeling of areas on a magnet by the names "north" and "south" makes it more convenient for us to discuss the relative physical position of magnets—but it is not fundamental to greater understanding. We could label the extremities of a bar magnet "voom" and "zoom." The "law of poles," using

these designations, would state: "voom" repels "voom" (like repels like) and "voom" attracts "zoom" (unlike attracts).

One very important, yet subtle point to emphasize in discussions related to Activity 1 is that "magnetism works at a distance." A magnet exerts a force on things that can be called a **magnetic force.** It is an interesting force because it acts through a distance—direct contact between the magnet and the thing affected is not necessary! Most forces children have a daily awareness about are contact forces—pushes, pulls, and bumps between objects that are touching each other. Another example of a "noncontact" force—one that operates whether objects are touching or not—is the **gravitational force.** Gravitational force is a universal force and exists between and/or through all objects, whereas magnetic forces can be shielded and may not exist between or through all objects. An early beginning of the understanding and acceptance of the "force at a distance" concept can begin at this level.

We can "see" magnetism. Iron filings sprinkled on a piece of paper placed over a magnet will form an interesting pattern. The pattern formed by the iron filings represents the magnetic field surrounding the magnet. The iron filings help in visualizing ("seeing") the magnetic field, but the field is in no way dependent on the use of iron filings. The magnetic field of a magnet can be thought of as the "realm of influence" of the magnet. Objects in this "realm of influence" are acted on by a magnetic force. Where the force is large (close to the magnet) the "realm of influence" (magnetic field) is strong, and where the force is small (farther from the magnet) the "realm of influence" (magnetic field) is weak. The iron filings cluster together where the magnetic field is strong.

The pattern formed by iron filings sprinkled on a piece of paper covering a magnet may not be a new experience for your students. The concept that this pattern represents a magnetic field is new. Try to develop further class consideration of this concept of **field** by discussing current space age technology which must contend with the gravitational field of our earth. Close to the earth

the "realm of influence" (earth's gravitational field) is strong—farther away the realm of influence (earth's gravitational field) is weak. At points where the "realm of influence" is large the force exerted on an object is large. At points where the "realm of influence" is small the force exerted on the **same** object is small. As was true about our discussion of the "force at a distance" concept, the discussion of "field" and "field strength" should begin to develop the early beginnings of acceptance and understanding of this important concept.

Activity 2

For Activity 2 each child should be given a magnetic compass, a nail, and a collection of paper clips or pins. The following questions placed in the form of an activity sheet are suggested:

1. You have been given a magnetic compass. What is a magnetic compass?
2. What does the magnetic compass tell you?
3. When you place your magnet near the magnetic compass is it affected? What does it do? Do other "things" affect the magnetic compass?
4. Make the nail into a "nail magnet." Stroke the nail 50 or 60 times in the **same direction** with the magnet.

How many paper clips will the "nail magnet" pick up?

5. Will the "nail magnet" affect the magnetic compass?

Is the "nail magnet" as strong as your bar magnet?

Did the bar magnet lose something when it stroked the nail?

The magnetic compass used by each child emphasizes the notion of a magnetic field. A magnetic compass responds to a magnetic field. Actually, a magnetic compass is an indicator of the presence of a magnetic field. The compass can be an indicator not only of the presence of a magnetic field but also, to some degree, of its strength (the compass deflects more rapidly close to the magnetic source than farther away). A magnetic compass used for navigation is affected by the earth's magnetic field. The direction of the earth's magnetic field (the pattern) is relatively constant and hence a magnetic compass always assumes an orientation which points in the general direction of north.

Making a nail magnet may not be a new experience. The difficult question that may stem from this activity is, How did the nail become magnetized? Most elementary explanations will begin by discussing this question in terms of the "lining up" of many tiny imaginary magnets within the nail (or other object). When a sufficient number of these tiny imaginary magnets are all lined up and remain in that configuration the nail will exhibit magnetic characteristics which can be observed. For the moment your concern should not be about the cause or origin of magnetism. You should be more concerned with its observable characteristics and effects. Do not discourage questions about the origin of magnetism, rather encourage thought on this topic. Just remember that all questions do not demand an immediate, understandable response by you. At this point encourage only the formulation of the question. Learning to shape good questions is just as important as developing an answer for them.

Activity 3

The magnets used in earlier activities have all been "permanent magnets." The origin of the magnetism has not been developed. From experiences and discussions connected with Activities 1 and 2 the youngsters should be aware of many of its characteristics. It is possible to develop the initial concepts connected with its origin from this activity.

Let students work in pairs. Give each pair of students one nail (8-10 penny), 3 feet of bell wire (plastic or cotton insulated, number 20, 22, or 24), one flashlight battery (size D), a collection of paper clips or pins, and a magnetic compass.

1. You have received a nail, a piece of wire, and a flashlight battery. Wind the wire around the nail about fifty times as shown in the figure.

Remove the insulation from the ends of the wire (about an inch).
Connect the ends of the wire to the flashlight battery.

2. Does the nail wound with the wire act like a magnet? Does it affect your compass?

3. Draw a picture of how you connected the flashlight battery to the wire around the nail.

4. What happens when you disconnect the wire from the flashlight battery?

5. What happens when you make only ten turns around the nail?

Prior to this activity some of the youngsters may have had experience with an electromagnet. They will undoubtedly know how to connect the wire to the flashlight battery. Other youngsters will be doing this for the first time. Do not be too eager to render assistance. It is best to let those students that do know how to connect the wires act as teachers. Always encourage youngsters to learn from one another. The connection should be as indicated in the figure.

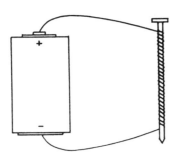

The nail magnet will exhibit the same characteristics as the bar magnet. It will pick up metallic objects. Iron filings sprinkled on a piece of paper covering the nail magnet will produce the same pattern as that caused by the bar magnet. The nail magnet will affect the magnetic compass in the same manner as did the bar magnet.

When the flashlight battery is connected to the wire the characteristics observed indicate the presence of a magnetic field surrounding the nail. These characteristics largely disappear when the wires are disconnected (some residual magnetism may remain).

The youngsters know that a flashlight battery "supplies electricity," and hence when the wires are properly connected the electricity moves through the wires. This "electricity in the wires" produces a magnetic field with the same characteristics as any magnetic field. Magnetic fields are produced by electric currents—**moving** electrical charges. The ultimate origin of **all** magnetic fields is moving electrical charges. This will not be apparent to the youngsters, for their experience will permit this conclusion only for the nail magnet, not the bar magnet.

In this activity you are not trying to convince or persuade the youngsters that all magnetic fields are caused by moving electrical charges. Sufficient will be accomplished if they begin to think about the relationship between the flow of electricity in a wire (moving electrical charges) and a magnetic field.

Activity 4

The formal study of electricity is not nearly as old as many other fields of science. About two

hundred years ago Benjamin Franklin experimented with his kite and key. A little more than one hundred years ago there were no electric lights, telephones, or radios. About twenty-five years ago television was a novelty.

With simple and inexpensive equipment children can discover for themselves some basic principles of electricity.

Let students work in pairs. Provide each pair with one flashlight battery (size D), one foot of bell wire (plastic or cotton insulated, number 20, 22 or 24), and one flashlight bulb (number 14 with a screw-type base).

1. You have received a flashlight battery, a piece of wire, and a flashlight bulb. Can you make the bulb light?

2. How many different ways can you make the flashlight bulb work? Connect the flashlight battery, bulb, and wire in combinations as suggested in the table (observe the diagram).

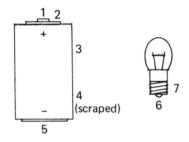

When these touch:	And the wire connects:	Will the bulb light?
6 and 1	7 to 2	Yes
6 and 1	7 to 3	?
6 and 1	7 to 4	
6 and 1	7 to 5	
6 and 2	7 to 1	
6 and 2	7 to 3	
7 and 1	6 to 5	
	(and so on)	

3. The flashlight bulb did not always work. Can you describe in your own words how the electricity was moving when the bulb did work?

4. A battery supplies energy to the flashlight bulb. When the battery and bulb were connected correctly the energy supplied by the battery caused the bulb to work.

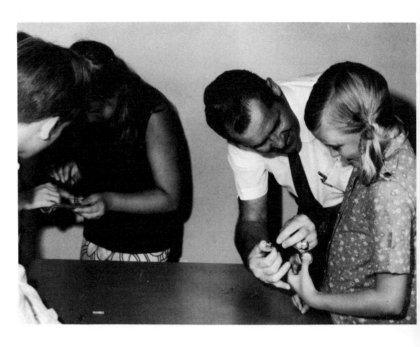

a. Did the bulb work for every connection?

b. When the bulb did not work was the battery supplying energy to the bulb?

c. There seem to be only certain connections which let the energy from the battery make the bulb work. These certain connections are called a complete path—a complete circuit—for the electrical energy.

5. You have received a second flashlight battery. Connect the batteries, bulb, and wire in combinations as suggested in the table (observe the diagram).

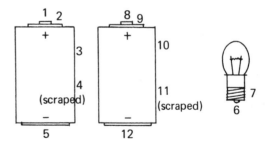

When these touch:		And the wire connects:	Will the bulb light?
6 and 1	8 and 5	7 to 12	Yes
6 and 1	8 and 5	7 to 11	?
6 and 1	8 and 5	7 to 10	
6 and 1	8 and 5	7 to 9	
6 and 1	8 and 5	7 to 5	

6 and 1	8 and 5	7 to 4
7 and 1	8 and 5	6 to 12
7 and 1	8 and 5	6 to 11
7 and 1	8 and 5	6 to 10
6 and 1	12 and 5	7 to 8
6 and 1	12 and 5	7 to 10
6 and 1	12 and 5	7 to 11

(and so on)

6. Did the bulb light with the same brightness in each of the connections you made for question 5?

When the bulb, the wire, and the battery are connected so the bulb lights, a circuit has been completed. In a completed circuit electricity travels through the wires—energy is transferred through the circuit to the bulb. Without a completed circuit, electricity does not flow—energy is not moved through the circuit to the bulb. There can be no gap in the circuit. A circuit which has a gap in it is called an "open" circuit. Whenever the bulb did not light there was an open circuit—the path was not complete and continuous for the flow of electricity (flow of energy).

This activity is a confrontation with the necessary materials for making electrical circuits. You can provide assistance in helping youngsters understand the directions or in setting up various experiments but do not try to provide explanations. You are primarily interested in the collection and organization of data. Using the data collected, have the class together note the situations in which the bulb did work.

The major points of understanding you want to start in this activity are:

a. A battery is a source of energy which causes electricity to move through wires, bulbs, etc.

b. Only a complete circuit will allow the energy to move through the wire, bulb, etc.

c. The way the circuit is "hooked up" determines how the energy is "used" in the circuit.

Activity 5

Now there should be considerably more experimentation with circuits. This experimentation will be more structured than in previous activities.

Students experimenting with flashlight batteries and bulbs learned that in some circuits, as flashlight batteries are added to a circuit, the bulb becomes brighter. Some students may have added too many batteries and actually burned out the bulb.

Flashlight batteries added to a circuit such that the point of one touches the base of another, thus making a line of flashlight batteries, are **in series**.

Whatever passes through one unit of the series must pass through all other units of the series;

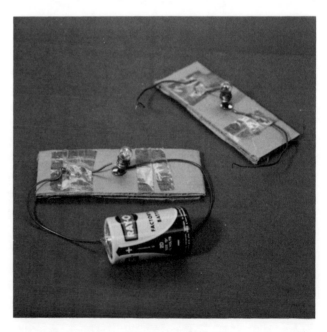

there is only one pathway. In a flashlight the parts of the circuit are in series; no electricity can move through one part of the circuit without moving through all other parts.

Let students work in pairs. The following questions will structure the activities:

1. Connect two flashlight batteries in series. An easy way to hold the flashlight batteries in place is to drop them into a cardboard tube from the inside of a roll of paper towel or foil. Connect one flashlight bulb to the two batteries. Did the bulb light?

2. Remove one flashlight battery and connect the flashlight bulb to the battery. Did the bulb light? Did the bulb receive as much energy as it did in question 1? How did you decide this?

3. Connect two flashlight bulbs in series with one flashlight battery. See the following diagram for how you should make these connections.

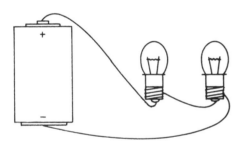

   a. Did the bulbs light?
   b. Were bulbs brighter or dimmer than when only one bulb was connected to the battery?
   c. Each bulb is receiving (more or less) energy than was received by one bulb connected to the battery. How did you decide this?
   d. What happens if you disconnect one bulb? Will the other bulb still work? Explain.
   e. If more batteries are added in series the bulbs receive (more or less) energy. Try it.

4. There are symbols for batteries and bulbs which make it easier to draw diagrams of circuits. The symbol for a battery is 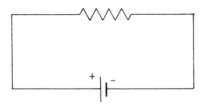 and the symbol for a bulb can be

   a. The diagram for one battery connected to one bulb is

   b. Draw the diagram for one battery connected to two bulbs in series.
   c. Draw the diagram for two batteries in series connected to two bulbs in series. Practice drawing other circuit diagrams.

The addition of batteries in series adds more voltage—more energy—to the circuit. This is evidenced by bulbs becoming brighter as batteries are added. Each additional bulb in a series adds a sort of bottleneck, making it more difficult for energy to be transferred through the circuit (more difficult for electricity to pass through the circuit). The tiny wire filament in a bulb resists the

transfer of energy (the flow of electricity), even though some energy does pass through it (some electricity does pass through it). It is this **resistance** to the flow of energy (the electric current) that makes the filament glow. Every object in an electric circuit has some resistance to the transfer of energy (the electric current). Objects with high resistance become warmed by the flow of energy (the electric current). Objects with low resistance remain relatively cool. The object of highest resistance in a series circuit becomes the warmest.

If two objects have equal resistances, they become equally warm (take the same transfer of energy). Three bulbs with filaments of equal resistance become equally hot (bright).

In a series circuit, the total resistance to the flow of energy (the electric current) is the **sum** of all the resistances. That is why adding another bulb in a series circuit makes all the bulbs dimmer. As each new bulb is placed in the circuit, its resistance is added to all the rest, and the flow of energy (the electric current) is reduced through all the bulbs. This is true in a series circuit no matter where the bulb or other electric device is added to the circuit.

A series circuit provides only one pathway for the flow of energy (the electric current). If the circuit is **opened** at any point, the pathway is broken and energy will not flow (no electric current). It will resume as soon as the circuit is **closed**—the pathway made complete. A **switch** opens or closes a circuit—breaks or completes the pathway.

For this activity simple light bulb sockets can be made from some wire, cardboard, a tack, and tape. See the picture. Zigzag the wire leading to the socket in order to help keep it rigid.

Activity 6

There is another basic circuit. When the flow of energy (the electric current) can take more than one pathway at any point in a circuit, the pathways are in **parallel**. Batteries or bulbs, or both, can be connected in parallel.

Let students work in pairs. The following questions will structure the activities.

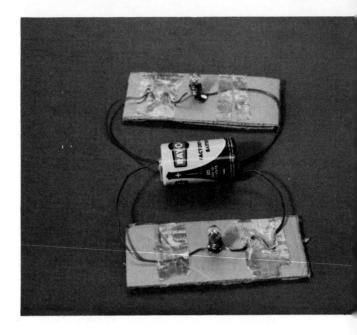

1. Connect your bulbs and batteries as shown in the circuit diagram.

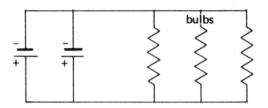

What happens if:
   a. You unscrew one bulb.
   b. You unscrew two bulbs.
   c. You use only one battery.
Here is a diagram of how the hook-up should look:

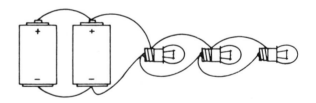

2. Make a **series** circuit using two batteries and three bulbs. Compare it with the circuit you made for question 1. Draw the circuit diagram.

Unscrewing a bulb from a parallel circuit has no observable effect on the other bulbs—they continue to burn as brightly as before. Removing one battery in parallel has no apparent effect on the energy provided the bulbs.

The energy from the batteries, arriving at the bulbs, can take any of the paths. If all bulbs are the same there is little difference which path the energy will follow (which path the electric current takes). An equal amount of energy (electric current) will go through each filament. Even though the filament in each bulb represents a resistance to energy transfer (electric current), three such filaments in parallel permit three times as much energy flow (electric current) as when only one filament is present. Each additional filament makes another path to permit energy flow (electric current). No matter how much resistance a pathway in a parallel circuit has, it can increase only the total energy flow (electric current) carried by the **supply wires.**

Electricity passing through devices in series and in parallel is analogous to people getting out of an auditorium through various arrangements of doorways. Suppose, for example, that all the people in an auditorium had to leave by one exit, a passageway with only one small door. There would be much pushing and shoving and probably a pileup at the doorway as all the people sought to escape by the one route. A second similar door in the passageway would only make a double traffic jam, and a third door would make a third jam. This is like a series circuit. All the electricity must go through a single route, regardless of how many devices are in it.

On the other hand, imagine the auditorium with more than one exit, each sharing the job of emptying the auditorium. Although each door is sort of a bottleneck, each is also a pathway for people, and the more pathways there are, the greater the flow of people from the auditorium in a period of time. This is like a parallel circuit in which the electricity has more than one route.*

*Jeannette Bakke and Verne N. Rockcastle, "Electric Circuits and Charges," Cornell Science Leaflet, Volume 60, Number 4, May 1967.

Home wiring circuits are parallel circuits. Usually each room is one circuit and all appliances or devices connected to each circuit are in parallel. These individual circuits are separately fused at some central point. For each appliance or device that is turned on, more energy flows (electric current) in that circuit of the house and more energy (electric current) is carried by the fuse in that circuit. If too much energy flows through the fuse, because too many devices are turned on in the circuit, the fuse will heat up and burn out—thus protecting the circuit from an overload.

Review some of the components in the circuits made in Activities 4, 5, and 6. All components (wires, bulbs, batteries, etc.) resist the flow of electricity (movement of charged particles—usually electrons). It is this effect which is labeled **resistance.** The flow of electricity (movement of charged particles in **a given period of time**) is called **current.** The energy supplied the "electricity" (electrical charges) is called **voltage.** The battery, the power station, etc., are the sources of energy for the electrical charges.

Do not draw analogies between an electric circuit and the flow of water in a closed system of pipes. Practically all such analogies result in wrong concepts. This analogy is used extensively in most science books and it usually is incorrect. A battery is **not** a pump—it **does not** supply pressure to a circuit. A battery merely supplies **energy** to the electric charges. The unit of this energy is the **volt**—which is defined as energy per charge. The larger the voltage of a battery the greater the amount of energy capable of being transferred by the battery to each charge. Large batteries (large in size) with the **same voltage rating as small batteries** (small in size) transfer the same amount of energy to each charge—the larger battery can do it for a longer period of time—it has greater total energy storage. Large energy transfer per charge means large current—small energy transfer per charge means small current. In simple terms, the battery does work on the charge and any time that work is done on any object energy is transferred to it. Remember, the definition of Work is Force times Distance, and the definition of Pressure is Force divided by Area. Pressure and Work are **not** at all alike. The origin of the energy in a battery is a chemical reaction within the cell. This is all that need be said about the origin of the energy. Children can have fun pointing out the errors in many of their science books after the function of a battery has been completely explained.

It is now advisable to encourage students to obtain a more fundamental idea about electrical charges. Therefore, we will consider some experiences with static electricity.

Not all electricity is contained in cells, batteries, and wires. Sometimes it is not useful in doing work. At times electricity moves as uncontrolled charges, making sparks, giving people shocks, or holding objects together. Especially when the humidity is very low (as in the winter) electric charges can be extremely annoying.

All objects are made up of charged particles of some kind. The wood in a chair, the paper in this book, and even persons consist of molecules and atoms, individual parts of which are charged particles. Some particles are neutral and do not take part in the currents of ordinary electricity. Two kinds of particles are involved in the production of electric currents—the proton, which is positively charged (found in the nucleus of the atom, relatively heavy, and not readily moved from the nucleus), and the electron, which is negatively charged (found moving rapidly around the nucleus, 1/1800th the mass of the proton, and easily moved from around the nucleus). It is important to note that the selection of the terms **positive** and **negative**, although having some historical significance, is purely arbitrary. The terms "zat" and "zap" might just as well have been chosen to indicate the different kinds of electrification. Nature did not supply the names positive and negative—they were invented by man.

Activity 7

Supply each child with one balloon, a piece of string, and a plastic strip (plastic vinyl and acetate strips can be commercially purchased, or use strips cut from the negatives of old X-ray plates, plastic straws, etc.).

1. You have walked across a wool carpet and touched a doorknob or a person and noticed the "crack" of a spark. Tear some paper into tiny pieces and place them on your desktop. Can you pick up any of the pieces with your strip of plastic? Rub the plastic between your fingers or against a piece of wool (fingers should be dry). Can you pick up some pieces of paper with the plastic strip?

2. Inflate your balloon and tie it with the string. Rub the balloon against a woolen cloth or your clothes. Then place the balloon against the desk or the wall. What happened? Hold your balloon next to the one your neighbor has and note what happens.

3. Cut two long strips of newspaper (about 2 inches wide and 12 inches long). Hold the two strips in one hand and run the other hand quickly down the strips, keeping one finger between the strips and one finger on the outside of each of them. Do this rapidly two or three times. What happens?

4. Rub the plastic strip quickly between your fingers or with a woolen cloth. Try to pick up chalkdust with the plastic strip.

5. Make a simple electroscope. See the diagram and related description for making a simple electroscope.

Material required: 2 large paper clips, small piece of modeling clay, 1 plastic top from a coffee can, 1 drinking straw, 1 needle or pin. *Directions*: Bend both paper clips as indicated,

insert the straight end of each paper clip into the plastic top by poking holes in the top which are about 3/8 inch to 1/2 inch apart; hold the paper clips in place with the modeling clay which is pressed on top of the plastic top; cut the straw to a 3 1/2-inch length and insert the needle or pin just to the left or right of the middle of the straw.

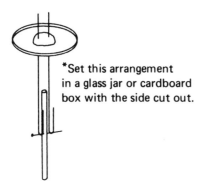

*Set this arrangement in a glass jar or cardboard box with the side cut out.

Charge your plastic strip and then touch the

electroscope with the strip. Note what happens to the straw in the electroscope.

6. Place two electroscopes next to one another. Connect a piece of wire between the two electroscopes. Touch one electroscope with the charged plastic strip. What happens to both electroscopes? Connect a piece of string between the two electroscopes and place a charge on one of the electroscopes with the plastic strip. What happens to both electroscopes?

7. Hold a charged plastic strip, comb, or straw next to a thin, unbroken stream of water. Describe what happens.

Activities such as those suggested can lead to the development of basic notions about electrical charges. This activity should initiate considerable discussion.

All objects contain a great many charges (billions or higher) and seldom are the positive and negative charges exactly equal—there are always slight differences. Only when fairly large differences occur are objects said to be charged. When an object is being charged, usually only the negative charges move. When you scuff your feet across a rug on a cold day, electrons move from you to the rug or from the rug to your feet, upsetting the balance of charges in both you and the rug. The spark you hear (and feel) when you touch a metal object is the "rush" of electrons from or to your body in order to once again establish the balance of positive and negative charges on your body.

The suggested activity sheets in this unit serve to motivate and supply some direction to student activity. Teachers are encouraged to modify the activities and/or add to the number of experiences suggested. Do not try to rush through this unit. For some classes it may be advisable to consider completing only a part of it.

The following projects are suggested as extra or supplemental activities.

Additional Activities—Currents and Charges

1. Demonstrate the relationship between moving electric charges and a magnetic field. Place a wire over a magnetic compass. Alter-

nately connect and disconnect the wire to a battery. Note the deflection of the magnetic compass.

2. Construct a simple circuit with a switch, light, and battery. Trace the flow of electric charges. Try more complicated circuit arrangements.

3. Obtain a fuse and take it apart to see how it is made. Find out how it works.

4. Construct an electromagnet with wire and a large nail. Any nail with ten, twenty, thirty, or more turns of wire will be satisfactory. Connect the ends of the wire to a battery. Compare the strength of different magnets containing varying turns of wire.

5. Use the simple circuit from item 2 above to find out how electric charges move in different substances. Break the circuit and insert, one at a time, various objects (nail, paper clip, eraser, chalk, etc.).

6. The atoms in a piece of iron or other substance are usually arranged haphazardly. When these atoms are arranged in a special orderly fashion we say the material is magnetized. Make up "models" using blocks or children to demonstrate that magnetism represents a unique kind of internal order. This order is frequently disturbed by heat or blows from a hammer and magnetism is "lost."

7. Acquire some pieces of magnetic iron ore, commonly called natural magnets. How does this natural magnet affect a compass? Can objects be picked up with it? How will the natural magnet affect finely cut pieces of steel wool sprinkled on a piece of paper? Do all parts of the natural magnet have the same effect on the compass?

8. The activities in 7 can be done with artificial magnets obtained from old radio loudspeakers or telephone receivers. Of course, they can also be obtained from scientific supply houses.

9. Magnets can be made from steel knitting needles or iron nails. Simply stroke the needle or nail with a magnet twenty or thirty times in the same direction. Test your results by using your "detector of magnetic fields"—the compass. Bar magnets can be made from metal hacksaw blades. Stroke opposite ends of each blade with alternate ends of a strong magnet. Hacksaw blades are made of hard steel and do not magnetize as easily as nails.

10. A magnetic compass can be made by simply stroking a needle in one direction with a permanent magnet, and sticking it through cork floating in a dish of water. Add some detergent to the water to keep the cork from sticking to the sides of the dish. Check your home-made compass with a commercial one. Be sure no other magnets are lying around when this test is made.

11. Insert a magnet into a box of tacks, nails, or paper clips. Most of the items will attach themselves to the ends of the magnet and hence it is usually stated a magnet's strength is concentrated at its ends—poles.

12. Magnetize a bar by hammering. An iron bar or old curtain rod will do. Test it with a compass at each end to see if it is magnetized. Hold the bar in a north-south direction and tilt it. Strike the rod several blows while it is in this position. Test it again with the compass. You will produce a magnet in this manner. In a sense the earth's magnetism stroked the bar as you hammered it, causing the material in the bar to be reorganized and hence the result is a magnet.

13. Make a magnet with iron filings. Fill a test tube or toothbrush tube about two-thirds full of iron filings. Place a stopper in the open end. See if a compass is affected by the tube of iron filings. Hold the tube carefully—do not shake or move it—and stroke the side of the tube twenty or thirty times with a permanent magnet. Bring the tube near a compass again—the tube of filings behaves like a solid magnet. Shake the tube up well and again bring it near the compass. It will not influence the compass. This demonstrates very nicely that magnetism is the result of many tiny pieces of matter (molecules and atoms) arranged in a unique order.

14. A permanent magnet held near but not touching a piece of nonmagnetized iron will cause this piece of iron to act as a magnet. This is called induced magnetism. The pieces of matter which make up the nonmagnetized iron (a nail) have been organized in a particular way because of the influence of the external magnetic field from the permanent magnet.

15. Place a magnet in a burner. Use one of the magnets made in an earlier experience (hacksaw blade). When the magnet has been removed from the flame is it still magnetized? Check it with a magnetic compass. Heating the magnet in some way disturbs the orientation of the pieces of matter within the magnet, causing it to lose its magnetic properties.

16. Cut some thin paper into small pieces and make a pile of cork particles by filing a cork. Obtain a plastic comb, ruler, rubber balloon, or other nonmetallic objects. Rub each of these objects with a piece of fur and/or a piece of silk and bring near the pieces of paper or pile of cork particles. Observe what happens.

17. Spread a sheet of newspaper out on a smooth dry wall. Rub over the entire surface with a ruler several times. Pull up on one corner and then let it go. It will snap back to the wall. On very dry days you can hear the crackle of the static charges.

18. Make an electroscope, which is a device for detecting charges. Obtain a glass jar, wire, a cork, and some pieces of thin aluminum foil or tissue paper. Insert one end of the wire into the cork and form the other end into an L-shape. Hang a piece of thin foil or tissue paper on the lower end of the wire. Insert the cork-wire assembly into the jar. Cover the cork with wax before final assembly. This will prevent the charges from leaking off. When a charged body is brought near the wire, the leaves of paper or foil will fly apart because they have received the same kind of charge. A permanent charge can be deposited on the electroscope by touching the wire with another charged object. When the charged object is removed the charge will remain on the electroscope as indicated by the way the leaves remain separated. In time this charge will leak off, causing the leaves to come together. When a charged object is placed near the electroscope, but not touching it, the electroscope is charged by induction. Removing the charged object from the vicinity of the electroscope will cause the leaves to come together.

19. Obtain some pith balls. Pith balls are made from the inside of a dried plant stem. They are also available from commercial supply houses. Coat them with aluminum or gold paint and attach them to pieces of silk thread. Suspend them from a wooden stand. Bring objects rubbed with fur or silk near the pith balls and see how they behave.

20. A good project for some children is making a motor. There is always information available in library books and regular textbooks about the best ways to construct a motor.

21. Magnets can be made other than by stroking a piece of iron with a permanent magnet. Wind some close turns of insulated copper wire around a piece of ordinary glass tubing. Insert knitting needles into the tube and connect each end of the coil to a flashlight battery. The magnetic field of the coil will induce a permanent field in the knitting needles.

22. Cut a dry cell in half with a saw, exposing the inside structure of the cell. Identify the parts and note any deterioration which is the result of the chemical reactions within the dry cell. The zinc covering is eaten away.

23. Connect dry cells in series—with two cells in series the light bulb will be brighter than with one cell. Connect dry cells in parallel. With two cells in parallel the light bulb will burn as brightly as with only one cell. What is the difference in the two arrangements? In the series connection the charged particles (electrons) have but one path to travel and in traveling this path charges move into and then out of each dry cell. Since the dry cell is a source of energy each charge (electron) re-

ceives additional energy in its passage through each cell. In the series connection each cell adds its energy to the circuit, which results in a larger current—more charges per second past a particular point because of this increased energy—and hence the bulb burns brighter with the addition of each cell in the circuit. In the parallel connection, the charged particles have more than one path to travel and in traveling these paths charges do not move into and out of each cell (provided all cells have the same voltage rating). Hence all charges receive only the energy supplied by a single cell. A bulb connected to a group of cells in parallel burns as brightly as one connected to but one cell. In the parallel connection each cell does not add its energy to the circuit in the manner observed in the series connection. Three 1½-volt cells connected in series add 4½ volts of energy to each fixed collection of charge passing through the circuit. Three ½-volt cells connected in parallel add ½ volt of energy to each fixed collection of charge passing through the circuit. The parallel connection provides a fixed amount of energy—a fixed voltage—which is available to all components in the circuit. Increasing the number of identical cells in parallel does not alter this fixed level of energy, but it does increase the circuit's ability to supply this same energy for a longer period of time. Adding more cells in parallel increases the "storehouse" of energy available, but does not change the rate at which it is "parceled" out. The series connection provides a fixed current—number of charges passing a particular point per second—for all components in the circuit. Increasing the number of cells in series increases the rate at which energy is supplied to the circuit and hence results in a larger value of current available to all components in the circuit. This value will stay fixed until more cells are added or removed from the circuit. Try connecting bulbs in parallel and in series.

24. One bulb can be controlled from two switches (see figure below). This sort of ar-

rangement is frequently encountered in homes with upstairs and downstairs hall lights. There are many other similar situations.

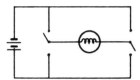

25. A simple fuse holder or fuse assembly can be constructed from cellophane tape (or masking tape), foil, and two paper clips. Foil strips are stuck to the tape and the paper clips will act as terminals for making connections (see figure below). This home-made fuse can be placed at various points in a circuit. Different lengths and widths of foil can be experimented with.

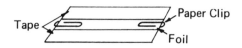

26. Dissolve some copper sulfate in a jar of water. Use enough copper sulfate to make the solution a deep blue. (Copper sulfate is obtainable from a hardware store or the high school chemistry department.) Insert a copper strip in the solution and connect it with a wire to the positive terminal of a dry cell. Attach a wire from the negative terminal of the dry cell to a clean iron nail which is also placed in the solution. In a short time the nail will be plated with a thin layer of copper. Other substances can be plated in this manner by attaching them to the negative terminal of the cell and placing them in this solution. This experiment serves as a good example to **illustrate the motion** of both positive and negative charges. When copper sulfate is dissolved in water, the copper sulfate molecule is broken apart. The copper atoms are detached from the copper sulfate

molecule. When this break occurs, the copper atom loses two of its electrons, leaving it with a net positive charge. The sulfate (SO_4) part of the copper sulfate molecule gains the two electrons the copper atom lost and hence has a net negative charge. The copper atoms, minus their two electrons, and the sulfate (SO_4) with these two extra electrons are now called ions. The positive copper ions are attracted toward the electrode connected to the negative terminal of the dry cell (in our experiment, the nail). The copper ions attach themselves to the negative electrode and hence form a thin layer of copper atoms. The dry cell supplies two electrons for each copper ion that plates on the electrode. Each sulfate ion is attracted to the positive terminal and this gives up two electrons to this terminal, leaving a residue (sulfate) in the vicinity of the positive terminal. Note that this container, with its copper sulfate solution, is in series with the dry cell. There is a current through the solution and this current is a result of both positive and negative charges in motion.

27. Electricity can be produced from a chemical reaction. Two metals are placed in a solution and one of these metals gives up electrons to the solution. This is an electric cell. An electric cell can be made from a carbon rod, a zinc strip, a glass jar, and a solution of ammonium chloride and water. The analysis of this cell is similar to the electrolytic cell in experience 26. The ammonium chloride molecule dissolves in water, leaving positive ammonium ions and negative chloride ions. The chlorine atom in breaking away from the ammonium chloride molecule takes away an extra electron. This chlorine ion is attached to the zinc strip. A reaction takes place between the zinc atoms and the chlorine ions and a new compound, zinc chloride, is formed. In the formation of this compound the zinc atoms give up two electrons which are collected on the zinc strip and then move along the wire attached to the zinc strip. An electric current is produced.

28. Pass a wire conductor through a magnetic field and charges will move through the wire—a current is induced in the wire. This experiment can be performed using two coils of wire, a magnet, and a magnetic compass. Connect the two coils of wire together. Place the magnetic compass near one of the coils and pass the magnet through the other coil. A current will be induced in the coil the magnet passes through. This current will pass through the other coil and produce a magnetic field about the other coil. This magnetic field will deflect the needle of the magnetic compass, thus indicating the presence of a magnetic field and verifying that a current was induced.

DRUG ABUSE

How to Begin

Drug misuse and abuse is a nationwide problem reaching into big cities, suburban communities, and small towns. Meeting the challenge offered by this problem will require the combined efforts of private and public agencies in every town and city.

Most authority figures—schoolteachers, parents, school administrators, businessmen, housewives, political leaders—are pretty ignorant of the problem. Therefore, when a young person starts talking about drugs, neither parents nor teachers are able to keep up with him.

Much of the information available about drugs is misinformation, but this does not relieve adults of this devastating problem. A public uninformed about drugs will not develop solutions to this serious problem.

This unit will attempt to set the stage for meaningful and serious consideration of the drug crisis. The objective is to get students and teachers to jointly start the development of a fundamental understanding about the health as well as social hazards related to drug misuse and abuse.

Why Do It This Way?

A feature of all the units in this book, as well as the philosophy which has always motivated the authors, is direct and independent involvement by children with actual materials. Obviously, a unit related to drug misuse and abuse imposes certain limitations on the extent to which this philosophy can be applied. There is still a great deal of independent involvement available to children in a unit on drugs. It will require extra effort on the part of the teacher to provide the right stimula-

tion to generate in students a real sense of involvement.

Today elementary, middle, and senior high school students are aware of their interactions with older people who are using substances which will require personal decisions by them in the near future.

This unit will focus on certain substances used by individuals (certainly not all individuals), under what circumstances they are used, and why people act as they do with each other when these substances are used.

Inherent in this unit should be the notion that many of the decisions related to drug use are judgment decisions made by society. These judgment decisions will never be made "absolute" or "once and for all." Changing views by society will always require a reassessment of attitudes and result in possibly new judgment decisions.

How to Begin

Do not start this unit by announcing to the

class "we are going to study drugs" or "have a unit on drugs." You can lead up to this unit by placing certain posters (available from many sources—see "Where to Find Out" section) around the room in advance of starting the unit. The teacher can develop some posters from current material in newspapers and magazines. In other words, establish the "class mood" to want to investigate the reasons for this sudden appearance of literature and posters on drugs. Stimulate curiosity and the class will react in a manner which can launch the unit for you.

This unit is subdivided into activities primarily for organizational reasons. Each activity can last a single day, several days, or weeks.

Activity 1

Hopefully, the posters and/or literature placed in the room prior to the start of this unit have stimulated general class interest. Try starting this activity with a questionnaire which each youngster will complete. Most questions can be answered by a "yes" or a "no."

1. How do you act when you are sad?
2. How do you act when you are happy?
3. How do you act when you are angry?

4. Do your feelings affect how you think?
5. If you feel confident can you think better?
6. Do your feelings toward others influence what you think about them?
7. When you are angry is it more difficult for you to learn?
8. If you are tired from playing outside in the afternoon, is it easy for you to study in the evening?
9. When you are sick and have a high temperature, do you feel like playing a game?
10. When you are tired from work or play, have you ever had a bottle of soda?
11. Do you seem to have more energy in the morning after a good night's rest?
12. Do you ever feel sleepy after you have had a big lunch or dinner?
13. Do you know any people who seem "moody" and hard to get along with?
14. Do you think adults are harder to get along with when they are tired?
15. Do you think the weather can make people unhappy and hard to get along with?

This questionnaire can be administered orally and answers recorded by students on separate sheets of paper, or separate question sheets can be made up and given to each youngster. Collect the results (names are not necessary on the papers) and display the results of questions 4 through 15 on the chalkboard. Return the papers and go back over each question to see if you can stimulate some general class discussion.

Your objective is to get the class to realize that the mood of an individual or group of individuals is a major factor in explaining behavior. Furthermore, that the mood of an individual or group of individuals is a changing thing which is altered by varying kinds of pressures and experiences. Sometimes an individual's mood is altered by external events—it rains on the day of a baseball game or it snows, causing cancellation of school. Sometimes an individual's mood is altered by internal events—something is eaten which makes the individual sick or the individual gets nervous thinking about a test in school the next day.

Following this discussion, or in conjunction with it (discussion can last for several days), assign youngsters the task of bringing in to class advertisements from newspapers and magazines about things that alter the moods of individuals or groups of individuals. You could tape-record some of the advertisements on radio and television for presentation to the class. The media have an abundance of material on smoking, headaches, tension relief, alcoholic beverages, pills for all kinds of congestion, etc. Please note, and include in your classroom work, that mood and changes in mood are related not only to the above-mentioned items. Beautiful music, an oil painting, a photograph, an exciting movie or play, a good book, an exciting sports event, events in local and national politics, tragic accidents, a walk through the woods, an interesting discussion, and many other examples all affect the moods of individuals or groups.

This activity should allow you to explore how feelings affect thinking (and vice versa) and how feelings affect physical condition (and vice versa). From knowledge about the interaction of feelings, thinking, and physical condition, the behavior of an individual or group can be assessed. Essentially this activity attempts to link emotions and behavior and cause youngsters to gain increased understanding about this relationship.

Additional activities suggested

1. Share stories, poems, and pictures which create different moods. Do the same for music.
2. Invite the school nurse or a local doctor to the class to explain how emotions affect body functions.
3. Start investigations of various body systems:
   (a) digestive (b) circulatory (c) respiratory (d) nervous
   Try to determine how emotional states affect these systems and vice versa.
4. Collect information on how lie detectors function.
5. Develop reports on the early use of medicine for changing moods.
6. Discuss some of the causes for quarrels between individuals.
7. Investigate the discovery or development of different medicines.

Activity 2

Certain substances affect our emotional and physical condition. Most of these substances are taken into the body through the mouth.

Initially students are involved in this lesson through questions asked by the teacher. The youngsters respond to these questions on paper at their desks or by oral responses which the teacher records on the chalkboard.

Questions:

1. Certain very common substances are taken into our mouths. Name as many as possible.
2. Which of these substances is labeled a stimulant?
3. Which of these substances is labeled a depressant?
4. Possibly you cannot answer questions 2 and 3 because you do not understand the meaning of the words **stimulant** and **depressant**. Can you guess?
5. Do you know of any common substances that relieve pain?
6. Do you know of any common substances that reduce tension and anxiety?
7. Have you ever heard of people taking pills to stay awake?
8. Where do you get these substances for tension, pain relief, or for staying awake?
9. If you knew something about the body systems—circulatory system, respiratory system, nervous system, digestion system—do you think it would help you in understanding how these common substances affect you?

Discussions can continue for several days after you have utilized these questions.

There are many substances taken into the body through the mouth and used by people to change or alter their behavior and physical comfort or discomfort. Some very common substances used by most people are chewing gum, candy, and soft drinks (carbonated drinks). Most adults drink coffee or tea, both of which contain the stimulant caffeine. Tobacco can be chewed or sniffed, but generally tobacco is smoked. The nicotine in cigarettes is a depressant. There are wide ranges of beverages which contain ethyl alcohol. Beer is probably the mildest, containing between 3 and 6 percent alcohol. Wine is probably next, containing between 12 and 20 percent alcohol. Distilled beverages (whiskey, vodka, gin, rum, brandy, and liqueurs) are much stronger, containing between 30 and 50 percent alcohol. Alcohol is a depressant.

Drugs obtainable from the drugstore, with or without a prescription, can be properly used or misused. There is increasing evidence supporting the misuse of drugs in our society. Drugs such as aspirin relieve pain and tension. The barbiturates (stronger drugs) reduce anxiety and tension and induce sleep. Aspirin and barbiturates are depressants. Amphetamines reduce appetite and postpone sleep. The amphetamines are stimulants.

A stimulant increases alertness, reduces hunger, and provides a general feeling of well-being. A depressant appears to stimulate the central nervous system by releasing inhibitions.

Some characteristics of an individual abusing the use of depressants are:

(a) symptoms of alcohol intoxication
(b) drowsiness
(c) lack of interest
(d) staggering and stumbling movements

Some characteristics of an individual abusing the use of stimulants are:

(a) very active—argumentative and nervous
(b) chain smoker
(c) dilated pupils
(d) goes for long periods without eating or sleeping

Additional activities suggested

1. Collect pictures and articles from magazines and newspapers which are related to smoking, alcohol, coffee, sleep inhibitors, relaxing agents, etc. Have youngsters discuss the material they bring to class.
2. Continue the investigation of various body systems started in Activity 1. (If this was not started it should be initiated in this activity.)
3. Have youngsters collect drug advertisements and use them in class discussions for the purpose of identifying amphetamines, barbiturates, pain relievers, and tranquilizers.
4. Collect news items on the effects of glue sniffing, LSD, narcotics, overdoses of sleeping pills, crimes committed while under the influence of drugs, etc. These news items should motivate discussions about group and individual behavior.

Activity 3

There are artificial ways of altering moods and these include the use of certain chemicals or drugs. Their improper use will result in unpredictable effects, lead to habit-forming addiction, or hide symptoms of more serious personal problems.

Some of the discussions stimulated by Activities 1 and 2, and their additional suggested activities, undoubtedly have caused youngsters to consider drugs and narcotics prior to the start of this lesson. In this lesson, drugs and narcotics will be given more detailed attention.

It is very important for the class to have become involved in body systems that carry out different life processes (suggested in Activities 1 and 2). The level of involvement, and hence subsequent understanding, will be determined by the teacher. There are *many* good teacher and student reference sources designed to explain in simple and understandable terms the basic life systems of the human body. Please note the bibliography in the Where to Find Out section of this book.

It is noted that the study of the basic life systems, when motivated by a real purpose, will be more exciting to the youngsters than studying these systems just for the purpose of completing a science requirement in a particular curricular guide. Body functions, physical and emotional, are altered by certain chemicals or drugs. Hopefully, an understanding of these systems will better prepare young people to examine both the good and bad effects of certain chemicals or drugs on each system and on the complex interrelations between the life systems.

The groundwork has already been established

for this activity if you have completed the discussion questions and suggested additional activities in the preceding activities.

In this activity you will motivate discussions specifically on certain chemicals or drugs. The information supplied should assist you in developing these discussions.

There are dangerous chemicals and drugs available. The names of these chemicals and the associated dangers related to their use are indicated below:

1. Barbiturates (sleeping pills, *i.e.* Amytal, Nembutal, Phenobarbital)

    Dangers are:
    a. overdose results in coma or death
    b. physically addictive
    c. withdrawal painful and dangerous
    d. symptoms of other ailments masked

2. Amphetamines (diet or pep pills, *i.e.* Dexedrine, Benzedrine)

    Dangers are:
    a. mental illness or death from poisoning
    b. need for increased doses and in larger amounts
    c. can lead to paranoiac states, malnutrition, or exhaustion
    d. abnormal heart action and high blood pressure

3. Hallucinogens (*i.e.*, LSD, DMT, Mescaline, psilocybin)

    Dangers are:
    a. possible chromosome change
    b. distorted perception
    c. serious change in mental attitude
    d. possible violent and/or suicidal reactions

4. Marijuana

    Dangers are:
    a. introduction to other drugs
    b. depth perception distorted
    c. unable to separate reality from unreality
    d. sleepy or drowsy
    e. loss of concentration
    f. confusion and possible hallucinations

5. Tranquilizers (*i.e.*, Equanil, Librium, Miltown)

    Dangers are:
    a. drowsiness
    b. apathy and listlessness
    c. lead to drug dependence
    d. excessive and continued use can damage white blood cells
    e. mental confusion and lack of coordination if excessively used

6. Alcohol

    Dangers are:
    a. can lead to alcoholism
    b. produces unconsciousness if used excessively
    c. interferes with brain functioning
    d. affects ability to concentrate, reason, and exercise judgment
    e. can damage vital organs

7. Tobacco

    Dangers are:
    a. increased heartbeat
    b. prolonged use increases chances of lung or throat cancer
    c. aggravation of respiratory conditions
    d. irritates nose, throat, and lungs
    e. contributes to emphysema and heart disease

8. Deliriants (inhalants, volatile chemicals, *i.e.* airplane glue, gasoline, lighter fluid, paint thinner, shellac, varnish)

    Dangers are:
    a. confusion
    b. distorted perception
    c. possible hallucinations
    d. prelude to drug use
    e. drowsiness, loss of memory
    f. aggressive impulses released
    g. damage to brain, liver, kidneys, and bone marrow if continued

All of the above-mentioned substances will affect individual behavior. The effects on behavior will range from mild to strong. The actual effect any of them actually has on an individual depends on the individual's personality needs, current mood, the situation in which the substance is used, and the amount and frequency of use.

Additional activities suggested

1. Continue study of body systems.
2. Investigate local laws dealing with the sale of alcohol and tobacco. Determine the local definition of "minor."
3. Invite a medical doctor to the class to discuss the correct uses of drugs when given by prescription.
4. Identify many of the useful medicines contributing to our well-being—*i.e.* antibiotics, insulin, antiseptics, analgesics, antihistamines.
5. Arrange for a visit to your class by a registered pharmacist in order to have him discuss the use and misuse of certain drugs.
6. Investigate the Food and Drug Administration's standards and procedures for determining the safety of different medicines.
7. Collect some empty containers of patent medicines to investigate the information which appears universally on all such con-tainers (name, directions for administering, dosage, possible effects or side effects, warnings, conditions under which to be taken).
8. Invite representatives from local community agencies to discuss drug abuse and its impact on your local area as well as on the country.
9. Investigate the legal restrictions on the illegal use and/or sale of narcotics.
10. Invite representatives from the local police department to talk to the class about drug use and abuse. Obtain information on the role of the police in dealing with the drug problem.

This unit can be expanded and made a part of various learning situations throughout the school year. The use of materials suggested for students and teachers working on this unit (see bibliography in Where to Find Out section) is encouraged. The unit primarily supplies teachers an approach to utilize in dealing with this timely topic of drug use and drug abuse. This approach should be considered a beginning which offers a great deal of flexibility for classroom development.

GROWING CRYSTALS

How to Begin

According to the unabridged edition of *The Random House Dictionary of the English Language* a crystal is: "a solid body having a characteristic internal structure and enclosed by symmetrically arranged plane surfaces, intersecting at definite and characteristic angles." A specific crystal is a collection of fundamental building blocks (atoms and molecules) arranged in a unique and always repeated regular "space arrangement." Nature has grown crystals over long spans of geological time. The smooth, hard surfaces of a crystal are not shaped by the tools of man. The unusual symmetry of crystals has always fascinated man and shiny crystals have been considered collector's items ever since the days of the caveman. The amazing uniformity of crystals which have their "birth" in a jumble of inorganic disorder certainly must conceal some of the secrets of the nature of matter. How can such beauty and order be the product of disorder?

For the intermediate school youngster, probing into the secrets of matter and developing a beginning appreciation of its building-block nature can start with the study of crystals in this unit. Your goal in the unit is to emphasize the fundamental nature of this building-block scheme in crystals by permitting extensive independent student work with crystals.

Why Do It This Way?

This unit is subdivided into activities. Each activity does not necessarily represent one class period for science. This is a **student-centered** unit in which youngsters respond to their own experi-

ments. The various activities merely serve as starting points or "catalytic agents" to encourage development of a student's investigative procedures.

This unit can set the stage for worthwhile discussions about the states of matter—solid, liquid, and gas. The molecular theory of matter can be developed, using crystals as representative of many solids. Molecular activity is chaotic in gases, considerably less chaotic in liquids, and extremely orderly in crystals. Students will find it amazing as well as difficult to comprehend how such order can result from disorder as characterized by the liquid growing solutions. Furthermore, the "crystalline order" is precise and never fails to reproduce itself in the order unique to each crystalline substance.

How to Do It

The activities for this unit can center around written question sheets developed by the teacher.

Each activity has a suggested group of questions which have been used with intermediate school youngsters. These questions can be made into worksheets to stimulate individual experimentation. The important thing is to give each youngster time to practice making independent decisions. Always encourage youngsters to give both written and verbal descriptions of their results.

In working with your children on this unit, discourage them from seeking teacher approval for what they do. Don't look for "right answers" and above all do not permit the worksheets you develop to assume too great an importance. The worksheets are for written responses and should not be graded. Some youngsters will do more than others in responding to questions, for certainly some can think independently better than others. Independent thought will not develop in those who most need it unless they are given the opportunity to practice thinking independently, without being constantly aware of the need to secure teacher approval.

The success of this unit is largely dependent on the availability of the necessary number of microscopes in each class. Ideally each youngster should have his own, but the unit can be successful with one microscope for each pair of youngsters. These do not have to be expensive, high-power microscopes. This unit has been successfully completed by many youngsters using toy microscopes with a magnification of seventy-five to a hundred. In fact, higher magnification will present considerable problems to the children (field of view is diminished).

At appropriate times after completing an activity as well as during an activity the teacher should encourage general class discussion of the work being accomplished by the class. It is difficult to assign times for these discussions. The classroom teacher can best determine this on a day-to-day basis. Certainly there should be many general class discussions—not to evaluate right and wrong answers but to share findings and student opinions.

Remember, you are using the activity of growing crystals as a vehicle to get youngsters to practice all forms of expression and to help develop improved work skills in dealing with unfamiliar problems. The final goal is not merely memorized

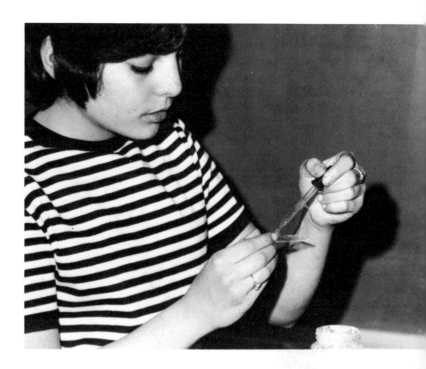

facts about crystals and how these facts relate to other memorized facts. Youngsters in their work with crystals are developing a process. This process will lead to a method of thinking and a scheme through which they learn to organize their own personal experiences.

Activity 1

For this first activity youngsters will require inexpensive microscopes, microscope slides, salt, and sugar.

There are many materials in every home, such as salt and sugar, that reveal interesting shapes when viewed under a microscope.

1. Place some salt on a microscope slide and look at it through the microscope. Describe what you see. Draw a picture of what you see.
2. Place some sugar on a microscope slide and look at it through the microscope. Describe what you see. Draw a picture of what you see.

When these substances are dissolved in water they seem to disappear. We know the substances (salt and sugar) have not been destroyed, for the water tastes salty or sweet. If the water is evaporated the solid substances may be restored.

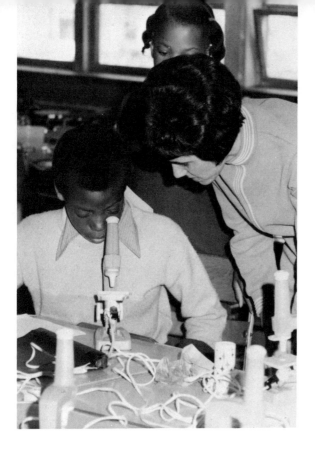
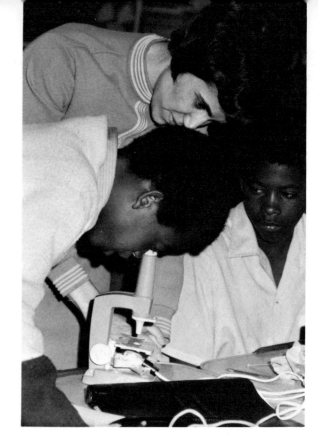

3. Make a small solution of salt and water. Place a drop of this solution on a microscope slide (use a toothpick). Observe the drop through the microscope as it evaporates. Describe what you see.

4. Make a small solution of sugar and water and do the same thing with a drop of sugar solution. Describe what you see.

Most youngsters (and teachers) have never given very serious consideration to crystals and their growth. For this reason the unit on growing crystals can be fascinating to both youngsters and teachers. In this first activity students are introduced to the basic techniques and procedures which they will follow in their study of crystal growth.

For many youngsters this may be their first introduction to the use of a microscope. These youngsters will require some indoctrination in the use and care of a microscope. This indoctrination should not begin with a long list of don'ts about the microscope. Teach what you do with a microscope—not what you should not do. In other words, be positive in your approach.

The microscope enlarges and inverts objects.

When viewing through the microscope if you move the object viewed to the right with your hand it appears to move to the left. The opposite is true when you move the object to the left. The field of view (the total area the observer sees when looking through a microscope) of a microscope is very small. It gets smaller with higher magnification.

Teach proper viewing techniques from the beginning. Look through the microscope with both eyes open. Do not look through the microscope holding one eye shut—this can cause excessive eye strain. Covering one eye with a small cardboard square initially may assist in learning to view in this manner.

Children will require practice in developing their techniques with the microscope. Take the time in this first activity to permit practice and experimentation in the use of the microscope.

Activity 2

Activity 2 is very long and will require careful work. Discourage youngsters from trying to hurry up and finish so they can move on to the next activity. Let them know that you realize that Ac-

tivity 2 is long and will understandably require considerable time.

The following materials will be required for a class of about 30 students:

alum (1 pound)
copper sulphate (1 pound)
cream of tartar (1 can)
Epsom salt (magnesium sulfate, 1 pound)
Rochelle salt (potassium sodium tartrate, 1 pound)
table salt (1 pound)
sugar (1 pound)
washing soda (sodium carbonate, 1 pound)

These items can all be obtained from the drugstore and grocery store. They are also available from the high school chemistry department or a commercial chemical supply house. (The amounts suggested will be sufficient to last for several years.) Other material required will be a measuring cup, a tablespoon, and about a dozen baby food jars (with tops).

Good organization of the materials within the classroom is essential. Children will be moving freely about the room obtaining various samples to view through their microscopes.

In the first part of Activity 2 the youngsters examine the appearance of various substances *before* they are dissolved in water. They are asked to draw pictures of what each substance looks

like when viewed through the microscope. During this activity some children will attempt to draw a picture of what they see as they simultaneously look through the microscope. This is very difficult. Although it is suggested that this procedure be encouraged, it should never be required.

Part A

In Activity 1 "grains" reappeared out of the liquid as the drop evaporated. These grains are called crystals (salt and sugar crystals). Many other crystals can be observed as they grow.

Before making observations of how different crystals grow let us find out something about what some substances look like under the microscope.

Place a little bit of each of the eight substances listed above on a microscope slide and notice its appearance as you view it through the microscope. Describe in words what each one looks like and draw a picture of what you viewed.

Prior to the start of *Part B* the teacher must

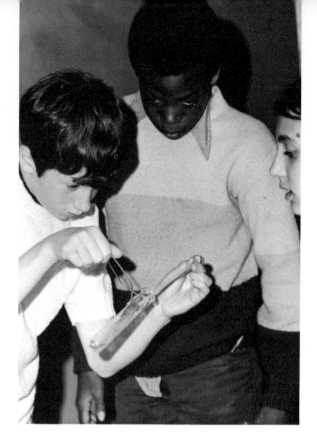

make up several solutions. Students could assist the teacher after school hours in this activity. The recipes for the solutions are found in the table on page 138. Be sure to use *boiling water* when making these solutions. Place each solution in a properly labeled jar. When not in use each jar should be sealed. One complete set of solutions should be sufficient for an entire class.

Part B

Solutions have been made of the substances you viewed earlier. Place a drop of one solution on a microscope slide (use a toothpick) and watch the drop through the microscope as it slowly evaporates.

For *each* solution try answering the following questions:
1. Do you see crystals right away?
2. Do you see them in a half a minute? A minute? More?
3. How fast do the crystals grow?
4. How large do they get?
5. Where do crystals start to grow in the drop?
6. Are the shapes familiar? Compare them with the ones you saw in Part A.

7. Why do the crystals seem to stop growing?

Remember, there is no rush to get this activity completed. Many of the questions which are raised in this activity will receive additional consideration later in the unit. Not all questions must receive an immediately understood reply.

It is interesting to note that some crystals show up more clearly when viewed against a dark background. Take two little pieces of polaroid glass or plastic (as found in polaroid sunglasses) and hold them up to the light. Rotate one in relation to the other. You will find a position where the pair let very little light through. If you place one piece on the microscope stand and another on top of the eyepiece, turning the top one until you find the position where very little light goes through them, you will have a dark background. Place a microscope slide with a drop of solution on it on the stand (over the polaroid disk) and view through the microscope the evaporation of the drop. Suddenly for some crystals bright and varied colors will be observed. This can be a very useful way to see what is going on more clearly—somewhat like staining cells. The table at the end of this activity indicates those substances which show up using the polaroid pieces.

There are very valid reasons as to why the use of polaroid pieces produces the results indicated. It is not intended that the children understand why nor is it intended you take class time to try to explain it to them. Some of the better students may become interested and their questions can be considered after class time.

The following comments briefly indicate the characteristics of polarized light. (It is suggested the teacher review some of this material in a basic physical science book or an elementary physics book.)

Light has wave characteristics. Light waves are believed to be like waves in a vibrating rope (transverse waves). In light there are many waves. They vibrate in all directions at right angles to the direction the waves are traveling. Light waves are like a combination of many ropes, each vibrating in a different direction. A piece of polaroid is able to separate these light waves. If the waves were vibrating between two upright vertical sticks, the waves moving up and down would pass through. The waves moving in other directions would be stopped. The upright sticks would represent one piece of polaroid. If a second piece of polaroid is turned at right angles to the first, both waves are stopped. When the polaroid sheets are positioned on the microscope to produce a dark background, the two polaroid sheets are turned at right angles relative to each other. When you see some light through the microscope, some crystals are growing in the solution. The crystals altered the direction of light vibration which was permitted through the first polaroid (one on the stand) and hence this vibration will not be stopped by the second polaroid at the eyepiece. This ability of some crystals is a very interesting physical characteristic (see diagrams).

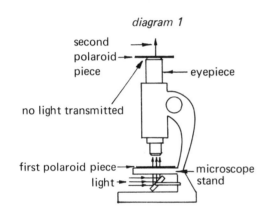

diagram 1

second polaroid piece
eyepiece
no light transmitted
first polaroid piece
light
microscope stand

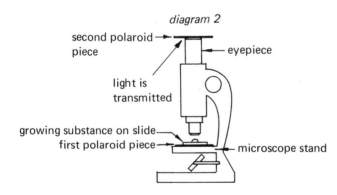

diagram 2

second polaroid piece
eyepiece
light is transmitted
growing substance on slide
first polaroid piece
microscope stand

After the class has completed this activity a general class discussion should center around the observations made by various individuals.

Activity 3

Activity 2 should have indicated that crystals grow from a solution of their own substance. In this activity youngsters will try to find out if crystals will grow from a solution of a different substance. The answer is no, for each crystal is strangely unique in selecting the substance which will support its growth. Actually a crystal of any substance will dissolve in a solution of a different substance, even while that crystal of the different substance is growing. It is especially easy to check that the two kinds of crystals are different. Try using the two polaroid disks as indicated in Activity 2. Salt and alum will appear dark and the washing soda and Epsom salt will appear light. Youngsters should be encouraged to find other pairs.

You have observed crystals grow. Do you think the growth of crystals is like the growth of living things? The following suggestions may help you answer this question.

1. What kinds of substances will these crystals grow on? We have already seen they grow from a solution of their own substance. But will they grow from the solution of a *different* substance? We can find out.

Let a small drop of salt solution evaporate to dryness on a microscope slide. After examining the dry crystals that have been deposited, place on these dry crystals a drop of washing soda solution. What happens to the salt crystals? Do new crystals start to grow?

Do this experiment again with alum and Epsom salt. Place a drop of Epsom salt solution on dry crystals of alum. What happens to the alum crystals? Do new crystals start to grow? Are these new crystals alum crystals or Epsom salt crystals?

2. Now can you answer our original question: Will crystals of one substance grow from a solution of another substance?

Activity 4

This activity will supply further evidence about the unique nature of crystal growth.

1. We learned in Activity 3 that crystals of any one substance will dissolve in a solution of a different substance, even while that different substance is growing. Do you think crystals will grow from *any* solution of its own substance? Add a drop of water to a drop of solution you are watching grow under the microscope. What happened?

2. When there is no longer any material for crystals to grow from, and they have consequently stopped growing, do crystals ever lose their ability to grow more?

3. Let us find out. Place a drop of salt solution on a microscope slide and watch the crystals grow as you look at them through the microscope. Drop into this solution a few crystals of salt. Do these crystals grow or disappear?

4. Do crystals ever lose their ability to grow?

The first question deals with the growth of crystals from any solution of its own substance. Crystals will not grow from any solution of its own substance. A crystal growing in a drop of solution will begin to dissolve again if a drop of

Table for Use with Activity 2

Substance	Recipe*	Shows Up With Polaroid	Dehydrates	Type Crystals
Alum	4 tbsp. 2 oz. water	—	Yes (not easily)	octahedra, starts growing well
Copper sulfate	2 tbsp. 2 oz. water	No	Yes	"pointed" parallelograms
Cream of tartar	1 tbsp. 2 oz. water	No	No	chunky, begins growing soon, does not grow too large
Epsom salt	8 tbsp. 2 oz. water	Yes	Yes	fat needles, grows fast
Rochelle salt	6 tbsp. 2 oz. water	Yes	Yes	plates and fat needles—may need to be seeded
Table salt	2 tbsp. 2 oz. water	No	No	grows in cubes—growth suggests nuclei
Sugar	8 tbsp. 2 oz. water	—	Yes	chunky—needs to be seeded
Washing soda	4 tbsp. 3 oz. water	Yes	Yes	long needles, grows fast

*Dissolve in boiling water.

water is added to the drop of solution under the microscope. The crystals will again start to grow when this added drop of water has evaporated. Crystals are very "choosy" about the conditions under which they will grow.

When there is no longer suitable and sufficient material for a crystal to grow from, and it has consequently stopped growing, the crystal does not lose its capacity to grow. A dry crystal is only "dormant." A crystal never loses its ability to grow. At any time in its history, if given the correct conditions, a crystal of a particular substance is always prepared to grow.

Activity 5

A crystal never loses its ability to grow whereas a living cell does. This activity is intended to show that crystals never "die" in a way similar to cells.

Three additional substances will be necessary for this activity. They are chrome alum, ammonium alum, and Salol (phenyl salicylate). Make your solutions for these substances following the recipe given for the alum solution in Activity 2.

1. Crystals never lose their ability to grow. Dry crystals remain **dormant**. They will always grow more when placed in a solution which is growing similar crystals. Are crystals like living cells? Do living cells ever lose their ability to grow?

2. You have seen crystals growing and dissolving. What is different about the shapes of growing crystals and dissolving crystals?

3. Check your answer by adding a drop of water to any solution of growing crystals. How did the shape of growing crystals compare with that of dissolving crystals?

4. How does a crystal grow? Does it have a cell wall like a living cell? We can do an experiment to find out how a crystal grows. **Chrome alum** and **ammonium alum** are closely related substances. Chrome alum crystals have a purple color and ammonium alum crystals are colorless. Grow a drop's worth of chrome alum crystals, then add a drop of the ammonium alum solution, and observe the crystals continuing to grow. Does a crystal grow by adding material to its outside or to its inside? Check your decision by making a careful observation of salt crystals growing from a salt solution.

5. All crystals grow only at their surface—the inside stays put. How do living cells grow?

6. Is the surface of a crystal like that of a cell? Does a crystal have a "crystal wall"? Do crystals have nuclei, or something that looks like them?

7. Grow Salol crystals from their **molten state**. What do you note about the shape of Salol crystals as they begin to grow? What do you note about the shape of the Salol crystals after many have come into contact with each other? Does a Salol crystal continue to grow after it bumps into a neighboring crystal?

As crystals grow, the sharp corners of the crystal can be observed. As crystals dissolve, their shape is characterized by rounded corners.

A crystal grows from its outside. Careful observations of salt will verify this. The little square of salt seems to include within itself a square outline which stays imbedded at the spot it first appeared while the crystal grows on.

Chrome alum and ammonium alum are closely related substances. It is possible to grow a drop's worth of chrome alum crystals, then add a drop of the ammonium alum solution, and have crystals continue to grow from the new substance (very few crystals will behave this way). If you start with chrome alum crystals you can see their purple color. Then continue growth with the colorless alum. The demarcation line shows as a change in color. In all cases a crystal grows only at its surface. The inside does not change. The crystal's cell wall is constantly being pushed out by the addition of more layers of unique atomic and molecular order.

Since a crystal, like a cell, has a natural shape, has it also, like a cell, a natural size? No. With patience and luck one can grow any crystal bigger and bigger by supplying enough of its growing solution. Hence, if the crystal has a cell wall, that wall must be able to expand as fast as the crystal grows.

It is noted that observations in this activity have not truly answered the question as to whether a crystal has a crystal wall. They have only shown that, if there is such a wall, it has very peculiar properties. It is usually assumed that there is no crystal wall.

It is hard to be certain from microscopic observations whether or not a crystal has a nucleus like an organic cell. Many crystals appear to have nuclei, but many others are entirely clear and transparent. As crystals grow they often develop little flaws that suggest the appearance of nuclei as the growth continues (noted in salt). Further, most crystals are enough thicker in the middle for the light to appear to have some difference in its quality at this point. Therefore, it seems reasonable to say that a crystal does not have a nucleus.

It is very easy to observe that crystals stop growing where they bump into each other. A crystal needs substance to grow from. Where there is no substance—for instance, at points where crystals come in contact—the crystal stops growing. This characteristic of growing crystals is demonstrated nicely in the case of Salol. To grow Salol crystals from the **molten state** means to heat the Salol until it melts and then permit it to cool down and solidify, forming crystals. No solution is prepared. This can be accomplished by heating a microscope slide containing a little Salol over a lighted match or hot plate. Very little heat is necessary. The crystals of Salol are exciting and very

easy to view through the microscope. The final shape of each crystal will depend on how all of the growing crystals came into contact with one another.

Activity 6

Crystals assume various geometric shapes, the names of which may be unfamiliar to many students. The objective of this activity is to identify some of the more common crystalline shapes and develop a "three-dimensional sense" for these shapes. This can be accomplished by constructing paper models of certain three-dimensional shapes.

Make ditto masters for the following shapes: hexagonal, tetragonal, monoclinic, triclinic, rhombohedral, and orthorhombic. Follow the design suggested by the following diagrams. These diagrams can be cut out and glued together (using tabs indicated) into three-dimensional shapes. After this has been accomplished encourage students to research which crystalline substances possess these various shapes. Furthermore, see if students can return to viewing crystals growing under the microscope and more easily identify the shapes they have constructed.

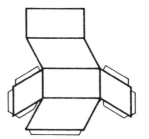

TRICLINIC

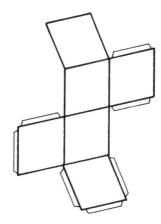

RHOMBOHEDRAL

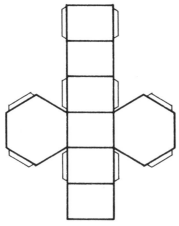

HEXAGONAL

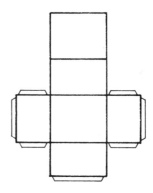

ORTHORHOMBIC

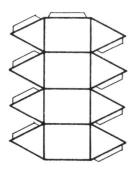

TETRAGONAL

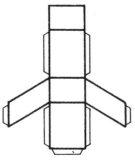

MONOCLINIC

Activity 7

This activity will require no special worksheets. It can center around a class activity about what some crystals are "made of." Individual projects may result from this activity. They should be encouraged.

Some crystals contain water and can be dehydrated. When the crystals are placed in a closed container with calcium chloride, the calcium chloride will absorb the water they contain. Any container which can be sealed will be satisfactory. A frozen juice can covered with Saran Wrap is suitable—also small baby food jars, etc. Only a small amount of calcium chloride is needed in each container—enough to just cover the bottom. Use equal arm balances for weighing. Any unit of measure for weighing is satisfactory—for example, washers. We are not interested in the absolute measurement of weight at each weighing—the important item is the difference before and after dehydration. This difference is as well expressed in terms of washers as in terms of ounces.

Note that the list of recipes on page 138, for Activity 2, indicates which substances dehydrate. Some do and some do not. Leave the various substances sealed in containers with calcium chloride for at least one day.

When the water is removed from crystals (dehydrated) the substance is not destroyed. Crystals which contain water crumble into finer dust when their water is removed. These finer particles, when viewed under the microscope, have shapes different from the original crystals. If some of the dried particles are dissolved in a drop of water, crystals similar to the original ones will be re-formed as some of the water evaporates. Children should be encouraged to perform these investigations.

Now review all the observations about crystals. It should be clear that crystals are like and unlike cells in the following ways:

Like cells: They grow from suitable substances and have characteristic shapes.

Unlike cells: Crystals are very particular about the concentration of the growth substances; they always retain the capacity to grow after they have been dormant; they grow to any size; after melting, dissolving, or dehydrating they can form new crystals of the same kind again and again.

There are several valid and interesting comparisons between living cells and crystals. Considering the similarities and differences will enhance the student's understanding of cells and crystals.

Additional Activities—Growing Crystals

Hopefully all the previous work with crystals has generated considerable general class interest in the nature of crystals. Some students may desire to continue their investigation into crystal growth

on a larger scale. Hence you may have many children interested in growing large single crystals from some of the substances used in this unit. This can be done in class, at home, or both. The teacher will probably have to spend extra time after school hours to help some students get started in this activity. Extra encouragement to a few students will reap considerable dividends with all the students, for you may be able to get the entire class busy in this interesting activity. It is not wise to make all students grow large single crystals. This activity can serve as an on-going culminating activity on growing crystals for some students—not necessarily all.

There are two general methods which are convenient for growing crystals. In both, you suspend a seed crystal by a thread in a jar of solution. In one, the **sealed jar method**, you supersaturate the solution and seal the jar to keep water from evaporating. The seed will grow as excess salt in the solution slowly crystallizes on it.

In the other method, **growing by evaporation**, you start with a saturated solution and permit it to slowly evaporate. The jar is not sealed, but the top is covered with a piece of cloth. The cloth top reduces the rate of evaporation and keeps dust out of the solution. The crystal grows as water evaporates.

In both these methods even temperatures are important because temperature changes alter the amount by which the solution is supersaturated.

The first step in either method is to make a saturated solution—one that is saturated at the temperature at which the crystals will grow. Making saturated solutions requires time and patience.

Refer to the recipes for crystal growing in the book *Crystals and Crystal Growing* by Alan Holden and Phyllis Singer—pages 108 to 119. These recipes give quantities of substance and of water which will produce solutions that are supersaturated below about 80°F.

A suggested recipe to start with will be for the growth of aluminum potassium sulfate (potassium alum) crystals. Mix three ounces of potassium alum to one cup of water.

Heat the mixture of the substance and water to about 125°F, stir the mixture occasionally, and the substance will dissolve in the water fairly rapidly. Keep a top on the vessel between stirrings to reduce the loss of water by evaporation. After the substance is dissolved, pour the hot solution into a one-quart Mason jar and seal to prevent evaporation. Then cool the solution to your growing temperature. The solution is now supersaturated. Seed it with a pinch of the substance, thus providing a place for the excess substance in the solution to deposit. Seal the jar, shake it thoroughly, and keep the solution at your growing temperature for at least two days, shaking it twice a day to give it time to become saturated.

A precipitate will form in the bottom of the jar. When this precipitate stops growing (after about two days) the solution has reached saturation. Pour off the clear solution into another container, carrying over as little as possible of the substance at the bottom of the jar. Scrape the bottom of the Mason jar, dry out the precipitate, and return it to the supply bottle (it is still good). Wash out the Mason jar, pour the saturated solution back into it, and seal it. Further evaporation would make it supersaturated in a short time.

In order to grow crystals it is necessary to start with a "seed." The seed should be about 1/8 to 1/4 inch long in order to enable you to tie (with a slip knot) a thread to it. It must be a single crystal so the crystal grown from it will also be single. These seeds can be obtained by placing an ounce of your saturated solution in a glass, set it in an undisturbed place, and a few crystals will grow in the bottom as a few crystals evaporate. It may be necessary to add a very small amount of the substance to this sample in order to obtain some crystals. Observe this small sample once or twice a day, and "harvest" your seeds (with tweezers) before they grow enough to touch and interfere with each other. Dry them well with paper tissue and tie a thread about the seed. Collect several seeds, for your crystal growing efforts may fail, or you may wish to grow several crystals when you do succeed.

The "sealed jar" method requires a supersaturated solution. For the recipes described in the book *Crystals and Crystal Growing*, weigh out the amount of substance called for in (a) or (b) or Part II (whichever is applicable) and add it to your saturated solution. Heat it slowly, stirring it until the substance has dissolved (this step is performed in a container other than the original Mason jar). Wash the Mason jar, let it drain, place the solution in the jar, seal the jar, and let the solution cool slowly. While the solution is cooling prepare a cardboard disk to support the thread from which the seed will be suspended. Adjust the thread length such that the seed will be suspended an inch or two above the bottom of the jar. Bring the solution to a temperature about 5 degrees F above your growing temperature, place the seed in the solution, and seal the jar. This is a very critical step. If you are unsuccessful the first time in planting the seed, the solution can be reheated, cooled, and seeded again. As the solution cools to growing temperature after it has been seeded, it will become supersaturated, and the crystal will begin to grow. Observation of currents in the jar adjacent to the seed will indicate whether the seed is growing or dissolving. An upward current means the crystal is growing, a downward current means the crystal is dissolving. The descending current means the solution is carrying in it extra substance dissolved from the crystal. The ascending current means the solution has been depleted of some of its substance, the lost substance being deposited on the crystal. The descending current indicates the solution is not supersaturated at the growing temperature and the ascending current indicates the solution is supersaturated at the growing temperature.

The growing by evaporation method is different in few respects. Heat the original saturated solution in a separate container, dissolving any spurious seeds, place in a clean jar, and cool to a temperature a degree or two above the growing temperature (stir with a thermometer to make sure the temperature is uniform). Tie the seed to a wire support. The thread must not extend above the surface of the water when placed in the jar. If it did extend above the water the thread would act as a wick, for water would evaporate from the thread. Seeds would form on the thread and drop on the growing crystal. Drop the wire support with the thread and seed attached into the slightly unsaturated solution and cover the top with a cloth. Hold the cloth in place with a rubber band. Growth will start when the solution cools to the growing temperature. The rate of growth depends on the rate at which water evaporates from the solution.

Both methods of growing crystals have advantages and disadvantages. The evaporation method allows a progressive supersaturation of the solution. In principle you can get back all of the solid in the form of a single crystal. The rate of evaporation is hard to control. It depends on the humidity of the environment and on how often casual drafts remove the evaporated moisture. Since evaporation takes place at the surface of the solution, the supersaturation tends to be greatest there and spurious seeds often form at the surface and may drop on the desired crystal. In the sealed jar method supersaturating the solution by cooling it below its saturation temperature is only as effective as your control of the temperature of the environment. As the crystal grows, the supersaturation declines, and then automatically provides the slower growth rate usually desirable for larger crystals. The amount of material which can be deposited from the solution is limited to that amount originally dissolved in the saturated solution when it was made. Probably the quickest way of growing crystals is by use of the sealed jar method.

While the crystals are growing they should not be disturbed. Keep the temperature fairly constant, using a bucket of water for thermal ballast if necessary. Place the jars in a large bucket of water. The water will not change temperature rapidly with changes in room temperature and hence will keep the jar at a relatively constant temperature. The crystal will grow to good size in from three to six days in the sealed jar method. Some crystals will form in the bottom of the jar, but as long as the desired crystal continues to grow, this formation on the bottom of the jar will cause no damage. When crystals are "harvested" remove them from the solution and quickly dry them with a paper tissue or a soft cloth. Be careful how you handle them, for they are water soluble and perspiration on your hands will damage their clear, plain faces. They are best stored wrapped in cloth and placed in screw-top jars to keep them at constant humidity.

More crystals can be grown from the same solution. To do this, weigh what you took out of the jar—including the crystals that formed on the bottom of the jar—and add this substance (alum, copper sulfate, etc.) to the old solution to make the new growing solution.

Additional Activities—Growing Crystals

1. Display a chart of the atoms—Periodic Chart—and note a few of the general characteristics (symbols, atomic numbers).
2. Construct models of an atom. Select a simple one first. Remember that this is a model and does not have to be identical to the atom in every respect.
3. Disassociate water (electrolysis). Make a solution by dissolving one tablespoon of sodium carbonate (washing soda) with every one cup of water. Make enough solution to fill a glass container to the halfway mark. Fill two test tubes with this solution and invert them in the large container. Connect the bare ends of two wires to two nails. Insert the nails up into the test tubes and connect the other ends of the wires to three 1½-volt dry cells connected in series. Gas will bubble up from each nail filling the test tubes. Determine which tube contains hydrogen and which one contains oxygen. This is a chemical change.
4. Observe molecular motion. Use a medicine dropper to place one drop of ink into a glass of very cold water. Perform the same activity using a glass of hot water. Notice the difference in the speed with which the ink is scattered by molecular bombardment.
5. Observe the characteristics of a mixture. Mix some salt and iron filings. Remove the iron filings with a magnet or remove the salt by placing the entire mixture in warm water and dissolving the salt. If the latter is done, then allow the water to evaporate, leaving the salt.
6. A chemical reaction. Place some steel wool loosely in the bottom of a test tube. Invert the test tube in a pan of water and allow it to sit overnight. In a short time the oxygen will combine with the steel wool, forming rust. The rise in the water level will indicate that some oxygen has been removed from the trapped air in the test tube.
7. Note some chemical changes. Burn a lump of sugar and note the black charry product as well as the formation of water. Burn a piece of wood and note charry product. Heat some mercuric oxide (powder) in a container. Insert a glowing splint into the container during the heating. Note the silvery, heavy liquid formed (mercury) and how the glowing splint bursts into flames (oxygen released).
8. Discuss mixtures and how the constituents can be separated. Make a solution of salt and water. Boil until the liquid disappears. The residue will be salt. Mix sugar and iron filings. Separate with a magnet or by dissolving the sugar in water and removing the filings.
9. Make lists of mixtures, elements, and compounds. Examples are: **mixtures**—fruit salad, concrete, air, garden soil, baking soda; **elements**—oxygen, hydrogen, carbon, iron; **compounds**—water, salt, sugar, marble, alcohol, turpentine.
10. Use some common examples to demonstrate the chemist's shorthand notation and what it means.

water—H_2O—two atoms of hydrogen combine with one of oxygen

carbon dioxide—CO_2—one atom of carbon combines with two of oxygen

calcium chloride—$CaCl_2$—one atom of calcium combines with two of chlorine

hydrogen peroxide—H_2O_2—two atoms of hydrogen combine with two of oxygen

nitrous oxide—N_2O—two atoms of nitrogen combine with one of oxygen

sodium chloride—$NaCl$—one atom of sodium

combines with one of chlorine

sulfuric acid—H_2SO_4—two atoms of hydrogen, one atom of sulfur and four of oxygen combine

11. Example of two different substances with the same chemical formula but different geometric structure for the atoms:

ethyl alcohol C_2H_6O
   1. some people drink it
   2. melts at $-11.3°$ C
   3. boils at $78.5°$C

dimethyl alcohol C_2H_6O
   1. poisonous, not used as an anesthetic
   2. melts at $-138.5°$ C
   3. boils at $-23.65°$ C

12. Observe the burning of a candle and record as much information about the candle and its burning as possible. This may seem to be a very simple activity. It is not. There are approximately 53 valid observations.

13. Examine the Periodic Chart of the Elements. What information can be obtained from it? Where are the metals located? Where are the gases in the chart? Can the chart tell something about the size of atoms? There are many other good questions which can be a part of this activity with the Periodic Chart.

14. Collect information on nuclear reactions—fission and fusion processes. Associated with these reactions are the dangers of radiation. Investigate how radioactive radiation can affect living material and hence have an impact on the world society.

HEXAPODS—INSECT TRAPPING

How to Begin

Insects (Hexapoda—6 legs) are an infinitely varied lot. Many species are harmless and even useful to man. However, many are pests which are all around man, living in his house, puncturing his skin, consuming his food and clothing. Most are voracious eaters during some stage of their life. A single flight of locusts, for example, can weigh 50,000 tons, as much as a flight of bombers. Fifty thousand grasshoppers each consuming its own weight in food daily would take the food of five million humans per day. That's roughly equivalent to the combined populations of Delaware, Idaho, Maine, Montana, Nevada, New Hampshire, and North and South Dakota. Most insects are tiny, much smaller than grasshoppers, but a million of them make a hungry giant. Many millions constitute an army of giants and they fast become a rival world to man.

Insects can reproduce with incredible speed. In a summer season, the descendants of one pair of houseflies, if all lived, and reproduced normally, would make a total of 191,000,000,000,000,000,000. That's 191 quintillion, or 1.91×10^{20} ; a figure that large would need a computer to handle it.

There are about 700,000 species of insects known today and several thousand new ones are classified each year. No one knows exactly how many species of insects there actually are. Estimates range from one to ten million but the total already known is nearly triple the combined number of all other species on earth.

Insects can be found almost everywhere. Some species can live in water nearly boiling hot; they have been found in deep underground caves;

others on the Himalayas, the driest of deserts, or the surface of the ocean. Some survive at freezing temperatures and still others make their homes in the corks of cyanide bottles. A few thrive on opium, nicotine, or strychnine. At least six different kinds of insects inhabit wine bottle corks, and the diet of one species of beetle consists solely of cayenne pepper. Some insects have a sweet tooth, and sugar beets are favored by caterpillars of various kinds.

Wherever they live and whatever they feed on, they endure and have endured for millions of years.

They are so adaptable that possibly, except for

aware of the tremendous variety to be found in nature. Using this activity in conjunction with the unit titled "Unknown Objects—Ecology," the students may study insects and other living forms in greater detail and learn to use the various keys to identification of insects provided by simple field guides.

In this way they can begin a study of the vast world of nature with its complexities, enigmas, and joys. Many of today's world-famous entomologists began in just this way.

Living things are often found in places where the untrained observer does not expect them and in places where they cannot be located by visual inspection alone. Insect traps are widely used by research scientists to collect insect specimens for scientific study or to determine what insects are found in certain areas.

The objectives of this exciting activity will be to show students how insect traps operate and how insect survey and detection work is conducted. They will also learn how to use a "bug betrayer" and realize that insects can often be driven from their hiding places with nothing more than the heat of a light bulb and secondly that insects and other living things, both destructive and beneficial, are frequently present in materials where their presence is unsuspected.

man himself, they constitute the only threat to man's dominance of this planet.

> When the moon shall have faded out from the sky, and the sun shall shine at noonday a dull cherry-red, and the seas shall be frozen over, and the ice-cap shall have crept downward to the equator from either pole . . . when all cities shall have long been dead and crumbled into dust, and all life shall be on the very last verge of extinction on this globe, then on a bit of lichen, growing on the bald rocks beside the eternal snows of Panama, shall be seated a tiny insect, preening its antennae in the glow of the worn-out sun, representing the sole survival of animal life on this our earth—a melancholy "bug."*

Why Do It This Way?

Most young students are generally unaware of the vastness of the insect world and the scope and organization of the natural world around them. By learning how to find, trap, and classify a number of species of insects, youngsters can be made

*W. J. Holland, *The Moth Book*, New York, Doubleday, 1949.

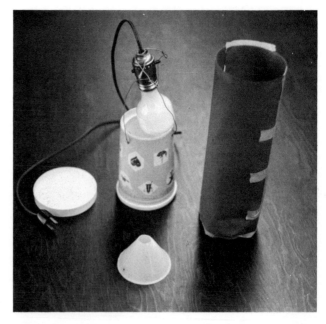

Materials needed for light trap

1 outdoor extension cord approximately 30 feet long with a weatherproof socket

1 40- or 60-watt light bulb

1 transparent plastic container approximately 5 inches high with a 3-inch diameter opening (like the kind used to package ice cream)

1 plastic funnel 3 inches in diameter

1 piece of white construction paper 5 inches wide and 6 1/2 inches long

3 pieces of lightweight wire, each 10 1/2 inches long, masking tape, small nail (4 or 6 penny), pair of pliers, one piece of heavy cord about 2 feet long

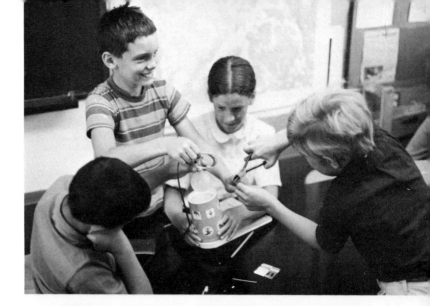

Materials needed for "bug betrayer"

1 sheet of tag board or heavy construction paper 20 inches by 30 inches

2 sheets of aluminum foil 10 inches by 30 inches

1 half-pint jelly jar or a 1-quart fruit jar

2 pieces of window screen 12 inches square

1 piece of 1/4-inch mesh wire hardware cloth, 12 inches square

1 75-watt light bulb and drop cord

1 aluminum pie pan, 10 inches in diameter, or a commercial reflector for the drop cord

How to Do It

The following procedure and instructions for use of the light trap and bug betrayer were developed by the U.S. Department of Agriculture* and are included here for use with this unit.

Insect traps are widely used by research scientists to collect specimens for scientific study or to determine what insects are found in certain areas. One of the most frequently used attractants is light, and the trap described in this section closely approximates the kind used by scientists to survey an area for night-flying insects. Children will enjoy constructing and using this trap since many of the insects captured in this manner are never seen during daylight hours.

*U.S. Department of Agriculture, Office of Information. An Agriculture 2000 project.

149

Using the wires previously attached to the container, hang the trap below the light bulb which has been screwed into the extension cord socket beforehand. The bulb should be positioned directly over the center of the funnel with the lower end of the bulb approximately 1 to 1 1/2 inches above the top of the container. Tie the piece of cord securely around the socket. This completes construction of the light trap.

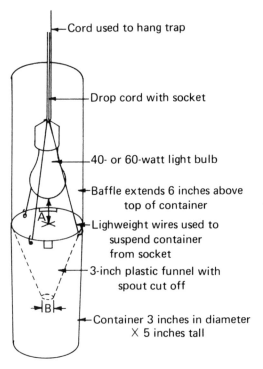

A = 1-inch distance from bulb to container
B = 1/2-inch to 5/8-inch diameter

Procedure (see diagram)

Hold the nail with the pliers and heat the point. Then burn three small holes through the plastic container approximately 1/2 inch below the top. Space the holes an equal distance apart around the container. Next, insert the ends of the three pieces of wire into the holes, one piece of wire per hole, and bend the ends up inside the container. For simplicity, use lightweight wire easily bent by hand. The wires should be cut off to equal lengths, each approximately 10 inches long. These wires are used to suspend the container beneath the light.

Next, cut the spout off of the plastic funnel with a sharp knife, leaving a hole 1/2 to 5/8 inch in diameter. Then place the funnel on the container with the plastic rim of the funnel resting on the top of the container. Using two pieces of masking tape, fasten one side of the funnel securely to the container. This forms a hinge, allowing the other side of the funnel to be raised when removing insects from the trap. Use one piece of masking tape to hold the side of the funnel opposite the hinge down securely while the trap is in operation.

Tape the construction paper to the rim of the plastic container on the side where the hinge is located above the holes where the wires are attached, forming a baffle approximately 5 inches wide around one-half of the container and 6 inches high.

Operation of the Trap

Using the cord that was tied to the socket, hang the trap outside the schoolroom window, in a tree in the schoolyard, or in the teacher's or a pupil's backyard. (During early fall or late spring, the light trap will catch insects almost any place outdoors.) Plug the extension cord into an electrical outlet.

Turn on the light at dusk. Larger insects attracted to the light fly toward it, strike the baffle, and fall into the trap. Smaller ones are attracted to the light, fly around it, and many fly into the trap. Within an hour after dark, at least a dozen insects will have entered the trap. Ideally, the trap

should be operated all night, but several dozen insects can be collected before midnight if the operator wishes to turn off the light then. About 25 percent of the insects trapped manage to escape; the remainder fail to find their way back up through the opening.

After turning off the light, plug the hole at the bottom of the funnel with cotton or a rag to keep the insects inside until the class is ready to remove them. To remove the insects, simply release the piece of masking tape opposite the hinge and baffle and dump them into a quart glass jar for further observation. Moths that have entered the trap can be so transferred by cupping one hand over the edge of the container and the glass jar to prevent their escape during transfer. Most of the smaller insects will allow themselves to be poured into the jar without attempting to escape.

Building your "bug betrayer"

Procedure (see diagrams)

Using masking tape, attach the aluminum foil to one side of the piece of tag board or construction paper. The foil should be stretched and smoothed against the tag board or construction paper, and then should be taped securely in place at the center seam. Next, roll the board or paper into a cone with the aluminum foil on the inside. The cone should be constructed so that it will be 10 inches in diameter at the top, 16 to 18 inches high, and have a 1/2- to 1-inch opening at the

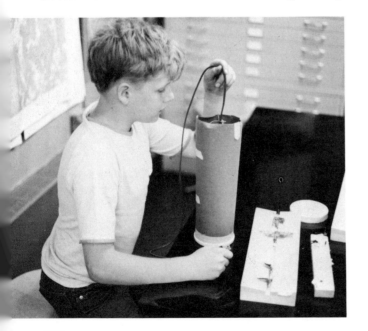

proximately 12 inches below the top. Make sure it fits tightly against the sides of the funnel and cups down slightly in the center. Cut the piece of 1/4-inch mesh wire hardware cloth to a size that will allow it to be placed inside the funnel approximately 6 inches below the top. (It should not be farther down than 7 inches or closer to the top than 5 inches.) Then cut the second peice of screen wire the same size as the hardware cloth and lay it on one side for use later.

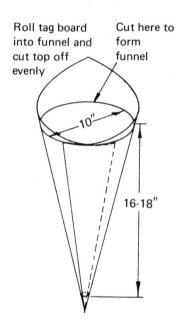

Roll tag board into funnel and cut top off evenly

Cut here to form funnel

10"

16-18"

bottom after the excess material at the top is cut off. Use masking tape to fasten the cone together and hold the shape, then cut off the extra material at the top to form the finished cone. Place a strip of masking tape down the inside seams of the funnel so that the interior is smooth and free from crevices.

Cut one piece of the screen wire to a size that will allow it to be placed inside the funnel ap-

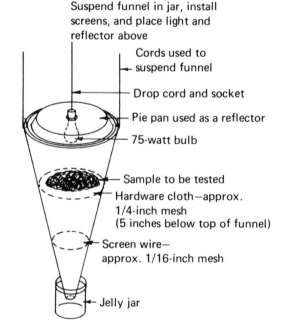

Suspend funnel in jar, install screens, and place light and reflector above

Cords used to suspend funnel

Drop cord and socket

Pie pan used as a reflector

75-watt bulb

Sample to be tested

Hardware cloth—approx. 1/4-inch mesh (5 inches below top of funnel)

Screen wire— approx. 1/16-inch mesh

Jelly jar

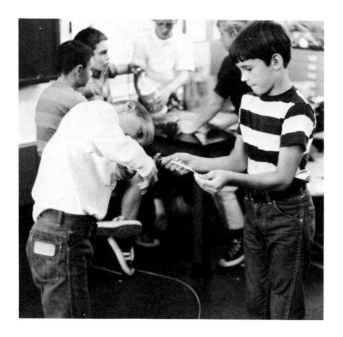

hole with the pie pan turned upside down, and screw the bulb into the socket of the drop cord. The pie pan should touch the glass portion of the bulb only, and it acts as a reflector. Position the drop cord over the center of the funnel and lower it to a point where the bottom of the bulb is 4 to 5 inches above the top screen inside the funnel. This completes construction of the bug betrayer, which is known scientifically as a modified Berlese funnel.

Note: An easy way to measure the sizes required for all screens is to place an ordinary compass normally used to draw circles inside the cone at the points where the screens will be located. When opened to touch each side of the cone, the compass will show the inside diameter of the cone at the point, and the radius of the screen required will, of course, be one-half the diameter.

Suspend the funnel in a vertical position, large end up. The funnel may be supported in any one of the following three ways:

1. Hung by four wires attached to small holes in the top.
2. Set inside a wire coat hanger that has been previously bent outward (so that it forms an approximate square) to the correct size to fit around the funnel several inches below the top. The hook of the coat hanger is then placed between books stacked to the proper height to hold the funnel upright.
3. Set the funnel in the neck of an ordinary 1-quart fruit jar. This is the least desirable method, as the funnel tends to tip and wobble when in use.

Cut a hole in the center of the aluminum pie pan slightly larger than the small end of the 75-watt light bulb. Insert the bulb through the

153

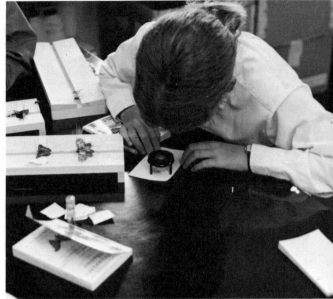

Operation of the "Bug Betrayer"

Have students collect samples either at home or on the school grounds. Samples may be collected in paper sacks. After a sample is collected, the student should twist the neck of the sack shut securely and tie a piece of string around it to prevent the possible escape of any living organisms in the material. Samples may be collected anytime during the day or evening in fall or spring. In the winter, living organisms generally burrow down too deeply to be detected.

Place an individual sample on the top screen of the funnel. When using soil or other fine material, place the second piece of screen wire on top of the 1/4-inch mesh screen so that the material will not drop through. Crumble the soil up finely not more than 1/2 inch deep.

When using leaf mold, forest litter, and decayed plant material, place it directly on the 1/4-inch screen. Loosen the sample with the fingers and make a layer 1 1/2 to 2 inches deep.

After a sample has been placed on the top screen in the funnel, place the half-pint jelly jar under the funnel. Elevate it so that the edges of the jar touch the sides of the funnel. (If a 1-quart jar has been used to support the funnel, let it be the collecting jar instead of using the half-pint jar.) Lower the light bulb and reflector into place and turn on the light. The heat drives living organisms in the sample downward. Most of them will

be small enough to drop through the lower screen into the collecting jar. Any larger organisms will be found on the screen wire at the end of the experiment.

Specimens usually begin to drop into the jar within 10 to 15 minutes after the light has been turned on, although soil samples sometimes require a longer time. It requires 1 1/2 to 2 hours to drive all living organisms out of a sample. At least 75 percent of the samples listed for this experiment will yield living organisms if collected and tested in the fall or spring. Avoid use of sand, gravel, or peat moss as such materials do not normally contain living organisms. When using extremely dry material (such as dead leaves), keep the light bulb at least 2 inches above the top of the material in the funnel and be alert to any possible fire hazard. Never operate, or allow the funnel to be operated, unattended. If a pupil has piled the sample too high and smoke is detected, turn off the light immediately. Adjust it higher and sprinkle water on the sample. This reduces the fire hazard without impairing operation of the funnel.

Making an insect collection

If your efforts prove successful with the light trap and bug betrayer, sufficient insects will be captured to begin your own insect collection.

Cigar boxes may be used to contain the insects

collected. Line the bottom of the box with corrugated cardboard or 1/4 inch of paraffin (which can be melted directly into the box). If paraffin is selected, the collection should be stored in a cool place or the paraffin will melt and the insects may fall in and be ruined. Additionally, mothballs or moth flakes should be placed in the boxes to keep out carpet beetles or other insects which may find that your collection presents quite an interesting menu.

Collections should be mounted on special insect pins available from biological supply houses. Ordinary straight pins may be used but are awkward since they are too short and too thick.

Killing Insects

A simple killing agent which can be used is rubbing alcohol or carbon tetrachloride. (Caution: children should not inhale the vapor and should avoid getting any on their fingers and then putting their fingers into their mouths.)

Killing bottles may be made from baby food jars and set up as illustrated in the diagram below.

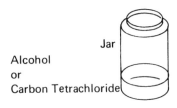

The bottom of the light trap itself can be connected into a killing container by simply adding alcohol to about 1/2 inch in depth. If this method is used be sure to keep the level of fluid at least one inch below the funnel. Remove specimens from the fluid with a toothpick and place on a paper towel to air-dry.

Pin insects soon after their death. Make sure they are dead or you may be stung. Pin beetles through the right wing cover. Grasshoppers should be pinned through the prothorax on the right of the mid-line. Bees, wasps, and hornets should be pinned to the right of the thorax. Grasshoppers should have their two left wings extended and spread. Beetles, flies, and dragonflies are pinned through the mid-thorax and both pairs

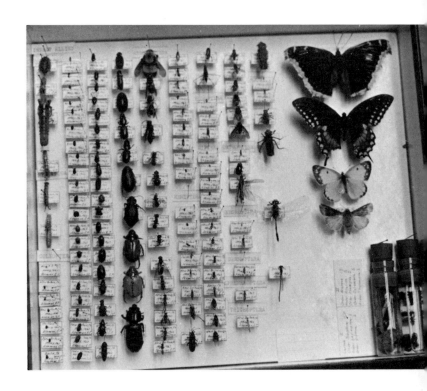

of wings extended for identification purposes. Do not pin insects on the slant or low on the pin. All insects should be at similar elevation on the pin. Small insects should be attached by glue to the tip of a cardboard triangle made from a 3" X 5" card. The triangle should be small and of uniform size and the insects located at the tip for observing.

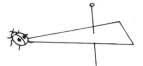

Only insects in good condition should be pinned. Try not to pin insects with damaged wings and antennae or missing legs.

If you touch your insects after they are pinned and dried out, they will break for they are very brittle.

Labels

Applying labels is a very important part of making an insect collection. When the specimen is mounted, place a bit of paper under the pin with the date and locality of area in which collected.

Label 1. area collected
date

> AVON, CT.
> 6/30/70

Label 2. Order
Family
Genus
Species

> DIPTERA
> etc.

The insect order and often the family name as well can readily be found using an insect key. However, genus and species may prove too difficult for elementary school children to determine. (See the "Where to Find Out" section for references on insect identification.)

At the end of this unit is a simplified version of an insect key for 25 orders of adult insects. See "Unknown Objects" unit elsewhere in this book for more specific information on construction and use of insect and other animal and plant keys.

Additional Activities

Once the class has learned to construct and use this simple light trap, construct several and allow

pupils to collect night-flying insects in their backyards, orchards, or outside city apartment windows. Compare and catalog the various collections, noting the hours during which the traps were operated, location, type of light used, and number of different types of insects collected.

The 3/8" to 5/8" opening in the bottom funnel is a medium size, allowing collection of a wide variety of insects. A larger opening will allow most of the smaller insects to escape, trapping only larger moths; a smaller opening can be used to collect mostly small insects, keeping out the larger moths, which often prey on the smaller bugs.

Use different color bulbs and compare results of two traps placed near each other utilizing (1) a clear bulb, and (2) a colored bulb. Blue bulbs will attract some different insects than clear ones. Yellow bulbs repel most insects (hence, their use in porch lights) but will attract a few.

Some insects eat others while in the traps. Moths often flutter about and lose scales off their wings. For this reason, scientists place a killing agent in light traps so that all specimens will be retained whole.

After the class has learned to use the bug betrayer effectively, have several students visually examine a sample before placing it in the funnel. Collect and record the number and types of living organisms detected. Then place the sample in the funnel, using care to include all debris that was separated out during the visual examination. Then record the specimens missed during the visual inspection but detected by the funnel. In at least half the cases this will demonstrate the students' inability to detect the presence of all living things by visual inspection alone.

Identification may be undertaken if the students wish to do so. Using the key included in this unit the order of many common insects may be discovered.

A magnifying glass is needed as most specimens are very small. Exact identification is extremely difficult and is further complicated because many specimens are immature stages instead of adults.

However, students can learn to separate spiders from mites (and both from any tiny 6-legged insects obtained) by using a simple key, paperback

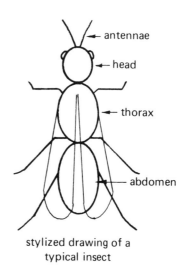

stylized drawing of a
typical insect

guide, or textbook showing specimens by orders and families.

From this starting point show pupils that all living organisms of the animal kingdom including man are divided into approximately **15 phyla** (plural for **phylum**). The phyla are then subdivided into **classes**. All insects belong to the class **hexapoda** but the mites and spiders are in another class. The classes are then divided into **orders** and these are then divided into **families**, **genera** (plural for **genus**), and finally into **species**. Have the class learn the meaning, relationship, pronunciation, and spelling of **phylum, class, order, family, genus,** and **species**.

Often this is a youngster's first realization of the vastness and variation found within nature's world. This is the concept of diversity and fundamental to an understanding of the bigger area of ecology.

Pupils will better appreciate this vastness by realizing that 75% of all known kinds (or species) of living animals in the world are insects.

Insects, General Characteristics:

Body divided into three parts: head, thorax, abdomen

One pair of antennae on head

Three pairs of jointed legs

Two, one, or no pairs of wings

Mouth parts for chewing, sucking, or lapping

SIMPLIFIED INSECT KEY FOR 25 ORDERS OF ADULT INSECTS

1. No wings (2)
1. Wings (10)
2. No antennae, no eyes, small insects. **Protura** (found in dead leaves)
2. Insects with antennae (3)
3. Insects with body laterally compressed. **Siphonaptera** (Fleas)
3. Body not laterally compressed (4)
4. Insects with spring (furcula) under abdomen for jumping. Found in all areas where it is moist. **Collembola** (spring-tails)
4. Insects without spring (furcula) under abdomen (5)
5. Body covered with fine scales, cerci (three long projections 1/3 of body length) on abdomen directed posteriorly. **Thysanura** (silverfish)
5. Body without scales or cerci (6)
6. Body flattened (dorsal-ventral) (7)
6. Body not flattened (dorsal-ventral) (8)
7. Flat body, **wide** head ectoparasite on birds and mammals, biting mouth parts. **Mallophaga** (biting lice)
7. Flat body, **narrow** head, mammal ectoparasite, sucking mouth parts. **Anapleura** (sucking lice)
8. Small prothorax, small insects, chewing mouth parts, may have wings or not. **Corrodentia** (book lice)
8. Prothorax average or normal size (9)

157

9. Chewing mouth parts, looks like stick, long antennae, found near water or on water plants. **Orthoptera** (walking stick)

9. For other wingless insects which may have wings at some stage of their life cycle, follow the key from number 10 on. If you have a grub or caterpillar or other immature insect form, this key will not aid in its identification.

10. One pair of wings, other pair replaced by halters ("balancers") (11)

10. Two pairs of wings, or at least wings for males and females during the mating season (12)

11. Minute insects, males have fan-shaped hind wings, no forewings, females larvalike (endoparasites in other insects), mouth parts vestigial or nearly so. **Strapsiptera** (stylops)

11. Mouth parts well-developed, membranous forewings, hind wings reduced to small halters ("balancers"), larva as maggots. **Diptera** (flies, mosquitoes)

12. Wings covered by fine scales (like shingles on a roof) **Lepidoptera** (butterflies, moths)

12. Wings fringed with long hairlike structures. **Thysanoptera** (thrips)

12. Wings on male only, absent in female, tarsi of foreleg enlarged, found in Texas, California, and tropical areas. **Embioptera** (embiids)

12. Wings without scales or long hair fringes (13)

13. Anterior wings—thickened or leatherlike, all or part of wing (14)

13. Anterior wings—membranous (15)

14. Anterior wings leathery at base only, triangular scutellum between base of wings. **Hemiptera** (true bugs)

14. Anterior wings long and all leathery. **Orthoptera** (grasshoppers, roaches)

14. Anterior wings very short and hard, forceps at posterior end of abdomen. **Dermoptera** (earwigs)

14. Outer (anterior) wings form hard, often brightly colored wing-cover. Under wings are folded underneath. **Coleoptera** (beetles)

15. Both wing pairs membranous, base of abdomen near thorax restricted but not narrow (16)

15. Both wing pairs membranous, connection between thorax and abdomen *very* narrow. **Hymenoptera** (bees, ants, wasps)

15. Both wing pairs membranous, connection between thorax and abdomen not constricted. **Homoptera** (cicada, leaf hoppers, aphids, scale insects)

16. Sexual forms pigmented, workers unpigmented, live in colonies, eat wood. **Isoptera** (termites). Wings only during mating season.

16. Insects not white (17)

17. Wings folded or pleated, one or both pairs. (18)

17. Wings not folded (19)

18. Wings pleated and flat on back, moderate to large insects, hind wings larger than anterior wings. **Plecoptera** (stone flies)

18. Wings if present folded and roofed. **Corrodentia** (book lice)

19. Wings filmy and roofed (20) Roofed: folded to make inverted V over back.

19. Wings not roofed (21)

20. Wings nearly alike, short cerci, head elongated as beak, chewing mouth parts. **Mecoptera** (scorpion flies)

20. Wings hairy coated. **Trichoptera** (caddis flies)

21. Wings nearly alike, eyes large, no cerci. **Odonata** (dragon flies)

21. Forewings large, hind wings small, mouth parts vestigial, adult lives only a day or so. **Ephemeroptera** (May flies)

HYDROPONICS—SOILLESS GARDENS

How to Begin

Hydroponics is the art and science of growing plants without soil by feeding them on chemical solutions. Plants can be raised in the absence of organic matter simply by giving them, in artificial form, the nutrients they usually draw from the earth through their roots. The basic principles of soilless culture are not new but its widespread application is relatively new. Until about 1930 the idea of producing plants artificially remained a laboratory technique. Mainly due to the work of Professor W. F. Gericke of the University of California, the practical nature of soilless culture was revealed. He named his new technique "hydroponics"—a word derived from Greek and meaning, literally, "water working."

Today, hydroponics is an established branch of agronomical science. Progress has been rapid and results obtained in various countries have proved it to be thoroughly practical and to have some very definite advantages over conventional methods of horticulture. The two chief merits of the soilless cultivation of plants are much higher crop yields, and the fact that hydroponics can be used in places where ordinary agriculture or gardening is impossible. Thus it is not only a profitable undertaking, but one which has proved of great benefit to humanity. People living in crowded city streets, without gardens, can grow fresh vegetables in window boxes or on roofs. Deserts, rocky and stony land in mountainous districts, or barren and sterile areas can be made productive at relatively low cost.

Introduced to a class, hydroponics will encourage study of plant growth and nourishment. Students will make their own "chemical garden," prepare their own solutions, nourish their own

plants, and discover the nourishment requirements of all plants. The students will not become chemists, but they will learn about the basic elements needed for proper plant development. They can have fun recording their observations as they vary the nourishment supplied their "chemical garden."

Why Do It This Way?

Plants can be raised without soil if they are supplied with the nutrient chemicals they require. In this unit students will make their own chemical gardens.

The complete unit will take several weeks. It has considerable possibilities for related work in social studies. This is especially true during those periods when there is apparently little progress being made in this unit. Because of the high interest which may be generated and its implication for exciting discussions in social studies you may wish to extend this unit through a major portion of the school year. There should be no time limitation. Let interest dictate how involved or prolonged this unit will be for your class.

How to Do It

The study of plant nutrition and growth is a vast and complex subject. Only a brief outline of certain salient points will be supplied in order to give at least a general idea of the fundamentals of plant physiology.

In order to become familiar with the basic principles of soilless cultivation, some knowledge of the elementary processes which go on inside a plant is necessary. Most of us accept the existence of flowers and vegetables as a simple matter of fact. We know soil and water are considered to be the essentials the gardener deals with and that some people are more clever at raising seeds than others. Have we ever paused to consider what a wonderful and complex mechanism plantlife really is? The involved physiological reactions which take place daily within the cell wall of the most despised weed are, in fact, just as important and vital as the complicated processes by which life is sustained in the human body. How plants grow and why is a subject of real consequence to the student of hydroponics.

Growth is the natural result of certain chemical changes which take place regularly in all vital organisms. This gradual building up of living matter requires suitable surroundings and adequate nutrition to insure continual healthy development. In the case of green plants these essentials consist of water, air, light, mineral salts, and a support for the roots.

A plant is really a sort of natural workshop, each section of which is employed in the business of changing raw food material into living tissue. All plants are built up of numberless masses of tiny units called cells—the building blocks. Generally speaking, the cell consists of protoplasm, which is the actual vital substance, surrounded by a delicate membrane (cell wall). Chloroplasts, containing the green pigment chlorophyll, are enclosed inside this cell wall. Green plants absorb their nourishment from the air and from solutions of inorganic salts or chemicals. These simple substances are built up by the various departments of the plant into living protoplasm through the expenditure of energy. How this energy is obtained is a subject of fascinating interest, for while the bulk of an animal's food, consisting as it does of fats, proteins, and carbohydrates, contains a large store of potential energy, the simple, inorganic diet of a plant is virtually devoid of any such properties. The answer is, of course, that plants possess the ability to build up sugars and other carbohydrates from compounds such as water and carbon dioxide, using light as the source of energy. This process is known as photosynthesis, and can be carried on only when light acts upon chlorophyll in the presence of water. Chlorophyll, which is the green coloring matter in plants, enables the sun's radiant energy to bring about such amazing transformations.

It is generally known that a special relationship exists between plants and animals called the "carbon cycle." A plant absorbs carbon dioxide from the air through a series of minute pores (stomata) situated on the underside of the leaves, while as a by-product of photosynthesis, oxygen is liberated. Animals breathe in oxygen and exhale carbon dioxide. Plants do, however, need some oxygen since it forms the basis of important processes which form a part of normal growth. In addition to air, light, and water, certain mineral salts are required for production of chlorophyll, and the other functions preceding and following photosynthesis. These elements in conjunction with water are absorbed by tiny hairs on the roots of a green plant (osmosis) while the roots themselves are supported by the firmness of the soil in which they rest.

There are basically five essentials for healthy plant growth. These will be considered briefly.

Water

Pure water is a compound consisting of two parts hydrogen to one of oxygen. In actual practice it often contains traces of other elements. In many plants water constitutes 90% of the total weight; in green foliage leaves it is often as high as 80%, while even in "dry seeds" 10 to 12% may frequently be found. Germination cannot take place in the absence of sufficient moisture.

Another phenomenon for which plants need ample water is transpiration. Cells in a leaf give up water in the form of vapor to the atmosphere. Unless this water is replaced the leaf wilts. Of the elements necessary to plant life, all but carbon and to some extent oxygen are derived from the water containing dissolved mineral substances or chemicals which are continually being absorbed by the roots. Osmosis is vital to plant life since it is by this means the water containing chemical nutrients is taken in by the root hairs and made available for the intricate process of photosynthesis.

Light

Sunshine consists of many different kinds of light rays. Experiments have shown that the green leaf synthesizes carbohydrates most actively in blue and red light. The illumination supplied by light provides the energy necessary for the conversion of carbon dioxide into organic compounds. Chlorophyll provides the mechanism through which this light energy is made available for the process. The rate of photosynthesis is affected by the intensity of illumination and the supply of carbon dioxide.

Air

Plants derive the greater part of their food requirement from the air, and over 40% of their dry matter is accounted for by carbon obtained from the carbon dioxide in the atmosphere. This gas, together with oxygen, diffuses through the leaf, where it is built up into sugar and other carbohydrates for nourishment of the growing plant. Air is important for plant respiration, or the taking in of oxygen. The oxygen which diffuses in through the stomata and passes into solution combines with that absorbed by the roots to meet the plant's requirement of these elements.

Mineral Salts

Chemical analysis of plant material has revealed that about forty different mineral elements are involved with the processes of growth and nutrition. The chemicals absorbed in solution by the roots may be divided into two classes, major elements and trace elements. The major elements are required in abundant quantity while the trace elements are needed in very minute quantities only. The major elements are:

Nitrogen: Extremely important for the production of proteins in plants. It promotes leaf and stem growth and is the foundation upon which protoplasm is built up.
Phosphorus: Stimulates the growth of flowers and fruits. It encourages healthy root growth and expedites the process of ripening.
Potassium: Plays a vital part in the synthesis of sugar and starch within the plant. It hardens and strengthens the tissues and framework.
Calcium: Stimulates root growth and strengthens cell walls. It also produces conditions in the nutrient solution that bring about absorption by the plant root of ions, especially of potassium, which would otherwise remain insoluble.
Magnesium: It is important for the movement of phosphorus within the plant and enters into the composition of chlorophyll.

Some other elements which may be labeled minor elements are: sulfur, iron, manganese, boron, zinc, copper, silicon, chlorine, aluminum, sodium, and iodine.

Support for Roots

It is essential there be suitable support for roots. Plants derive both food and support from the earth. Roots require a firm support, plenty of moisture without excess, and plenty of aeration. Roots need to breathe just as much as leaves do. For these reasons any good support for the roots, whether soil or soilless culture, is not only porous but capable of retaining moisture for a reasonable period.

Materials needed: chemicals (sodium nitrate, superphosphate, potassium sulfate, and magnesium sulfate—all obtainable from the high school chemistry laboratory or a commercial supplier), an assortment of seeds (bean, corn, pea, etc.), aluminum pie plates, paper towels, quart bottles, measuring cups, frozen juice cans, measuring spoons, tops from wide-mouth jars, and gravel, sand, or vermiculite.

Activity 1

1. You have examined seeds before, but have you really examined the stages of seed development? Place a paper towel in the bottom of a pie plate. Moisten the towel and put four or five bean seeds on it. Cover the seeds with another paper towel and moisten it with water. Keep the pie plate in a warm place and daily add a *little* water to the top paper towel. Examine the seeds every day. Keep a daily record of your observations.

2. Will a seed develop into a plant if it is supplied only with water? Try growing a collection of seeds using only water to help growth—no soil. Use your pencil to puncture four or five holes in the side, right along the edge of the bottom, of a frozen juice can (a nail or drill will be necessary for a tin can). Cut the juice can in half so it is about 2 inches tall. Place the juice can on the top from a wide-mouth jar (see diagram).

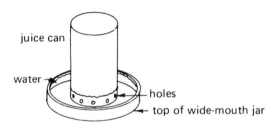

Fill the juice can halfway with gravel, sand, or vermiculite (no soil). Pour water into the juice can. The water will drain out through the holes and fill the top of the wide-mouth jar. Stop adding water after the top is completely filled.

1. Plant two or three seeds in the sand, gravel, or vermiculite.
2. Daily replenish water (through the juice can).
3. Record the growth of your seeds. This may take several weeks.

This activity will stimulate student interest and will also provide you and the students the opportunity to collect all the necessary materials for the coming activities. Students should work in pairs. Each pair of students should have two or three "juice can—wide mouth top" setups.

The seeds placed in the moist paper towels will start to germinate in a short time. Students should be encouraged to periodically take some seeds apart and examine their content and structure. A hand magnifier may be helpful. Some seeds will take a long time to germinate. Orange seeds, for example, will require seven or eight weeks. Bean seeds will provide the fastest results.

The seeds placed in the juice cans will germinate, but water alone will not sustain the life of the plants which begin to develop. The teacher can provoke a discussion about a plant's need for nourishment. The combination of gravel or vermiculite and water does not provide the necessary nourishment and possibly students can suggest methods for supplying the needed nourishment. The teacher can direct some of the discussion to the topic of hydroponics in preparation for the start of the next activity.

Activity 2

Refer back to the comments about plant nutrition just preceding Activity 1 and continue the class discussions from Activity 1 related to hydroponics, but with specific attention devoted to some of the nutrient needs of plants (water, light, nitrogen, phosphorus, potassium, calcium, magnesium, etc.).

In preparation for this activity the teacher and some students should prepare "plant food." The following proportions are suggested:

Chemicals	Amount	Major Nutrient
sodium nitrate	12 spoons	nitrogen
superphosphate	14 spoons	phosphorus, calcium
potassium sulfate	4 spoons	potassium, sulfur
magnesium sulfate	6 spoons	magnesium, sulfur
water	3½ cups	

Place water in a quart bottle and add chemicals in the amounts indicated. Shake the bottle to dissolve the chemicals. Place the label "plant food" on the quart jar. Two or three quarts should be prepared for class use.

1. Fill a juice can with gravel or vermiculite. Place the juice can on the wide-mouth jar top. Pour a little water over the gravel or vermiculite to wet it thoroughly. Place three bean seeds in the gravel or vermiculite. Fill the wide-mouth jar top about three quarters full with water. Place this unit on the windowsill or in some other spot where it will receive sunlight.

2. Maintain a daily record on your setup. After the beans have sprouted and the roots are visible, remove the juice can and empty the water out of the jar top. Replace the water with the prepared plant food. Completely fill the jar top after replacing the juice can on it. Check the jar top every day, keeping it filled with plant food.

The growing period for various plants will require time. Make sure students maintain daily records—time of sprouting, feeding schedule, height of plant, development of leaf, need for plant support, etc. This activity should proceed along with the regular class routine. Formal class discussions will result from individual student discoveries. Be alert to the many opportunities individual student observations can provide.

Activity 3

1. It is interesting to see how plants develop when proper nourishment is not provided. Basically, the major nutrients for all plants are nitrogen, potassium, and phosphorus.
2. The plant food can be made leaving out certain chemicals. Make the following three solutions as suggested by the chart.

	Solution I	Solution II	Solution III
	no nitrogen	no phosphorus	no potassium
sodium nitrate	none	12 spoons	12 spoons
superphosphate	14 spoons	none	14 spoons
potassium sulfate	4 spoons	4 spoons	none
magnesium sulfate	6 spoons	6 spoons	6 spoons
water	3½ cups	3½ cups	3½ cups

Prepare each of these solutions in a quart bottle. Carefully label each bottle correctly so there is no mix-up on which bottle contains which solution.

3. Follow the same procedure indicated for Activity 2, remembering to maintain accurate records.

The results using these three solutions can be interesting. Plants without nitrogen will be yellowish instead of green. The plants become yellowish because the lack of nitrogen in some way keeps chlorophyll from being formed. The plants will be small and appear sickly, for without nitrogen the plant cells cannot grow in a healthy way. The cells cannot make chlorophyll that will provide food for the plant.

Plants without phosphorus will be small and very dark green. Phosphorus plays an important role in the younger, rapidly growing plant material. Without phosphorus the plant does not make enough food chemicals for itself. The plant is dark green because nitrogen, necessary for the production of chlorophyll, builds up and is not used up as it should be.

Plants without potassium will have spotted leaves. The edges of the leaves turn brown (oldest leaves turn brown first). Potassium is apparently needed more in the root tips than in the growing tip of the stem. Potassium is also important in forming the flower and fruit of a plant.

When first experimenting with chemical gardens it is probably best to start with a bean seed. Experimentation with other seeds should certainly be encouraged after the initial start.

Each pair of students need not make Solutions I, II, and III. One way to handle this is to have the class divided into thirds with student pairs in each third making one of the three solutions. This procedure encourages growth comparisons between groups. Be sure to have each pair of students grow plants with the *correct* plant food besides experimenting with the three solutions. These plants act as "control plants" against which comparisons are made. Various combinations and experimental situations are possible. The students will have several ideas of their own—try them.

After considerable work has been accomplished growing plants in a soilless culture it may be fun to experiment with the proportions in the basic mixture—the plant food initially made by each team. For example, use all the chemicals but considerably more sodium nitrate in making a mixture. How would this affect growth? Does this mixture have the same affect on all plants—beans, corn, etc.?

Try not changing the amount of chemicals, rather change the amount of water in which they are mixed. *Whatever combination is used always make one change at a time so the effects of each change can be adequately evaluated.*

Information on the progress of seed or plant development should be recorded by each team. There is no best way to do this. The teacher can help in arriving at an organized manner for recording daily observations. Some students will devise their own method. A few items of importance are: solution used, seeds used, amount of sunlight, daily amount of water or solution added, height of plant, color of leaf, and rate of growth.

The elements nitrogen, phosphorus, and potassium are the major ones in the compounds used for the solutions. Various compounds contain these essential elements. In most discussions with students it is sufficient to name the compound that contains the essential element: for example, sodium nitrate contains the element nitrogen. It is not intended that the students learn chemical formulas but rather be able to observe different growth characteristics as solutions with varying ingredients are used. Interest in the chemistry of the compounds is not a major objective in the unit. Some students may want to know more about them—if so, help them, but do not force it.

This unit on hydroponics can extend through a large part of the year. There is no time limitation. Let interest dictate how involved and prolonged this unit is for each class.

Additional Activities—Hydroponics— Soilless Gardens

See activities suggested for the unit "Observing Cells."

MEASURING RAINDROPS

How to Begin

Unlike most activities, this one is designed to be performed outdoors and when it is raining. It may be simulated indoors but is much more exciting when done in the rain.

A little role-playing may be attempted during this activity in which the children can pretend that they are astronauts exploring an unknown planet and are uncertain as to the nature of rainfall in this new environment. (See Aerospace unit.) They may be concerned with such questions as: How often does it rain here? How hard will it rain? How big will the drops be? Will the drops be very small or will they be so large as to be dangerous when they fall? Is there a limit to the size a raindrop might grow to be? Rain gages and other weather instruments constructed in the "Thermobarometers and Other Weather Investigations" unit may be put to good use here.

Why Do It This Way?

One of the prime reasons suggested for doing it this way is that again the emphasis is placed upon exploring fundamental concepts in nature using simple materials. Few other areas of science lend themselves so well to exploring with everyday materials than does the subject of meteorology.

Many teachers are deluded by the rapidly developing technology of our space age into thinking that science can be accomplished only by a few specially trained individuals using sophisticated equipment such as electron microscopes, nuclear reactors, computers, and weather satellites. Even with all this advanced equipment there remains much that is still unknown.

Intermediate school youngsters should be encouraged to use simple materials in exploring the

wonders which surround them. The day of paper clips, sealing wax, and string may be gone (particularly sealing wax), but what about all the present-day materials generally available in almost every home and school, such as cellophane tape, plastic foam, polyethylene bags, plastic containers, nylon cord, flour, food coloring, plasticene clay, and the like?

One of the mistakes most frequently made by those of us who work with children is to insist that a right answer be obtained else all effort has been for nothing. Often the converse is true, for when all our energy is focused upon getting

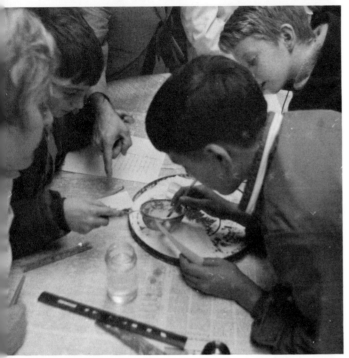

low-up to either the Snowflake unit or the Thermobarometer unit.

Begin by gathering the following materials in sufficient quantity for your class. Logically it should be done on the first day when it is raining and it is convenient for the class to go outdoors. The follow-up activities and supplementary experiments can be carried out anytime afterward.

Materials:

15 tin or aluminum pie plates or trays
15 one-foot plastic rulers (clear type)
15 flour sifters or pieces of screen
10 pounds of flour
several hand lenses
food coloring
toy baking oven
shellac (small can)
string
large sewing needles and thread

a correct answer—one that must satisfy the teacher—much else is lost in the process. The journey may often be more interesting than the destination. This investigation is intended to serve as a starting point for an individual or group project on weather. There is no magic road to success, no special method, for diligent effort with the simplest devices will often lead to success by the young experimenter. Much of scientific discovery is serendipitous in nature and exhibits itself only to the careful observer who is watchful for the subtle differences that may occur during an experiment.

How to Do It

This activity may be used as a natural fol-

Rain slickers and boots or rubbers are in order for this activity.

Have this equipment ready for the first rainy day. It should be a real rain and not a drizzle, for the drops formed during a drizzle will probably be too small to sift.

Have the students work in teams of two, one pan or tray serving for each team. Prepare the pans of flour before going outside. A one-inch fluffy layer will do nicely.

Take the children outside and ask them to allow a number of raindrops to fall into their trays of sifted flour. Wait for several dozen to hit the pan but don't overdo it or the flour will turn to paste. Bring the trays back inside and using a cup or piece of stiff cardboard as a shovel have each team sift its flour and search for raindrops. The little pellets of dough remaining in the sifter after all the loose flour has fallen through are the raindrops transformed into little flour balls.

Suggest that each team sort out its raindrops. A number of interesting questions may be raised from a close examination of raindrop replicas. These questions could be arranged in the form of activity sheets for the students.

Which are rounder, big drops or small ones?

Does the size of the mesh in the sifter or screen affect the size of the drops collected?

What is the size of the smallest drop?

What is the size of the biggest drop? Measure it with your ruler.

What is the average size of the ten smallest drops?

Is the average size of these drops more accurate than the size of one individual drop? Can your ruler be used to measure the smallest drop?

Sort your raindrops from the largest to the smallest. If the scale on your ruler proves too big to measure the smallest drop, what might you do to get the size indirectly? (Hint: If you were looking out a partially covered window on a slowly moving train and you saw some cows in a pasture but could see only their legs, how could you tell how many individual cows there were in the field?)

Try this same activity indoors by simulating your raindrops with a medicine dropper. Or simply dip your fingers in some water and sprinkle the drops into the flour. Let the drops go from various heights. Are the drops from higher up bigger or smaller than those dropped from lower down?

The following table indicates a relationship between cloud height and size of drops. See if this will help you in your experiment.

Type of Rain	Cloud Height	Size of Drops
THUNDERSTORM	Very high (30,000 to 50,000 feet)	Large drops (up to 1/4 inch in diameter)
STEADY ALL-DAY RAIN	10,000 to 30,000 feet	Medium-size drops (about 1/10 to 1/16 inch in diameter)
DRIZZLE	Low (sometimes only a few hundred feet thick)	Small-size drops (about 1/50 of an inch in diameter)

Raindrops form primarily in two ways, as ice crystals in sub-zero temperature clouds or as condensation on dust or salt particles in the air. (Thus rain, just as snow, can act as a cleansing agent in helping to clear our atmosphere of pollutants.) Only those of sufficient size are large enough to reach the ground before evaporating. Sometimes you may observe a relatively rare situation in which you can see what looks like rain falling off in the distance, but it doesn't seem to reach the ground and disappears on the way down. This phenomenon is called **virga**.

Encourage the children to examine their "raindrops" with a magnifying glass. Are the drops perfectly round? Can you think of a reason for the various shapes you got? Re-examine the drops you made earlier in the laboratory. Are the drops which were formed from the higher heights rounder than those from lower heights? Can you suggest a reason for the difference?

Allow the students to devise their own record sheets, for amounts of rainfall, size of drops, estimate of cloud heights from which drops fell, etc.

After the drops have been examined and measured the students may want to try to preserve their drops. The little raindrop replicas—the flour balls—can be dipped in various food colors and baked in either a toy oven or a real one. Food coloring may also be added to the water prior to dropping. When they have baked sufficiently to become hard, they can be threaded with a needle on thread or fine string and unique "raindrop" necklaces and bracelets can be manufactured. Imagine the fun of wearing a necklace, bracelet, or belt made of raindrops!

Raindrop Sizes: What Do They Mean?

The following table is an arbitrary listing of raindrop sizes and approximate heights from which they may have fallen, assuming nothing happens to them on the way down. This is a purely theoretical chart, for in actuality raindrops collide with others on the way down and are wisked up, down, or sideways by winds. What the chart does indicate, however, is that there is a *relationship between cloud height and raindrop size.* Children should enjoy placing their flour-ball raindrops on a chart to develop a rough idea about the height-of-fall/size-of-drop relationship. This table shows one possible relationship.

If the drop appears this big	·	it fell about 1000 feet through the air.
If the drop appears this big	·	it fell about 3000 feet through the air.
If the drop appears this big	·	it fell about 6000 feet through the air.
If the drop appears this big	●	it fell about 10,000 feet through the air.
If the drop appears this big	●	it fell about 15,000 feet through the air.
If the drop appears this big	●	it fell about 20,000 feet through the air.
If the drop appears this big	●	it fell about 30,000 feet through the air.
If the drop appears this big	●	it probably fell off the roof. Try again.

Astronomers use a similar scale method to determine magnitudes of stars. Caution should be exercised in using charts of this kind for there are many variables that need to be taken into account to make the data reliable.

Going Further

These activities are suggested for more advanced students or for those who may be stimulated to find out more about the physics of a raindrop.

1. *Weight of single drop* (laboratory method)
   Weigh a small beaker or bottle empty. Using a medicine dropper count exactly 100 drops of water into the empty container. Reweigh the bottle with the water and divide by 100 to find the weight of a single drop.

2. *Volume of a single drop*
   Once the weight of a single drop is calculated, we can plug it into the formula for density:

   $$\text{density} = \frac{\text{weight}}{\text{volume}} \quad \text{or, volume} = \frac{\text{weight}}{\text{density}}$$

   The density of water in the English system is 62.4 pounds per cubic foot and the arithmetic involved is a bit complicated. This is an opportunity to introduce students to the metric system with its decimal base, which, generally speaking, makes calculations simpler. In this instance, the density of water, in the metric system, is 1 gram per cubic centimeter.

3. *Radius of a single drop*
   Once the volume of a single drop has been determined and it is assumed that the drop is

a sphere, then the formula for the volume of a sphere can be transposed to find the radius of one drop. Doubling the radius will give the diameter: volume = $4/3\pi r^3$ or, $r = 3\left(\dfrac{3V}{4\pi}\right)^{1/3}$

4. *Surface area of a single drop*
   The surface area of a single drop can be determined by substitution in the following formula: area = $4\pi r^2$

5. The teacher may work individually with mathematically oriented students to continue along this line and try to determine additional physical characteristics of a raindrop such as the velocity of a drop in free fall or the distance traveled during free fall; terminal velocity, resultant velocity; potential and kinetic energy, and so on.

   Even if the foregoing experiments seem beyond the reach of the average intermediate school student they should prove very motivating for the bright or gifted child. The child with a real proclivity or exhibited ability for science may want to go even further and try to calculate the intensity of a particular rainfall. A project may develop for determining what effect the impact of rain can have over a small area. The young scientist may then try to relate this to the problem of soil erosion and develop an understanding for the amount of work that can be done by the rain. Even the horsepower of a single tiny raindrop can be figured out. There is almost no limit to the number of things that can be discovered from a close observation of raindrops. The old chant of "Rain, rain, go away, come again some other day" may give way to an exciting learning activity that will prove to be a lot of fun.

6. *What is the real shape of a raindrop?*
   A generally held misconception about the shape of a raindrop is that it is tear shaped. This is not true, as evidenced by the shape of most of the raindrop flour balls made in the preceding activity. The shape of a falling raindrop is strongly influenced by such things as hydrostatic pressure, aerodynamics, and surface tension forces.

Hydrostatic pressures are caused in any liquid by the weight of the liquid above it. The painful pressure one feels on one's ears when diving into deep water is an example of this pressure. This pressure is present in all liquids and increases with depth and exerts itself in all directions. An imaginary minuscule man diving into the top of a raindrop would experience the same increase in hydrostatic pressure as he plunges downward as a full-sized man would, diving into a life-sized body of water.

Aerodynamic pressures on a falling raindrop also strongly influence its shape but are too complicated to discuss here.

Also, the attraction that exists between water molecules themselves and is known as "surface tension" tends to squeeze the drop into a spherical shape. Of all geometrical shapes, the sphere has the smallest surface area for any given volume.

All of these forces distort the falling raindrop so that instead of assuming the streamlined teardrop shape depicted in most texts and children's books, it looks instead, of all things, like a hamburger bun. Raindrops may keep falling on one's head, but they're not like tears.

Another interesting approach to examining raindrop sizes indirectly may be accomplished in the following manner: Stretch a woman's nylon stocking tightly over an embroidery hoop and coat it with powdered sugar. (A used stocking works better than a new one since natural body oils permit the sugar to stick better.) Then shake off the excess sugar and go out and measure raindrops. As the drops strike the nylon screen and pass through they leave a "rain print" behind. The size of the original raindrops can now be measured indirectly and quite accurately. The sugar-stocking screen will give very sharp raindrop patterns.

Still another unusual method may be employed to examine the minute drops of moisture which are suspended in fog. For this we will have to construct a very unconventional "drop catcher"—but one which may often be seen in nature. Have you ever observed the beautiful necklacelike drops of moisture clinging to a spider's web on a foggy day?

With a little patience and practice and a cooperative spider, a net for capturing some fog droplets can be devised.

Locate a small (harmless variety) spider, one not much bigger than a pencil eraser top. Larger spiders are unsatisfactory for they will spin a thread too fast.

Construct a little spindle frame from a paper clip. Bend the clip with a pair of pliers into the shape shown. Holding the frame between thumb and index finger, place the spider on the frame and coax it to drop off by tapping the frame with your finger.

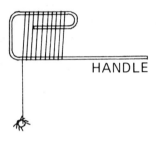

HANDLE

If it is cooperative and falls off, it will spin a fine thread behind as it descends. When the spider gets about halfway down, start winding up the thread. Try to wind the thread as fast as the spider spins it. If you don't, the spider will reach the floor and be off and running. This is the reason for selecting a small spider.

The threads are very small and may be difficult to see for a spider thread is from 50 to 70 times thinner than a human hair.

By waving this homemade spider net gently through some fog, you should be able to capture a few drops. You may want to try spraying a fine mist from an atomizer indoors on the net instead of waiting for a fog.

Try salt solution or seawater. When the drops evaporate, salt crystals will form. They will be perfect little cubes if kitchen salt is used, but will be somewhat irregular if seawater is used, because of its impurities. Look carefully at these crystals with a hand lens. Place a light bulb underneath to enhance evaporation. Try breathing on the drops as they evaporate to see what happens.

Thread with salt spray

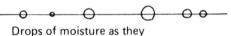

Drops of moisture as they may appear on your spider thread. Relative humidity should be above 70%.

Salt particles appear when humidity falls below 70%.

Additional Activities—Measuring Raindrops

See some of the suggested additional activities for the Commonplace "Things" unit.

MIRRORS AND LENSES

How to Begin

Most of the information that reaches us comes to us through the sense of sight. From the very beginning of history, men have puzzled about the nature of the light that affects our eyes. The questions they asked were probably the same ones that have occurred to you. What is light? How does it travel and how fast? Is seeing always believing? Why are some objects colored, some white, some black?

Mirrors can serve as the means to introduce a class to light. There are several in most homes and one in every woman's purse. Mirrors are found in cars, in front of the driver or just outside the driver's window. There are mirrors on vending machines, in barber shops, restaurants, and clothing stores. The dentist puts a little mirror in the patient's mouth. We see a "natural" mirror when we look into a pool of water.

Why Do It This Way?

Too often we have failed to utilize the commonplace, man-made, or nature-produced mirror effect to examine basic characteristics of light. In fact, light itself is so frequently taken for granted that our complete dependence on its presence is totally overlooked.

In this unit experimentation with simple materials should help in broadening student understanding of light and effects related to the use of light.

How to Do It

This unit is divided into activities simply for ease of presentation to the teacher. It can be sub-

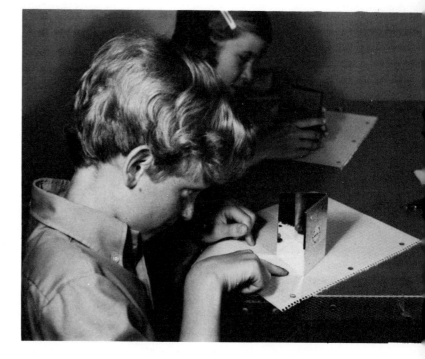

divided in other ways which may seem more suitable for a particular class. Mirrors and hand magnifiers must be available in quantity for this unit, at least one of each for each student.

Materials needed: small mirrors (about 3½" X 2½"—plastic preferable—one source, McGraw-Hill Book Co. #E0901), hand magnifiers (suggested source, Macalaster Scientific #4611-101), cellophane tape or masking tape, brightly colored wrapping paper, paper lined in half-inch squares (make a ditto and run off one hundred), small washers, and sheets with four-inch-diameter circles, divided in thirds, fourths, and sixths, drawn on them (make a ditto and run off one hundred).

Activity 1

You probably have had some experience with a

shape. Hold them in one hand and look through one end with your eye near the corner of the V. What do you see? Open and close the mirrors slightly while you look. Hold your finger or a pencil near the other end. Hold the two mirrors in a V shape with one eye at one end and a brightly colored piece of wrapping paper at the other end. What do you see as you slowly turn the wrapping paper?

3. Did you notice in your home-made kaleidoscope that you changed the number of images you saw by changing the V between the mirrors? Does the number of images increase or decrease as you make the V larger?

This activity introduces youngsters to mirrors and images formed by plane mirrors using the kaleidoscope as a vehicle. Do not try to use this lesson to explain image formation in a plane mirror. At this point encourage youngsters to construct more elaborate kaleidoscopes. Questions related to how images are formed in a mirror will be considered in later activities.

Activity 2

Mirrors reflect light and because of this we can "see" objects reflected in mirrors. What do you see when you look in a plane mirror?

1. Look in a mirror and then cover your right eye with your hand. What do you see? Cover

kaleidoscope. Do you know how they work? Do you know how to make one?

1. Place two mirrors face to face. Hinge them together along the long edge with some tape (see diagram).

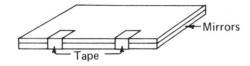

2. Separate the hinged mirrors, forming a V

your left eye with your hand. What do you see?

2. Hold the mirror close to your face. What do you see? Hold the mirror far away from your face. What do you see?

3. Mirrors form images. From your experiences in questions 1 and 2 do the images look exactly like the objects?

4. Your teacher will give you a piece of paper with squares lined on it. Set your mirror up in the middle of the paper. Support your mirror against a book. Do you see the pattern of the squares in the mirror? Position the mirror so the pattern in the mirror is matched to the pattern on the paper.

Place a washer in one of the squares in front of the mirror. How many squares in front of the mirror did you place the washer?

Look at the image of the washer in the mirror. How far back of the mirror does it appear to be? Count the number of squares.

Place the washer in another spot and count the number of squares it is in front of the mirror and compare that with the number of squares the image appears to be behind the mirror. Do this for several new locations of the washer. How does the count of squares compare?

Where does the image always appear to be in the mirror?

5. When you moved the washer to the left on the piece of paper which way did the image move? When it is moved to the right?

6. You discovered that the image of an object in a flat mirror is located right in line with, or in front of the object and as far behind the mirror as the object is in front of the mirror. Apply your understanding to the following problems:

Locate on the paper the image position

_____ mirror
        X object

_____ mirror
           X object

_____ mirror
  X object

Give the youngsters plenty of time to practice on problems in this activity. All youngsters should be able to find the location of an image in a flat mirror (question 6). Question 6 is a measure of the student's understanding of his experiences in previous questions. The image in a flat

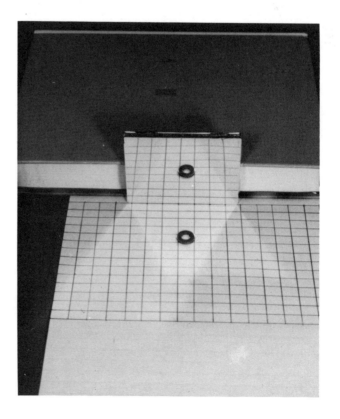

175

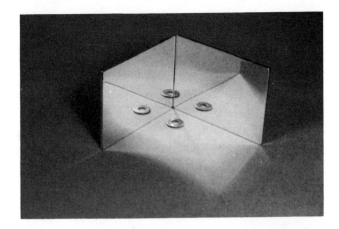

mirror is always directly in line with, or in front of the object and appears as far behind the mirror as the object is in front of the mirror.

Activity 3

Two mirrors can be taped together (see Activity 1) and several images viewed.

1. Hinge the short sides of two mirrors together with tape. Place the mirrors on edge, on a plain piece of paper (see diagram).

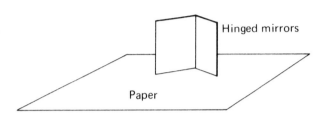

Place a washer on the paper between the hinged mirrors. How many images do you see?

Bring the mirrors together slowly. As the mirrors come together what happens to the number of images?

As the angle between the hinged mirrors increases, what happens to the number of images?

What will be the angle between the hinged mirrors when there is but one image of the washer?

2. Your teacher will give you drawings of circles that have been divided into equal parts. Place the hinge on the center of the circle and move the mirrors so they are on the lines from the center of the circle. Put a washer halfway between the mirrors. How many washers do you see when the mirror is on the circle divided into: thirds; fourths; sixths?

Is there any connection between the number of washers you see and the angle between the mirrors?

3. With the hinged mirrors and the washer you can divide any circle into equal parts—thirds, fourths, fifths, sixths, sevenths, etc.—just by counting the number of washers.

Place the hinged mirrors on a plain piece of paper. Put the washer halfway between the mirrors and adjust the angle between the mir-

176

rors such that you *just* see four washers (three images and the object). The angle between the two mirrors is one quarter of a circle, or ninety degrees. Draw lines where the mirrors are positioned and check the angle by measuring it with a protractor.

Make the angle between the mirrors smaller until you can *just* see five washers (four images and the object). The angle between the mirrors is one fifth of a circle, or seventy-two degrees. Draw lines where the mirrors are positioned and check the angle by measuring it with a protractor.

Make the angle between the mirrors smaller until you can *just* see six washers (five images and the object). What part of a circle is this angle? How many degrees is this angle? Check your answers by direct measurement as you did above.

You can continue to smaller angles, checking your results with a protractor.

This is certainly one way to measure angles but it is not as easy as using a protractor.

4. How would you draw a diagram showing the location of the images when the mirror is placed on the circle divided into thirds? (See diagram.)

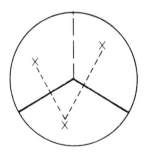

You make the drawing for a circle divided into fourths.

There are some difficult questions in this activity. Also, there are activities which can be used effectively in conjunction with work in mathematics (angle measurement). Question 1 requires quantitative responses and should not be difficult (except for the last section, which may catch some). Note that the word "angle" is used in the context

of question 1 for the first time. This may be troublesome for certain classes. Combine this science activity with an arithmetic activity related to angles and degrees. There could be considerable "pay-off." Questions 2 and 3 are quantitative and should be done in support of an arithmetic activity. Some classes may prefer to delete sections of questions 2 and 3. Question 4 could be difficult for many youngsters. Below is the drawing for this question. Note that image 3 is an image of an image.

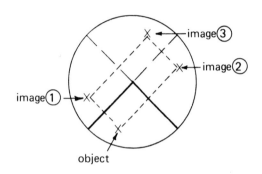

Recall the kaleidoscope the youngsters made in Activity 1. That fascinating toy is an application of the work learned in this lesson. As the angle between the two mirrors decreases, the number of images increases and the result is the production of images of images of images of images, and so on.

Activity 4

You have noticed several interesting things about flat mirrors. The image appears to be behind the mirror. It appears to be as far behind the mirror as the object is in front of the mirror. The image is right in line with the object and it is the same size as the object.

1. When you look into a mirror do you really see yourself as others see you?

   When you cover your left eye with your hand and look into a flat mirror which eye do you see covered?

2. Place a mirror on the line below.

———————————————————————

WHAT DOES THIS LOOK LIKE?
What happened?

177

3. Place a mirror on the line below.

_____

WHAT DOES THIS LOOK LIKE?

4. What happens to each of the letters below when you place a mirror on the line above and then on the line below each letter?

– – – – – – – – – – –

L S T U E V B O

– – – – – – – – – – –

What does the mirror do to the letters viewed in the mirror?

5. Can you use a mirror to help you write or draw figures?

Stand a mirror on a piece of plain paper. Draw a square and a triangle in front of the mirror. Now shield your eyes with a book from direct view of the square and triangle. Look into the mirror so that you see the image of the square and triangle. Try to trace the sides of the square and triangle as you watch your hand in the mirror. You will find this is a difficult task.

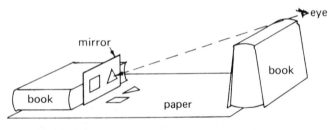

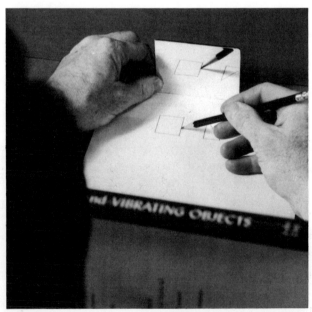

Your hand just won't go the way you want it to. It is a strange feeling because you seem to have no control over the movement of your hand as you try to trace the square and triangle.

Try mirror-writing your name. Watch your hand in the mirror as you write your name. Any problems?

6. You can arrange two mirrors to see yourself as others see you. You now know that the flat mirror does not show you the way you really look to others.

Hinge two mirrors together with tape. Stand them on your desk so that there is a 90 degree angle between them. Look at your reflection in the *corner* of the mirrors. You may want to change the angle a little to get the image of your face correct. What happens when you wink your left eye? What happens when you put your right hand to your face. Turn your head to the left. What happens? Try combing your hair.

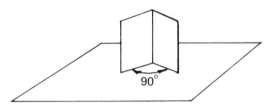

Activity 4 deals primarily with the inversion of images in a flat mirror. Although mirrors are commonplace items, most youngsters are not aware of how images are inverted in a flat mirror. In fact, we are so accustomed to this inversion that it has automatically been accepted by our senses when we look in the mirror to comb our hair, tie a tie, or try on a new dress or suit.

Youngsters will have considerable difficulty with question 5. It has taken many years for our hands, eyes, and brain to learn to work together. As you try to trace over the figures as you look into the mirror the mirror reverses your view, but your hand still wants to follow the way the eye normally directs it. The signals in the brain are reversed and the student becomes mixed up. This task can be learned but it takes considerable practice—new conditioning of eye, hand, and brain responses.

When the youngsters do question 6 and actually see themselves as others see them this becomes confusing for the same reason there was confusion in question 5. People are so conditioned to the inversion of an image in a flat mirror that eye, hand, and brain responses are not in confusion when using the mirror. There is considerable confusion when one tries to comb his hair while looking into the two mirrors hinged at ninety degrees to each other.

The image in the corner of these hinged mirrors is correct (not reversed) because it is actually an image of an image. It is a double reversal. If you reverse anything twice, it returns to the way it was at first. Therefore, the image shows you as you really look to others.

At this point a suggested topic of discussion could be reflected light in general. All objects reflect some light that falls on them. Most surfaces give diffuse reflection—they send off light in many directions. This is how we see most illuminated objects. Some surfaces are highly polished and reflect light in certain directions rather than in all directions. Such a surface is a mirror. Reflected light is essential to our way of life. What would you see if nothing reflected light? If there was no reflected light? Actually unless everything were painted with fluorescent paints, a world without reflectors would not be very different from the world of the blind. For example, all doors and passageways would have to be marked

with lights. You could not drive, or walk, unless roads were lined with lights and all objects were outlined by lights. Lights could not illuminate, they would merely be signals. You could never see anyone else or yourself, and you could not use a mirror. It is surprising how dependent we are on reflected light. A good discussion of our *total* dependence on reflected light will reveal its importance to our entire style of living.

It is possible now to go into the development of the laws of reflection of light. Lessons have not been developed for this purpose but the classroom teacher could pursue this topic through the preparation of teacher-devised activities. The teacher should not feel it is necessary to deal with these laws in order for the preceding material to have been worthwhile.

Activity 5

When light rays pass through a substance they are bent. A lens bends light rays and this effect is used to great advantage in the construction of various optical instruments. In this activity some basic features of a convex lens (hand magnifier) will be explored.

1. Look at various objects with your hand magnifier. Are the images you see larger or smaller than the actual object? Are the images right side up or inverted?
2. Hold your hand magnifier near the wall. Move it back and forth until you see an image formed of the windows in your room. Is the image larger than the windows? Is the image right side up or inverted? Do you see colors in your image?
3. Apparently what a hand magnifier does to an image depends on where the object is lo-

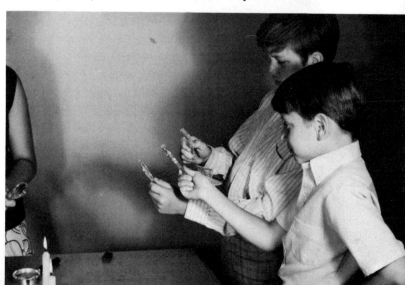

cated. When the object is very close to the magnifier the image is large and right side up. When the object is far away from the magnifier the image is small and inverted.

Project the writing and numbers on a light bulb onto the ceiling of your classroom. Point a lamp toward the ceiling. Hold your magnifier over the numbers on the bulb. Move the magnifier up and down until you get an image projected on the ceiling. What do you observe about the image?

4. In question 3 the object was very close to the magnifier. Was the image on the ceiling right side up or inverted?

Do you think the view of an image produced by a magnifier (lens) is partly determined by where you place your eye?

In questions 1 and 3 the objects were very close to the lens but the images viewed were different. When you had your eye near the lens and looked at the numbers on a light bulb they all appeared right side up and larger. When you turned on the light and held the lens near the bulb and viewed the projected image it was larger but upside down. In this case the eye was not looking through the lens but directly at the projected image on the ceiling.

5. Place the lens up to your eye and view a distant object. Do you observe a clear image?

Describe what you see.

Move the lens away from your eye and hold it at arm's length. What do you observe?

Hold the lens near your eye and move it out slowly away from your eye. Move the lens in and out while it is near your eye. What do you observe?

6. You can do some interesting things with two lenses. Hold one lens near your eye. With your other hand hold the second lens in front of the first lens. Move this lens in and out until you get a clear image. What do you observe?

Does the distance between the two lenses change for near and far objects?

180

What would happen to the image if you used three lenses all in line with one another? Try it and explain what you observe.

No attempt has been made in this activity to deal with the laws of refraction or to develop skill in ray diagramming for lenses. These items could be considered and made a part of the classroom activities. This activity will probably assist youngsters in shaping new questions about the nature of lenses and, therefore, cause various individuals to seek out new solutions or other resource material on the transmission of light through various substances.

Some of the following activities suggest ways of dealing with other features of light.

Additional Activities—Mirrors and Lenses

1. Make a mirror using a pan of water. Place about an inch of water in a pie pan or cookie pan. Observe the reflections at the water's surface. Compare reflections using a dark and a shiny pan. The darker pan will permit better reflections. Why?
2. Collect pictures of things that produce light such as kerosene lamps, incandescent bulbs, and fluorescent lamps.
3. Observe light through glass, cellophane, and other materials which we call transparent. Try looking through a mirror. Scrape off some of the back and try again.
4. How would it feel to live in a world with no light? Have children close their eyes and try to describe strange objects given to them.
5. Pass a beam of white light through a prism. Project the colors produced onto a white screen. Use a second prism to recombine the colors back into white light.
6. Use a rope to demonstrate the motion of waves. Explain the terms wavelength and frequency, using the rope.
7. Project a beam of white light at an angle to the water's surface in an aquarium. The light is refracted.
8. Place a pencil in a slanting position in a glass of water and note the appearance of the pencil. Refraction effects will be observed.

9. Glue a penny to the bottom of a paper cup. Move back until the penny is just hidden by the rim of the cup. Pour water into the cup and note that the penny is clearly observable. Light is bent in going from one substance to another.
10. Punch a hole in three cards. The hole should be in the same location on each card. Support the cards in an upright position. Arrange the cards in line so an object—a candle—can be seen by looking through the holes. Light travels in a straight line. Pass a long steel knitting needle (or piece of straight wire) through the holes to point out the straight path traveled by the light.
11. Light does not travel in exactly the same way through all substances. Some substances are **transparent** (glass), some are **translucent** (plastic curtain), and some are **opaque** (piece of wood). Show examples of these.
12. Place a flat mirror on a table. Shine a beam of light from a flashlight on this mirror. Notice where the reflected beam strikes the wall. Stretch a piece of string from the spot on the wall back to the mirror and then from the mirror back to the flashlight. This will show the path traveled by the light.

Compare the reflection of light from a piece of sandpaper and a piece of polished wood. The sandpaper will give diffuse reflection. It is important to realize that both specular (smooth surface) and diffuse (rough surface) reflections are basically the same. The rays of light travel in straight lines but in specular reflection the rays are reflected all in the same direction, whereas in diffuse reflection the rays are reflected in all directions.

A good way to view reflected light is demonstrated by use of a mirror and comb. Position a comb, upright in front of a mirror, on a piece of white paper. The shadows cast by the comb teeth clearly indicate how light is reflected from a plane mirror.

13. Obtain a shoe box. Cut one side out. Cover this side with Saran Wrap (or some other sort of cellophane). Punch three or four small holes in one end of the shoe box. Paint the

inside of the box a dull black. Fill the box with smoke and place the cover on the shoe box. Position a flashlight in front of the four holes at one end of the box and then observe the light rays made visible by the smoke. A plane mirror can be placed in one end of the box to demonstrate reflection of light.

14. Write a word on a piece of paper and place it in front of a plane mirror. The writing will be reversed. Images in a plane mirror are laterally reversed. Look in a mirror and note that your left eye is on the right side of the image. You can read reversed writing with a mirror. Place a piece of paper over some carbon paper—carbon side up. Write a word on the paper. Turn the paper over and view the reversed writing in a mirror. It will now be intelligible.

15. A mirror can be made with a piece of glass, a piece of white paper and a piece of black paper. Place the glass over the white paper. Can you see yourself in the glass? Do the same experiment with the glass placed over the black paper. You will see your reflection much better when there is a black background. With the white paper all the rays of light which strike it are reflected and hence primarily the white background is seen. With the black paper most of the light rays striking it are absorbed and the light reflected from the surface of the glass is sufficient to enable you to see yourself in the mirror.

16. Place a few drops of milk or some flour in a large jar of water. Punch a hole in a dark piece of cardboard. Position the cardboard near the jar with the hole just above the water surface. Place a flashlight behind the cardboard and the beam of light will come through the hole. Observe the change in direction of the light beam as it strikes the surface of the water.

The smoke box made in experience number 13 can be used to observe refraction. Position a jar of water in the smoke box and observe how the path of the light ray is altered when passing through the jar of water.

17. Make a cardboard disk half red and half blue. Pin this disk to the end of a wooden dowel. Spin the disk. What do you see? The disk appears purple! While viewing the spinning disk you see red one instant and blue the next. The color red still persists when you see the blue half. This results in a mixture of sensations—the red and blue sensations—and this is interpreted as the color purple.

18. The color of an object depends on the light it reflects or transmits. A solid object is said to be blue because only the blue portion of the white light striking it is reflected. The other colors are absorbed. An object through which light is transmitted is said to be red because only that portion of the white light striking it is transmitted. The other portions are absorbed. An object appears white because all the colors are reflected or transmitted. An object appears black because all the colors are absorbed and none reflected or transmitted. View a red object through blue glass or cellophane. It will appear black, for the red light reflected by the object is absorbed by the blue glass.

19. When light travels from one medium to another, its direction of travel is altered—the light is refracted. A convex lens will converge light rays to a point called the focal point. A convex lens can be made with a plastic bag, some water, and a cardboard frame. Obtain two sturdy pieces of cardboard. Cut a two-inch-diameter hole in each. Partially fill a plastic bag with water and clamp it between the two pieces of cardboard.

OBSERVING CELLS

How to Begin

For about three hundred and seventy years the primary tool of the biologist has been the microscope. Prior to the development of the microscope all that was known about living things was seen with the unaided eye.

The Dutch clothmaker Anton van Leeuwenhoek devoted his life (1632-1723) to constructing microscopes and using them to study microorganisms and minute structures of animals and plants.

The English physicist Robert Hooke had a homemade microscope and during his life (1635-1703) made many reports on what he was able to observe with his microscope.

Leeuwenhoek and Hooke were early pioneers in the use of the microscope. Their work opened the door to the unseen world of the microscopic and its sometimes unique order and random chaotic motion.

The intermediate school youngster can learn to use a simple microscope to probe some of the secrets of the unseen microscopic world. Your goal in this unit is to emphasize how the student, with the aid of the microscope, can extend his own senses to view the living world of the microscopic and make it a part of his experience.

Why Do It This Way?

This unit is subdivided into activities. Each activity does not necessarily represent one class period for science. This is a **student-centered** activity in which youngsters respond to their own experiments. The various activities merely serve as a starting point or "catalytic agent" to encourage

development of a student's investigative procedures.

The living cell is the basic unit of life. It is this basic structure and how it relates to the existence of all living material which this unit will amplify through experimental work and classroom discussions.

How to Do It

The activities for this unit can center around written question sheets developed by the teacher. Each activity has a group of suggested questions which have been used with intermediate school youngsters. These questions can be made into worksheets to stimulate individual experimentation. The important thing is to give each youngster time to practice making independent decisions. Always encourage youngsters to give both written and verbal descriptions of their results.

Note the comments in the How to Do It section of the "Growing Crystals" unit about "right" and "wrong" answers and about introducing the microscope to the children.

Before starting with suggestions for activities the following information about cells may be of interest to the teacher.

Plants and animals are built of unique arrangements of these tiny building blocks. The notion that life is based on the cell was first propounded by Schleiden and Schwann in 1839, but cells had been known about prior to this time. In fact, Robert Hooke in 1665 described the cellular structure of cork. Cells vary in size from the smallest, 1/250,000 of an inch long (bacteria), to the largest, three inches in diameter (ostrich egg). Cells also vary in shape. Some are large and round like the egg, others box-shaped like the onion cell. Even with this diversity in size and shape there are some features which are common to all cells.

Cell size is determined by several factors, two of which are the ratio of cell surface area to cell volume and the rate of cellular activity, or metabolism.

All cells have a definite size, implying a definite volume-to-surface-area relation, as determined by their metabolizing rate. There can be no answer as to what cell size is best, for it obviously depends on the function or activity of the particular cell. This is why there are cells of varying size in different organisms.

Surrounding the cell is a cell wall. It may vary in thickness and flexibility, yet it is always present. There are differences in the structure of the cell wall. In plants it is thick and rigid, primarily to act as support. Plant cells contain cellulose which forms the basis of wood, paper, and cotton. By comparison the animal cell may have only a thin membrane for a cell wall. The support in this case is supplied by the specialized cells such as those found in bone. Even in single-celled ani-

mals the cell wall varies greatly. For example, it is very flexible in the amoeba while it is fairly rigid in the paramecium. The cell wall is of great importance to the cell for it is through this partition that all substances must pass for the cell to live, grow, and reproduce.

Nearly all cells have a nucleus. One exception is the human red blood cell which lacks a nucleus. Experiments with cells have shown that cells which have had the nucleus removed cease to grow and do not divide. Further experiments have verified it is the nucleus that carries the genetic information and hence is responsible for the inheritance of characteristics from parent to offspring.

It is amazing how a single fertilized egg results in the production of thousands of cells that have identical genetic characteristics and yet some become bone, nerve, skin, etc. This process of cell differentiation and its control is still not fully understood.

The cell is filled with a substance called the cytoplasm. The green coloring matter in the cells of the green leaf is the result of small green disks called chloroplasts, which are suspended in the cytoplasm. The coloring in the skin of tomatoes or apples is the result of similar disks located in the cytoplasm. Recent studies of the cytoplasm with the electron microscope have revealed various structures in the cytoplasm.

Cells are active structures. Cells must have a source of energy. For plants this energy comes from the sun. The manner in which the plant captures this energy from the sun using the green chloroplasts is not fully understood. Animals cannot absorb energy directly from the sun. They must depend on receiving it from the green plants. The process of energy capture or exchange by cells is one of the most fundamental processes in cell development, for in order to live cells must have energy. It is noted this energy is captured and exchanged through the cell wall. This places added demands on the cell wall, for it must be capable of moving things through it while at the same time containing certain substances within it. The cell wall is a kind of unique sieve. It allows sugars, gases, and water to move freely through it while it will not allow proteins to escape. The cell wall is not a simple structure and how it performs this task is still not completely understood.

There are two major factors that determine the shape of a cell, external mechanical forces and the cell's function. The mechanical forces are the surface tension effects of the semi-elastic outer membrane and packing forces. On the molecular scale, surface tension forces are tremendous. Surface tension forces are always trying to form the cell into a spherical shape, for this is the most economical shape that can confine a given mass. Therefore, many cells have a spherical shape. The packing forces are one way in which the economical spherical shape can be disturbed. As cells grow they must adapt to a changing space availability between cells, just as oranges have their shape altered when packed tightly in an orange crate. Cells are not always packed in the same manner, and hence, different packing means different external forces resulting in new external cell shapes. Some cells are layered in flat sheets, as are the cells in the inner lining of the blood vessels. Bone cells are elongated structures that run parallel to the long axis of the bone.

The other factor affecting the shape of the cell is its function, and quite often this factor is of greater importance than the mechanical forces in deciding the shape of a cell. The human red blood cell is a double concave disk and when viewed from the side has a "dumb-bell" shape. Its function is to transmit oxygen from the lungs to the tissues and carbon dioxide from the tissues to the lungs. Its thin sections permit rapid exchange of gases between exterior and interior and its smooth contours allow it easy access to even the smallest capillaries. Other cells whose shape is primarily determined by function are the nerve cell and muscle cell. Both of these cells are long structures. The nerve cell in humans may be as much as three feet long. The nerve cells transmit information, serving as a communication system, and the muscle cells contract or expand rapidly when the muscle is in action. In general the cell shape is related both to the body plan of the organism and to the activities performed by the organism.

With their many similarities cells serve different functions. Nerve cells transmit messages. Muscle cells allow the organism to move about, glandular cells produce hormones that act to regulate certain activities, while others produce enzymes which aid in the digestion of food and hence the release of energy.

A major characteristic of all cells is that they multiply by division. All living cells no matter how complex increase in number by dividing. Cells double in each generation and hence this raises the problem of cell growth control. This control is another mystery of the cell still not fully understood. Possibly when the control of normal cell division is better understood the problems related to cancer, where there is no restraint on cell division, can be solved.

In this brief discussion there has been an attempt to convey some notions of what cells are and what things they do. It is interesting to note how much information is known about the cell while at the same time how much basic fundamental information remains to be learned.

As stated in the "Growing Crystals" unit the

success of this unit is largely dependent on the availability of at least one microscope for each two children. Once again it is emphasized that these microscopes do not have to be expensive, high-power microscopes. This unit can be successfully completed using toy microscopes with a magnification of seventy-five to a hundred.

Activity 1

For this activity youngsters will require microscopes and microscope slides. For many students this activity may serve as the first formal classroom introduction to the correct use of a microscope. The major purpose of this activity is to give your students an opportunity to find out how things look through a microscope. Most of the activity is teaching the mechanical skills in the use of the microscope. The activity sheets are written to lead the child to think about what is going to happen before he tries it.

Above all this activity should not be introduced with a long list of *don'ts* about the microscope. Once the room is organized and prepared for the unit, pass out the microscopes and let the students find out something about them. Have each child (or pair) tape his name to his microscope.

The microscope enlarges and inverts objects. When viewing through the microscope, if the object viewed is moved to the right with your hand, it appears to move to the left and vice versa. The field of the microscope is very small. Children will work for some time before they draw a circle small enough to be seen in its entirety under the microscope. It is important that the children understand the limitation of their viewing area.

Teach proper viewing techniques from the beginning. Look through the microscope with both eyes open. Viewing can be assisted by holding a small cardboard square in front of one eye and looking through the microscope with the other.

1. Sprinkle some chalkdust on a microscope slide. Look at this slide through the microscope. Find out how you focus the microscope so you can see the chalk dust clearly.
2. Cut a word from the newspaper. Moisten a

microscope slide with your finger. Place the word, right side up, on the slide and look at it through the microscope. Focus the microscope carefully. What do you see?

3. Look at your word again through the microscope. Move the slide to the left, while looking through the microscope. Which way did the word appear to move? Move the slide away from you. Move the slide to the right. How did the word appear to move in these two cases?
4. In question two you could not see the entire word through the microscope. How much can you see through the microscope? Draw a circle on a piece of paper the size you think you can see through the microscope. Look at your circle through the microscope. Can you see all of it? *Keep drawing* circles until you get one the right size so that all of it can just be seen through the microscope. What size circle can you see?
5. Pull a hair from your head. Look at it under the microscope. You can use a hair as a "ruler" and compare things you see under the microscope with the width of the hair. The width of a hair is very small. Objects you look at through the microscope will be either larger or smaller than the width of one hair.

It is quite possible that it will be unnecessary to pass out the worksheet for Activity 1 on the first day. There will be enough new things going on to stimulate interest, and passing out the worksheet at this time may cause more confusion than anything else. Let the microscopes and new arrangement of the room suffice for the first day. (For the more mature classes these remarks probably are not relevant.)

The children should be told that the activity sheets are a guide to help them discover things. The teacher should look over these sheets after each is completed, *but do not grade responses right or wrong*. Written comments are in order—comments that will encourage re-examination of an individual question. Some example comments might be: "I don't understand your answer"; "How many times did you do this, Mary?"; "Can you show me how you did this?" Some questions will be answered with completely unrelated and/or nonsensical answers—for example, one youngster may reply to the question "What does the cell look like?" by saying "The sun is shining." Don't be too fast at losing your patience with this individual, for this response may represent the first complete sentence this individual has written in many weeks. If this is the case, the response is great! You now can redirect the youngster back to the question and get him to explain his answer and perhaps try it again. The example selected may seem ridiculous, but it does suggest the attitude the teacher should be prepared to assume in the teaching of this unit.

A major problem in this unit (as well as in others) is slowing youngsters down. Because activity sheets are numbered they have become conditioned to receiving a new activity sheet when the present one is completed. This generates competition, causing children to hurry to get done so they can get to the next activity. It is difficult to control this and the teacher must constantly be aware of it. The teacher's comments made on the activity sheets can go a long way toward meeting this problem. Encourage all students to investigate other areas that are suggested by the activity sheet questions and also to base their decisions on more than one observation.

Activity 2

For this activity youngsters will require micro-

scopes, microscope slides, onions, and magnifying glasses.

1. You have seen an ordinary onion. What does it look like when it is cut in half? Draw a picture of what you *think* it looks like.
2. Now cut an onion in half. Compare it with your picture. Look at the onion with a magnifying glass. Can you see more detail with the magnifying glass? Does the onion have layers?
3. Break the onion apart and find a piece of *thin clear skin* on one of the layers. Place this *thin clear piece* of onion skin on a clean microscope slide. Look at it with your microscope. What does it look like? Draw a picture of what you see.

The little shapes you see are called *cells*. The onion skin you looked at through your microscope had many cells.

4. How big are these cells you are looking at? Use as your "ruler" a piece of hair pulled

from your head. Add a small drop of water to your onion skin, place the hair over the onion skin, and look at it through the microscope. Focus the microscope so you can see the "ruler" against a cell. You may have to move the hair. How wide is one cell in hair widths? How long is one cell in hair widths?

5. Can you see anything inside any of the onion cells? Draw what you see.

In this activity the student sees the cellular structure of a plant, an onion. He dissects an onion bulb, examines it with his naked eye, and then with a magnifying glass.

The piece of onion skin used under the microscope should be very small and almost transparent. The cells will not all have the same size or shape. Some students will have trouble getting a satisfactory onion skin sample. Do not be too eager to give assistance—*let them keep trying* until they achieve success. Usually students will use too large a piece of onion (hardly transparent) and it will take several tries to get the thin piece of skin which will reveal the unique orderly arrangement of onion cells. This first view of onion cells can be an exciting experience.

The section on measuring the cell is intended to help children understand that the cells they are viewing are not really as big as they look. Most children have an intuitive "feel" for the thickness of a piece of hair and hence the comparison of hair width with cells gives them a sense of size for an onion cell. Most onion cells will be about one hair width wide and from three to five hair widths long.

There are no right answers to many of the questions. Some children may be able to see some pulplike material between the layers of onion skin. Fine lines may also be visible in this pulpy material and some children may see dots in their cells—the nucleus. Sometimes these dots are really air bubbles trapped in the drop of water placed on the onion skin.

Note: Start growing some onions in preparation for Activity 6. In this activity children will view the root and leaf cells of an onion. Several onions will be needed. Place toothpicks in the sides of an onion. Suspend the onion, supported by the toothpicks, in a glass of water. The water should just cover half the onion. In a short while a leaf will sprout.

Activity 3

For this activity youngsters will require microscopes, microscope slides, onions, methylene blue, iodine, and eosine. The stains (methylene blue, iodine, and eosine) can be obtained from the school biology department. They should be placed in a central part of the room, along with the onions, so children have easy access to them.

1. Place a *thin clear piece* of onion skin on a microscope slide. Look at it through the microscope. Are the cells clearly visible?
2. Place a very tiny drop of methylene blue on the onion skin using a toothpick as a dropper. Look at the onion cells again. What does the methylene blue do to the cell? Can you

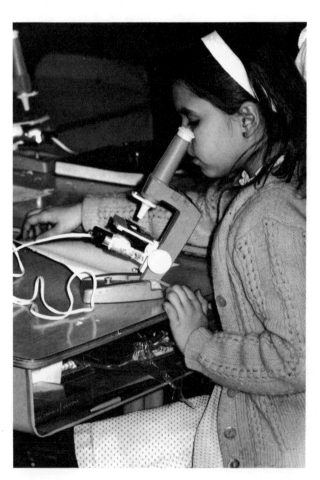

see parts of the cell better? What parts are stained darkest?

3. What do you think is inside a cell—what is it filled with?

4. Place another *thin clear piece* of onion skin on a clean microscope slide. Stain this onion skin with iodine. What parts of the cell does the iodine make darkest?

5. Place another *thin clear piece* of onion skin on a clean microscope slide. Stain this onion skin with eosine. What parts of the cell can you see easiest?

6. Does staining cells help you to see cells better?

7. Could you see anything inside the cells after they were stained?

In this activity the children learn to use stains. They see that stains make it easier to see some parts of the cell. Some children may notice that each stain colors a different part of the cell.

A review of the work in Activity 2 may be advisable. In this review discuss what the children saw. Have some students draw on the blackboard what they saw when looking at the onion skin. Bring out the fact that the outside is called the cell wall. Compare individual results regarding widths and lengths of cells in terms of hair widths. Some children may want to redo parts of Activity 2 as a result of this discussion.

When staining cells a common fault is to place too much stain on the specimen. This will create problems for some children. Let each child discover for himself the need to use very small amounts of stain. If coverslips are not available another microscope slide can be used instead. The coverslip or additional slide causes the drop of stain to spread out over the onion skin and squeezes out excess stain. If the stain remains in the form of a droplet on the onion skin, it can have an undesirable "lens effect" on the light.

It is possible that children may want to mix stains together or to try them on other things under the microscope. Experimentation of this sort should be encouraged—after the regular worksheet is completed.

Some students may note the small dot that appears in most of the cells. This small dot is the nucleus. Some of the cells may not appear to have a nucleus. In cases of this sort it is because the nucleus has been left behind when the piece of onion skin was pulled from the onion.

Methylene blue stains the cell wall and the nucleus a darker blue than the rest of the cell. This contrast is apparent only when using a very small drop of stain. Iodine stains the cell wall and the nucleus a deep brown. Eosine stains all the cell except the nucleus a light red. Usually the nucleus remains white or light gray.

Activity 4

You have examined the plant cell as seen in an onion. You will now look at an animal cell.

Stroke the inside of your cheek with the blunt end of a clean toothpick. Don't scrape hard. Rub the end of the toothpick gently on the center of a clean microscope slide. Do not leave the toothpick on the slide. Add a small drop of methylene blue. Look at it with your microscope.

1. Draw a sketch of what you see.
2. Place a hair under the microscope near a skin cell. Which is bigger?
3. Can you see a cell wall around the edges of a skin cell?
4. Which has the thicker cell wall, the skin cell or the onion cell?
5. What do you think is inside a skin cell?
6. Do skin cells look like onion cells?
7. Are they alike in any way? How?

In this activity the children observe human (animal) cells and compare them with onion cells.

Hopefully, by this activity the children will have improved in their ability to carefully read and follow directions. A major outcome of this entire unit should be closer attention to written directions.

Not all youngsters will be successful in getting a clear view of a skin cell. For some it will end up as a blob of "stuff" on the microscope slide. Encourage youngsters that are successful in preparing a good slide to share their view with other students.

Skin cells are flattened, pancakelike cells, which when joined together form the skin. They are formed in the deeper layers of the skin and move upward as the top layers are worn off.

Skin cells from different animals usually look the same. This is a result of the relation between function and structure—cells that do the same things are similar in structure. A muscle cell,

whether from a bird, fish, insect, or human, looks much the same.

Onion cells and human skin cells are different in size and shape. The onion cell has a thick cell wall whereas the human skin cell has a thin wall. The onion cells are thick like a brick, while the human skin cells are flat. Both cells have a nucleus.

After this activity is completed, a class discussion of the findings is worthwhile. Have children draw pictures of skin cells on the board and state how many hair widths wide and long the cells are. Do not rush into this class discussion—provide adequate class time for all students to carefully answer the activity sheet questions. Constantly be aware of your function in the class. It is not to dictate, suggest, or help in making observations. You want individual responses from each youngster—you want them to make decisions and hence you must be prepared to give the time decision-making requires. It is not easy "not to teach."

Activity 5

An assortment of additional substances is necessary for this activity. They can be obtained from the grocery store or brought in from home by the children.

You have seen two kinds of cells, a plant cell from an onion and an animal cell from the inside of your cheek. What about cells in other things? Are there cells in apples, plums, steak, squash, and bananas? *Use a very small piece. Mash it up well* and place it on a microscope slide. Stain it if you want. Look at it carefully with your microscope. Fill in the chart:

Name of substance		
Stain used		
Can you see any cells?		
Is there a cell wall?		
Is there anything inside the cell?		
How many hair widths wide is the cell?		
Make a sketch of the cell		

Now look at some nonliving things. Some examples are chalkdust, ink, and salt. Do nonliving things have cells? What things have cells?

In this activity the children look at cells in several living things such as steak, plum, apple, squash, and banana. They are asked to describe what they see. The children then look at several nonliving things such as salt, chalkdust, and ink to see if they can see any cells. It is hoped they will be able to generalize about what has or has not cells.

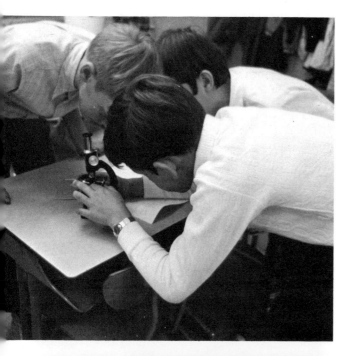

In looking at cells in steak, apple, banana, etc., only a small piece of substance is necessary. It should be mashed up on the slide so that individual cells can be seen. Children should be allowed to pick the stain they wish to use.

Some children may mistake grains of chalkdust and salt for cells. If this happens, you might inquire if they see a cell wall and dot (nucleus) as they did in the living things.

Not all students will notice the difference between living and nonliving material. It is interesting to note that squash and banana cells look most alike, whereas steak and banana cells look most unlike.

While looking at other substances, some children will wonder about wood, sawdust, or paper. These are made from materials which once were living and were made of cells. Whether cellular structure is visible depends on the state of the material.

The cell walls in banana are very thin and may go unnoticed by the children. All the cells will be about one to two hair widths in size except for the beef muscle cells, which are sometimes several inches long.

Each student need not look at all of the substances—two or three should be adequate for the average student. On the other hand, it may be interesting to see how many different substances can be viewed. Accept this challenge as one of the many this unit can present. Probably not all students will be able to make the desired generalization about what has and what does not have cells. After the children have completed this activity, a class discussion of this question is advisable.

Note: Collect a few jars of swamp water in preparation for Activity 7.

Activity 6

At the end of Activity 2 it was suggested that you start growing some onions. In this activity children will view through the microscope the root cells and leaf cells from these growing onions. Let us look at some plant cells. The root of an onion plant is interesting. Cut off the tip of an onion root. Place it in a drop of water on a micro-

specialized for the absorption of water and minerals and for the transport of these to the leaves. The cells of the bulb are for the storage of food and the leaf cells for the making of food. In the onion there is a variety of cells, each one designed for a unique function. The root cells are longer and thinner than the bulb cells. Inner bulb cells are smaller than those on the outside of the bulb. Leaf cells are smaller and squarer than the bulb cells.

A discussion after this activity could emphasize the differences in cells in the same plant. As said before, the cell shape and size are determined chiefly by its function. Some children may become interested in trying to find out something about the function of the root, bulb, and leaf cells in a plant. Outside reading can be encouraged here as well as at many other points throughout this unit.

scope slide and squeeze it flat. Now look at it through your microscope.

1. Can you see any cells?
2. How do onion root cells compare with the onion skin cells you looked at before?
3. Make a sketch of onion leaf cells.
4. How do the leaf cells compare with the *root cells* and *skin cells* of an onion?

Now look at pieces of onion skin from layers on the outside of the onion bulb and from layers on the inside (near the center) of the onion bulb.

5. Where are the larger cells found?
6. Do all cells in an onion plant look the same?
7. Do you think all cells in your body look the same?

In this activity the children will discover that cells are not the same throughout a plant.

When you look at cells from the root and leaf the piece placed on the slide should be very thin in order to see a single layer of cells. Some children may wish to use stains—let them make their own choice of stain.

Some children may begin to suspect that cells from different parts of plants or animals do not look the same. In the onion the root cells are

Activity 7

At the end of Activity 5 it was suggested that you obtain several jars of swamp water. In this activity children will see what they can find, with the aid of a microscope, in the swamp water.

Have you ever viewed swamp water through a microscope? Place a drop of swamp water on a microscope slide. Look at it with your microscope.

1. Can you see anything moving?
2. Are there any different things moving?
3. Do they move fast?
4. Can you see how they move?
5. Are they all the same size?
6. How big is the largest?
7. Can you draw some sketches of some of the "things" you see?

Look at several water samples—swamp water, water from puddles in the street, and water from the drinking fountain. What do you see? Do you see the same things in each sample?

One of the most exciting discoveries made by children will be in this activity dealing with life in swamp water. Microscopic life in swamp water is revealed to the child. Allow the children to

192

"play" by looking at all kinds of water samples they bring to class. This activity is designed to introduce the students to the strange single-celled animals and plants known as protozoa. All of the questions are intended to encourage the children to see what they can observe for themselves. Almost all answers are acceptable. Only general observations will be made in this activity. More detailed observations of protozoa will be done in the next activity.

Some students may wish to raise protozoa themselves. Good results can be obtained by collecting pond water in a jar and adding some dried grass or straw for food. Do not seal the jar, allow air into it. This is known as a hay infusion. After two weeks, protozoa will be found in abundance.

Protozoa (one-celled animals) are found in fresh-water ponds, streams, and swamps. Immense

quantities can be found in almost any stagnant puddle. There are many species of protozoans—about 10,000 have been identified and named so far.

Although these animals consist of only one cell, we want children to see that a protozoan cell does most of the things that more complex animals do; it moves, feeds, divides, excretes.

In the next activity we look at three of these one-celled animals—paramecium, euglena, and ameba.

Encourage children to bring in samples for this activity. Let them grow their own hay infusions. This project can continue after this activity is completed. Periodic examinations of animals grown in the hay infusions stimulate tremendous interest.

Activity 8

In this activity children make observations of paramecium, euglena, and ameba. Samples of each can easily be obtained from a commercial scientific supply house. The high school biology department may also be of assistance.

You will study in detail three kinds of protozoa. Place a drop of the culture to be viewed on a microscope slide.

Paramecium

1. Sketch one paramecium.
2. Is a euglena smaller or larger than paramecium?
3. What color is a euglena?
4. Do you think a paramecium can see?
5. What do you think a paramecium eats?

Euglena

1. Sketch one euglena.
2. Is a euglena smaller or larger than a paramecium?
3. What color is a euglena?
4. Does a euglena move faster or slower than a paramecium?
5. What do you think a euglena eats?

Ameba

1. Sketch one ameba.

2. Compare an ameba with a paramecium and a euglena. Make your own chart on how they compare:

The cultures of living material should be handled carefully—do not shake. Ameba are generally found at the bottom of the jar, paramecia near the top, and euglena on the side toward the light. Samples of each are placed (by the teacher) on microscope slides with a dropper.

The following is general background information on the paramecium, euglena, and ameba. The paramecium is completely covered with cilia and it moves about lashing the water with its cilia. Paramecia eat bacteria and small food particles. The food enters the gullet and it is collected by a food vacuole. As one food vacuole becomes filled, it moves to another part of the cell and is replaced by another empty one at the end of the gullet. Liquid wastes are thought to be voided by the contractile vacuole. The contractile vacuole fills with liquid and bursts at frequent intervals.

There is an extension in the front of the euglena which is used for "swimming." Scattered throughout the euglena are chloroplasts which probably contain chlorophyll similar to that in green plants. The organism is like a plant, for animals do not contain chlorophyll. Its other structures and habits are clearly animal. Because of this, the euglena is considered part plant and part animal.

The ameba is shapeless and a jellylike mass of protoplasm. Motion is provided by pseudopods (false feet), which carry the organism along. Ameba move slower than most protozoa. It obtains food by letting itself flow around microscopic plants, bacteria, and small protozoa. The engulfed particles become enclosed in a space called a food vacuole.

Concerning the questions in this activity, the following may be helpful. Most of the time the front end of the paramecium is the end which goes forward. Paramecia will bump into things and then back away. This seems to support the idea that they cannot see or at least ignore what they see. The paramecium flops over when it changes direction sharply. It cannot do this when confined by a coverslip. The euglena is smaller than the paramecium and is cigar shaped. The euglena spirals around as it swims and appears green under the microscope light. Ameba are much harder to find—children will have trouble. The ameba has many nuclei but is still considered a one-celled animal, as it has only one cell wall.

The interest generated in living animals during the last activity will be continued in this activity. Take time to consider other questions that can be asked about these protozoa. There is plenty of room for an active imagination.

This is the last activity in this unit. This does not mean that work with the microscope must cease—rather, encourage its continued use. One question not considered in the unit is, Do cells multiply and how? Many activities can be devised to find out. First, it is necessary to show they *do* multiply. The cultures used in this activity can assist in this problem. Check on the number of protozoa in one drop of culture each day: Is it increasing, decreasing, or staying the same? How about the abundance of animal life in the hay infusions started by the children earlier in the unit? Certainly samples from these will indicate an increase in numbers. Cells do multiply! The study of yeast cultures made from a solution of yeast powder, water, and molasses is a worthwhile activity.

Additional Activities—Observing Cells

1. Place a green plant in a dark place for several days. Compare it with a similar one left in the sunlight.
2. Plant several bean or corn seeds. Examine the progress of the seed daily. A sufficient number should be planted to insure the growth of several plants to maturity.
3. If possible examine the stems and leaves of many different plants. Cattails are interesting for they have a hollow stem through which air passes to the roots.
4. Have children note plants growing on the way to and from school. How does the environment affect the plants they see? Look in the schoolyard, shaded areas, and along the sidewalk.
5. Construct a terrarium. Place one inch of sand

on the bottom of a jar or glass tank. Then add a half-inch layer of charcoal and then a layer of garden soil or peat moss. Make valleys and add rocks for scenic beauty. Place a tiny container of water in the terrarium (a small pond). Add tiny plants (ferns, mosses) and small insects or animals and then seal with a cover (glass plate or cellophane). The effects of environment can now be viewed and controlled.

6. Sprinkle different seeds in a sponge and place in a can containing a small amount of water. Observe how the seeds grcw.

7. Place seeds on a piece of cloth which is laid over wet sand or sawdust in a pan. Cover with another piece of cloth and more wet sand or sawdust. The seeds will germinate and can periodically be observed.

8. Do seeds need air for germination? Place some on moist blotting paper and others under water. Seeds will decay in the water for they cannot take air from the water. How does temperature affect germination? Seeds planted in containers can be placed at normal room temperature, in the refrigerator, and in the oven (a few hours at moderate temperature).

9. Place a stalk of celery in water colored with red ink. Observe how water travels to all parts of the plant.

10. Draw diagrams of the various systems (root, leaf, stem, etc.) including the major organs in each system. It is preferable that a child be able to discuss the operation of a particular system using his own rough sketch than be required to memorize a diagram of the system.

11. Discuss certain common diseases and how they affect various body systems.

12. Examine the pores in your skin with a magnifying glass. Draw a picture of what you see.

13. Count how many times your heart beats in one minute. Compare the count with the count you get after doing ten deep-knee bends. Explain the difference.

14. In what way are sick people fed when they cannot eat food? Does this method (intra-venous feeding) bypass some of the normal systems?

15. Observe the bones of various animals—chickens, rabbits, birds, cows. These bones are obtainable from home, butcher shops, or slaughter houses. Consider how size and shape are related to function. A large collection can be obtained in time—try to build up your collection.

16. Construct a skeleton out of cardboard.

17. Examine models of the "Visible Man" during the study of the body's systems.

18. Make a chart showing heartbeats of various animals. Is there a relationship between the size of the animal and the number of heartbeats per minute?

19. Make a poster showing the various parts of the brain and where the nerve centers are located that control the various senses.

20. Remove a leaf from a plant which has been in the sun for several hours and place it in some hot water. Then soak the leaf in a corked bottle of alcohol overnight. Do the same thing with a leaf from a plant which has been in a dark closet for several hours. The leaves will be bleached white and the alcohol will be green (chlorophyll dissolved). Soak the whitened leaves in an iodine solution. The leaf which was in the sun becomes dark blue or black and the other leaf is stained brown. The dark stain indicates the presence of starch—a result of photosynthesis.

21. Grow some mold (nongreen plant). Place some bread in a dark, damp place. Wait several days before examining. Point out that some molds are helpful (medicinal) and some harmful (food spoilage).

22. Develop an experiment to observe how plants react to different colored lights. Grow four or five bean plants. Use different colored cellophane and different sources of light. What are the results?

23. Maintain an aquarium. It is not difficult to maintain a balanced aquarium. Obtain a square or oblong tank. Clean it thoroughly and place a few inches of clean washed sand on the bottom. Pile the sand a little deeper at one end for plants. Set the aquarium in a

location where it will receive diffused light, not too much direct sunlight. Place plants in the sand as desired. Plants from ponds are eel grass, water milfoil, duck weed, and pond weed. Purchased plants are Vallisneria, Sagittaria, or Elodea. Carefully fill with water (not disturbing the sand). Use pond water or tap water. Allow tap water to stand, until the chlorine evaporates, before using it. Stock the aquarium but do not overstock (one fish per gallon of water). Feed should be used sparingly.

24. Prepare yeast suspensions by dissolving yeast in a solution of sugar and warm water. Dissolve as much sugar as possible in the warm water. Prepare slides of the suspension for observation with the microscope. Careful observation will reveal the reproduction of yeast plants.

25. Invite a medical doctor to talk to your class about a specific body system and the major diseases that attack the system.

26. Investigate widespread famines and epidemics in regions of the world. How could they have been prevented? What steps were taken to meet the challenge presented by these disasters?

27. Make a field trip to the health department.

28. Invite representatives from the Heart, T.B., and Health associations and the American Cancer Society to visit your class and talk to the children.

29. Obtain a beef heart with vessels attached. Identify as many parts as possible.

30. Split bones obtained from the butcher—observe the red marrow. This is where the red cells are made.

31. Visit a laboratory where blood counts are made. Pay particular attention to the instruments used.

32. Consider the basic parts of the eye and compare with the basic parts of a camera. Obtain a pig, sheep, or cow eye from the butcher. Identify the parts.

SNOWFLAKE REPLICAS

How to Begin

How often have you tried to observe the exquisite beauty of a snowflake crystal only to have it evaporate before your very eyes? This same ephemeral quality has frustrated many a youngster as he attempted to capture these elusive gems of nature.

This activity is directly related to the unit on crystals and it is suggested that it be introduced as a sequel during the winter months if Crystals unit is taught during the fall. It may also be used prior to the teaching of crystals if the latter unit is tried in the spring. At any rate, snowflake activities naturally must be done during the winter months when there is available snow.

Begin by gathering the following materials in sufficient quantity for a classroom size.

black cloth (velvet or corduroy)
roll of commercial plastic wrap (Baggies or Saran Wrap)
toothpicks
spray can of clear plastic lacquer or art fixative spray (Krylon, clear #1301, or a 5% transparent spray in a push-button can usually available at art supply stores)
oak tag, or shirt cardboards
magnifying glass (hand lens type)
optional: overhead projector, slide projector, Formvar #15-45 (available from Monsanto Co.) and ethylene dichloride (available at the drugstore)

Why Do It This Way?

One of the most exciting ways of examining the delicate structure of matter is to observe it in

the pristine form of a snowflake crystal. Today there is much concern and justifiable alarm over the indiscriminate manner in which man abuses his environment. Tons of pollutants are poured daily into our atmosphere in the form of industrial wastes, automobile exhausts, and other particulate matter. They sit, casting a deadly veil of smog and irritating materials which create a very real and serious health problem. Were it not for winds that eventually blow the pollutant-laden air elsewhere and for precipitation (rain, snow, etc.), the great natural cleanser of our atmosphere, there would be little cause to study snowflakes for there would be no one around to engage in such study.

All precipitation begins with the cooling and condensing of water vapor on tiny nuclei, which may be particles of salt, a minute bit of dust, dirt, or a grain of pollen. Cloud droplets are formed and cold air turns the droplet into an ice crystal which enlarges as it falls and eventually reaches

Whatever the variations, snowflakes are things of beauty possessing a fragile elegance of design which must be seen to be believed. Intermediate grade children will thrill to the opportunity of capturing and examining the endless gallery of these dainty and compelling works of nature. Until comparatively recent times, analysis of snowflake crystals was accomplished only with painstaking care by drawings such as those of the Arctic explorer Scoresby, and later with the photographic process by W. A. Bently in Vermont.

How to Do It

The primary method of making snowflake replicas to be used in this activity, however, is based upon a technique developed by Dr. Vincent J. Schaefer, Director of the Atmospheric Sciences Research Center at the State University of New York in Albany, in 1941.

This technique encases a snow or frost crystal within a thin plastic film which, as it forms, makes an exact three dimensional impression of the surface features of the crystal. The replica solution, consisting of one to three parts of the synthetic plastic polyvinal Formal (Formar) dissolved in 100 parts of ethylene dichloride, readily wets an ice surface. By capillarity and surface activity it rapidly covers any ice crystal which comes in

the ground as a snowflake. This newly born "snowflake" is an individual crystal or a large clump composed of fifty or more crystals.

Snow may be a boon or a bane depending upon whether you are a skiing buff or own a long driveway that needs shoveling. Its beauty is difficult to deny and its cleansing effect on our dirty air is vital. Recent research by Edward R. LaChapelle, Associate Professor in the Department of Atmospheric Science at the University of Washington, also indicates that the type of snow crystals and the changes that take place deep within the fallen snow may be instrumental in the development of avalanches.

Contrary to popular belief not all snowflakes are the traditional hexagonal (six-sided) shapes depicted in most reference books. They may take many varied forms. The International Snow Classification guide shown elsewhere in this activity illustrates ten of the more common varieties, and some scientists have distinguished many times this number. The hexagonal versions usually have six arms or sides but under special circumstances or accidents can produce three, five, or even twelve. The arms can be broken off when flakes bump or separate from a clump. Other variables such as clouds, air, ground temperature, cloud height, amount of wind, and moisture content so influence the formation of the crystal that it is reasonably safe to say that no two snowflakes are alike.

contact with it. The solvent evaporates in five to ten minutes, after which the slide (glass, cardboard, etc.) bearing the samples may be warmed above freezing. Upon melting, the water molecules evaporate through the thin film, leaving a hollow shell which refracts and scatters light in a manner quite similar to the optical properties of the original crystal.[1]

The chemistry-oriented teacher may wish to try this method, but the following adaptation of a procedure also suggested by Dr. Schaefer should prove easier to implement.

Give each student a 5″ × 8″ filing card or cut pieces of oak tag or shirt cardboard to size. Place a sheet of commercial plastic wrap over the pieces of cardboard. Stiff sheets of clear acetate used with overhead projectors work nicely and eliminate the need for cardboard backing. Have the students work individually or in teams of two. Have a few cans of plastic spray in readiness and wait hopefully for the first snowfall. Chances are that snowfall will occur often enough during the winter in northern states to try this activity a number of times. Encourage the class to try it at home if the opportunity arises. Caution them not to spray the contents of the can at anyone and to store it in a cool dry place.

Go outside during a snowfall and allow five or six minutes for plastic wrap, slides, cardboard, or whatever is being used to cool to the outside temperature. The thicker the material the longer you will have to wait for it to cool. It is not necessary to cool the spray fixative since the gas under pressure will emit a fine spray at high nozzle speed and will be cool enough not to melt the snow.

1. Gently spray one side of your snowflake catcher until it is slightly tacky. Do not spray so much that it is gooey.
2. Wearing gloves to avoid heat from the hand melting your catch, hold your snowflake catcher out in the path of the falling snow.

3. Spray a toothpick or glass rod with the lacquer and select special or unusual crystals that may fall on your clothing and transfer them to your sheet.

When enough crystals are caught take your sheet to a protected area outside. Allow the sheets of plastic and cardboard to cool for a few minutes more and for the excess spray to evaporate. If you were lucky you should now have a number of flakes to look at. They may be brought inside after drying and shown directly on an overhead projector.

[1] Vincent Schaefer, "The Use of Replica Techniques for Studying Snow," *Compendium of Meteorology*, Waverly Press, Inc., Baltimore, Md., 1951.

Have the class search for and identify as many crystal types as possible. Let each individual or team elect the best crystals. Cut these out and prepare a slide for a slide projector, as illustrated in the diagram below.

If a microprojector or regular microscope is accessible, a much larger image may be obtained and finer detail observed.

Capturing and preserving snowflake crystals can be great fun and is an activity worth doing in itself, but a good deal more can be gained by learning to identify the myriad forms and shapes that will be collected over a period of time.

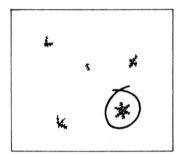

plastic sheet or wrap
with various crystals
caught

plastic sheet may be shown on overhead projection

commercial slide holders are available from most photo stores at nominal cost

selected crystal cut out and inserted in slide made from two pieces glued together with a window to project through

Examining snowflake shapes can indirectly tell you the approximate temperature and height from which the snow has fallen. While each snowflake has an individual identity that is never exactly like any other, yet certain shapes occur frequently enough to form groups or classes. The most commonly used classification for solid precipitation was proposed by the International Commission on Snow and Ice in 1951. The chart at the top of page 201 is a summary of the main types and applies only to falling snow.

The chart displays the main structural types of snow crystals, plus ice pellets, hail, and graupel (snow crystals with a crusty rime deposit of frozen cloud droplets). The primary seven snow crystal types are stellar crystals, columns, needles, spatial dendrites, capped columns, plates and irregular forms. The last category is a catch-all that embraces what cannot be placed in one of the others. Some examples are given in the chart beginning on the bottom of page 201.

An expanded version of the meteorological classification of snow crystals was developed by C. Magono and C. W. Lee[2] of Japan and is an amplification of the original classification of U. Nakaya[3] (see Where to Find Out Section).

The students engaged in identifying snow crystals may begin to see the relationship between cloud height, temperature, and crystal size. In general, the higher clouds exhibit lower temperatures and thus produce smaller crystals. The lower temperature causes the crystals to cool rapidly, thus inhibiting their growth. The higher the temperature, the slower crystals form and the larger they grow. This is a phenomenon common to all crystals whether in the laboratory or in nature.

Other Activities to Try with Snow

Before a snowstorm, set up these interesting experiments:

"1. Put a piece of black cardboard out on the grass. About two feet away, stake down a folded newspaper. Place both in locations where they will receive about the same snow-load as the surrounding lawn. Check daily after the storm to see the difference in melt rate on three different bases.

2. Stand a broom handle in the ground. After the storm, if there has been a high wind, check "saucer" shape around the broom handle.

[2] C. Mango and C. W. Lee, "Meteorological Classification of Natural Snow Crystals," *Journal of the Faculty of Science*, Hokkaido University, Ser. VII (Geophysics) II, No. 4 (November, 1966), s21-35.

[3] U. Nakaya, *Snow Crystals: Natural and Artificial*, Cambridge, Mass., Harvard University Press, 1954.

Types of Solid Precipitation

Term	Remarks	Graphic Symbol	Examples
Plates	also combinations of plates with or without very short connecting columns		
Stellar crystals	also parallel stars with very short connecting columns		
Columns	and combinations of columns		
Needles	and combinations of needles		
Spatial dendrites	spatial combinations of feathery crystals		
Capped columns	columns with plates on either (or one) side		
Irregular particles	irregular compounds of microscopic crystals		
Graupel (soft hail)	isometric shape, central crystal cannot be recognized		
Ice pellets (sleet)	ice shell, inside mostly wet		
Hail	layers (onionlike in cross-section)		

3. Stand a barrel stave or flat board in the ground at least two feet away from the broom handle. After the storm, check the difference in saucer forms and drift shapes to the front and rear.

After a snowstorm, take note of these oddities:

1. Watch a snowdrift vanish without melting. This "subliming" happens when snow crys-

Crystal Type	Size	Cloud Type	Approx. Height	Temp.
Prisms and Prism Clusters	Very tiny	slender, wispy cirrus	30,000 to 50,000 feet	below zero F.

These tiny prisms are common Arctic forms and a sudden below-zero cold snap may cause these shapes even in clear weather, under a moonlit starry sky. They will shimmer and shine as the air "sparkles."

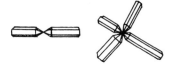

Crystal Type	Size	Cloud Type	Approx. Height	Temp.
Columns and Plates	1/1000" to 1/8"	alto-cumulus and alto-stratus	10,000 to 30,000 feet	medium temp.

Usually hexagonal columns with pointed prism ends; hexagonal plates with plain sides are also common in the clouds which form at this height. They are generally larger than the minute flakes which form at the higher levels, but the temperature is still low enough to keep available water vapor to a minimum and reduce the chances of extensions developing.

Crystal Type	Size	Cloud Type	Approx. Height	Temp.
Stellar Flakes	1/32" to 1/2"	low clouds: nimbo-stratus, stratus, or strato-cumulus	below 10,000 feet	between 26° and 32° F.

Usually abundant water vapor develops traditional-shaped crystal with number of fernlike extensions. Hexagonal plates formed at higher altitudes gather into clusters or add arms.

Crystal Type	Size	Cloud Type, approximate height, and temperature
Capped Columns or Tsuzumi	1/64" to 3/16"	Cloud type, approximate height, and temperature characteristics vary for this type. Capped Columns are in general similar to Columns and Plates.

These are unusually shaped crystals which resemble a Japanese tomtom or drum. They are sometimes called tea trays or collar buttons. They appear as columns wearing plates for caps and on occasion may have fernlike extensions.

Graupel

Most commonly found during the beginning and end of winter, they look like tiny, somewhat irregular snowballs. Formed as the result of small flakes which have picked up a deposit of frozen cloud droplets called rime.

202

tals pass into vapor without going through the liquid phase. It is particularly likely to happen in sunny weather.

2. Examine garden areas or lawn edges where there are still flower stalks or plant stems. You will see air spaces here where small tents are formed under which animals will sometimes shelter. The same phenomenon can be noted under bent-over cattails in swamp areas.

During a snowstorm, observe these phenomena:

1. Check roof insulation efficiency. Unless wind scours snow off as it falls, the roof with most snow has least heat loss.

2. See how snow piles up and supports itself beyond roof edges. If the flakes fall in just-below-freezing weather, the snow edge may curl over or even hang down as flakes are cemented by freezing. With very dry snow and a high wind, flakes may be wedged together so tightly that the drift may extend as much as a foot beyond the roof edge. Drifts may be quite vertical on the edge, with no roll-over until sun shines on them."[4]

3. Try preserving frost patterns. This may prove to be a little more difficult than snowflakes. If spraying the patterns after they have formed is too hard, try letting the spray fixative serve as its own medium. It may produce its own unique designs.

4. Collect new-fallen snow in plastic bags. Bring these bags of snow inside, allow them to melt, and then search for particles of dirt, dust, or pollen. Much of the material discovered will be particulate matter (pollu-

tants) of some kind collected by the falling snow as it cleansed the atmosphere.

5. Repeat this same activity by collecting snow in an area where the snow has already fallen but hasn't been disturbed. Scrape off the surface snow which has been contaminated with local dirt particles. Examine the underlying layers by following the procedure above and look for trapped pollutants.

6. If a cold chest of the type used for storing foods at $-4°$ to $-13°$F. is available, an interesting number of experiments may be performed. Line the inside with black velvet stretched on light wooden frames. Keep the cloth about one half inch from the cold box walls. Using the breath as a source of moisture supercooled clouds may be formed. Place your mouth close to the top of the chamber and exhale slowly with sufficient strength to reach the bottom of the chamber. Shine a bright flashlight or slide projector beam into the chamber at an angle of 45 degrees. A few ice crystals may be visible but not enough to be spectacular. To amplify this situation scratch a chunk of dry ice with a nail. Little contrails will appear consisting of numerous ice crystals which rapidly grow and spread throughout the supercloud produced by your breath in the chamber. Once some skill is achieved in this technique, apply some of your knowledge about snowflake replicas to attempting to capture some of these home-made crystals.

7. Try other materials as a source of condensation nuclei in the experiment above. Induce electrical charges by rubbing a hard rubber comb through your hair and see what effect it has on the cloud in the chamber.

8. Observe a small piece of ice or a clump of snow melting on a slide under a microprojector. Have the class write down as many things as they can observe happening to the material as it melts.

[4] Reprinted with permission from "That White Stuff—Little Known Facts About Snow and Things to Watch and Do," prepared by the Hartford Electric Light Co., January 1970, public service pamphlet.

THERMOBAROMETERS AND OTHER WEATHER INVESTIGATIONS

How to Begin

Perhaps no other area of science is of more concern to the average citizen on a daily basis than the science of meteorology. What is the weather at this very moment? Are you going to be able to accomplish what you planned for this weekend? Weather conditions each day help us to determine much of our daily activity. Undoubtedly weather is one of the most important influences in our lives. Weather affects how we feel, what we will wear, what we eat, what we do in our leisure time. Many of man's customs and traditions owe their heritage to the weather he has had to experience. He constructed his shelters, obtained his food, developed commerce and trade, organized social mores and customs in patterns allowable by the weather and climate in his particular area.

Why Do It This Way?

In a study of weather, teachers often ask their students to construct weather instruments. Many of these instruments often require very hard-to-get materials and a great deal of time for construction. This unit is designed to permit intermediate school children to build simple yet functional weather instruments. Probably no other science lends itself so readily to active experimentation with homemade instruments as meteorology.

The science of meteorology deals primarily with the measurement and analysis of the elements which make up weather. Many instruments are required to read and record the tons of data which must be reduced and interpreted for

weather forecasting. It would be difficult to have students attempt to build all the various types of instruments used by weathermen; however, an amazing amount of information can be gathered with just a few simple devices. This has led to its being named the "tin can science." Many of the basic instruments can indeed be made from tin cans by adapting them in a variety of ways. A few are illustrated in this activity.

How to Do It

Materials needed will be listed with each activity as they occur.

Activity 1: Making a Thermobarometer

Materials: tin cans (coffee or juice variety, one for each student)

balloons (9-inch size, one for each student)

a dozen or so 3" × 5" filing cards

scissors, masking tape, and rubber cement

A popular demonstration for illustrating the principle of the aneroid barometer usually involves the traditional tin can covered with a sheet of rubber or a piece cut from a balloon, with either a straw or a stick attached to the top to serve as an indicator of changes in air pressure.

It is ironic that this experiment has endured so long, for it is not valid and doesn't indicate air pressure correctly; the reason is that the effects of temperature are more noticeable than those of pressure changes. For example: A temperature increase of 20 degrees from early morning to afternoon will result in a 4 percent increase in the volume of air in the can. Changes in barometric pressure, on the other hand, are generally slight and a one-half-inch pressure change, which would be a rather large change, will barely change the volume of air 2 percent.

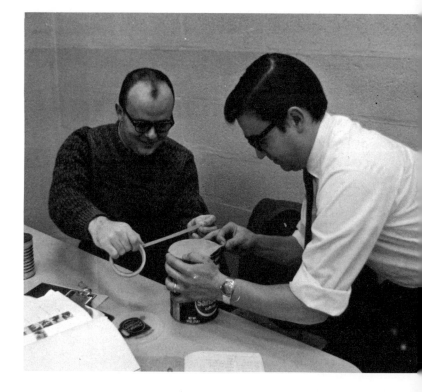

Does this mean that this familiar, easy-to-construct device should be abandoned? Indeed not. In fact, a more interesting learning situation may be experienced if the two variables are considered instead of being ignored.

Begin by asking each student to bring in a small

tin can and a balloon. Instruct the class to cut the necks from the balloons and stretch the remaining portion over the open end of the can. Seal the balloon with masking tape all around the perimeter of the can. Cut strips of the 3″ × 5″ cards approximately one inch in width and three inches in length. Measure or calibrate one strip by marking off every eighth of an inch or some suitable distance. Tape this perpendicularly to one side of the can after the balloon has been mounted. Take another strip and cut a point at one end and fold into a Z shape. With a spot of rubber cement, attach this pointer to the middle of the stretched balloon on the can (as shown below in diagram and accompanying photos). Instead of the Z-shaped paper strip a pointer may be made from a paper clip bent in a like manner. This will prove more durable.

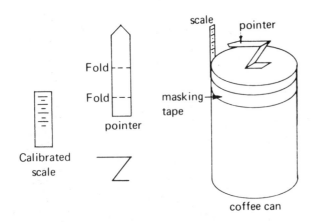

Once the children have all constructed their instruments, do not tell them what its function is even though they will want to know. Instead, ask them what they think it is for. Most of them will probably respond that it is some form of thermometer or a barometer of sorts. Before long there will be two opposing groups each staunchly defending its hypothesis.

Have all the students calibrate their instruments at the same time using the same zero point. You might make a dittoed scale to make sure that each starts at the same point. A thermometer and an aneroid barometer may be used as controls. Suggest that the students place their instruments in different places in the room. Some may put them by the window in the sun, others in the

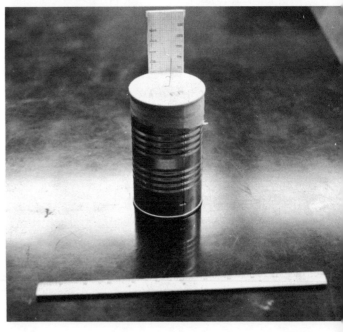

shade, some may be placed high and others low. Suggest also that they construct a graph of their recordings and compare their devices with the control barometers and thermometers. Ask what other factors might affect the accuracy of the instrument. Are there any differences if one can is colored dark and the other light? Does the size of the can influence the rate of change? What would happen if some pointers were made larger than others? Will those in the north window show more activity than those in the south? What can be done to negate the effects of temperature? (Hint that the difference caused by temperature might be recorded and corrected for, or better still, that the temperature could be kept uniform, as in a classroom heated in winter.) If the effect of temperature can be controlled, then the instrument may very well indicate pressure changes more accurately. In one class of children using this homemade instrument a meeting of minds occurred and they decided to compromise and not call their device a thermometer or barometer. They coined a new phrase instead: thermobarometer. Once the students have learned to negate, or correct for, temperature differences (by whatever means they choose) they have a reasonably good indicator of barometric changes. When the pressure indicator goes up, the chances for good weather are improved. When the pressure indicator goes down, it may be associated with the portent of bad weather.

Activity 2—Calibrating Thermometers

How good is a measure?

The exercise described here, which explores relative temperatures by calibrating ungraduated thermometers, is designed both to arouse the interest of the students and to create an appreciation for the built-in limitations of any measurement. Furthermore, it gives them an opportunity to discover some of these restrictions first-hand by utilizing rather simple equipment.

For a class of thirty, the following equipment is needed:

15 ungraduated thermometers, approximately 25 centimeters in length (available from most scientific houses at about $1.50 each). Household thermometers, removed from their backing, might work reasonably well.

6 beakers (1,000 ml are satisfactory) for holding ice cubes or crushed ice

6 Bunsen burners (or hot plates)

15 grease pencils for marking

15 shirt cardboards or large pieces of white construction paper

Procedure

To prepare for the exercise, challenge the class by asking if anyone can read the temperature in

the room by using one of the uncalibrated thermometers. You will get the obvious answer that it can't be done, which opens the whole problem for discussion. The following is an effective means of generating ideas: ask each student to submit a brief outline, for the next lesson, on how he thinks the thermometers can be adjusted to give a reasonably accurate reading. No matter what technique you use, do not give an answer outright.

Invariably, there will be suggestions to use fixed points of some medium, usually culminating in the proposal that the freezing point and boiling point of water could be used. There is no difficulty in getting agreement that these limits will provide a convenient and accurate range. At this point, the problem of devising a method of calibrating begins.

Divide the class into groups of two or three and permit each group to start calibrating from either end of the scale. Thus, half may attempt to record the freezing point with the buckets of ice, and the other half may concentrate on the boiling point.

When this has been accomplished, lay the thermometers out on a shirt board or construction paper and trace around them. When the points experimentally arrived at have been marked, the

class is ready to figure out a way in which the space between the two points can be graduated. Again, this should be left to the ingenuity of the students, with the only requirement being that they represent both the Centigrade and Fahrenheit scales, preferably one on each side of the thermometer, as shown. You will probably be surprised at the wide variations in methodology achieved by the individuals in the class.

By having the students work from the Centigrade side first (usually by dividing zero to 100 by some base measurement of 10) it is readily seen that from 32° to 212°F is a range of 180°, while 0° to 100°C is a range of 100°. This proportion is 9/5. The two scales become easier to calibrate and the old enigma of formula conversion is bypassed.

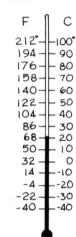

It is helpful, of course, to start with the Centigrade side by measuring the distance between zero and 100 degrees on the basis of some length divisible by 10. If this is impractical, then use a system which halves the total length. Further division into 20 readings of every 5 degrees will make the relationship between the two scales more evident, when the equivalent of 9 degrees is used on the Fahrenheit side (see note to diagram).

When the students describe their conclusions, these questions should be answered:

Are you measuring heat or temperature?
Is there any difference between the two terms?
Are there any limits to the degree of fineness of your calibrations?
Are the only limits imposed those of your measuring devices?

As a result of the exercise, the students will undoubtedly have many questions of their own. Common ones that come up are:

How do we know when we have reached the end point of freezing when using water and ice?

Can an ice cube be colder than 32° Fahrenheit or zero Centigrade?
What is temperature really a measurement of?
What is heat?

Each of these questions can provide enough discussion for a lesson in itself; you can explore each of them as fully as time permits. You may find, for example, that it will come as a surprise to many students to know that ice can get as cold as other things; they have long associated ice with the freezing point of water.

With the groundwork thus laid, you can introduce the most challenging of all questions for discussion: How cold can anything get, and what are the limitations, if any, of man's ability to measure this? This could lead, of course, into discussions of absolute zero.

Activity 3—Balloon Launching

Materials needed

11-inch balloons in assorted colors
a small cylinder of helium, approximately 35 cubic feet, fills 80 to 100 balloons; or a large cylinder, approximately 280 cubic feet will fill approximately 600 balloons
Postal cards, one for each student

This activity may well prove to be the most exciting experience for intermediate school children exploring the vagaries of weather. This can be done as a class activity or it might be fun to invite parents in not only to observe but to help and actually participate.

It is probably best to fill the balloons inside the classroom first and secure the postcards, with the following information written on them, to the balloons.

date_____time_____

This card was launched by a weather balloon filled with helium from_____school by a student in the _____grade.

Please fill out the following and return: Thank you.

Finder's name_____
Where found_____
When found_____
Weather conditions_____

You might ask the students to design their own cards and decide what information they would like to seek. The cards may be secured by string or even attached directly to the balloon by inserting the knotted end of the balloon through a hole punched in the card. A rubber band looped through the hole and the other end snapped around the balloon knot also works well. A plastic bag enclosing the card will give it additional protection against the weather.

The balloons should be filled just prior to launching since helium has a very high rate of diffusion and can pass right through the skin of the balloon. In an attempt to reduce the costs, students may wish to purchase their own balloons and postcards and contribute toward the cost of the helium gas. Hydrogen gas will work very well, but it is not recommended, for it is very highly inflammable.

Tying balloons is a little tricky for intermediate school children but they will improve with practice. Perhaps this is one area where the parents may be of help.

Now we are ready for the launch. Try to select a clear area away from trees, electric wires, and telephone poles. A trial balloon might be launched initially to determine the direction of the wind. As the balloons begin to rise, have the students measure the altitude by the following method. Let the class practice this method often until they become skilled at it.

1. Teach direction finding by using simple compasses and having students identify landmarks around the school or at home.
2. Show students how to measure angles by using the human fist. Have each student stand and extend his left arm parallel to the ground and clench his fist. In much the same way as one would climb a rope, the student places his right fist upon his left and so on, fist over fist successively as shown in the dia-

gram, until his fist has reached a position directly overhead.

Ask students to count the number of fists required to reach the 90-degree position. The average number of fists needed after a few trials should be nine.

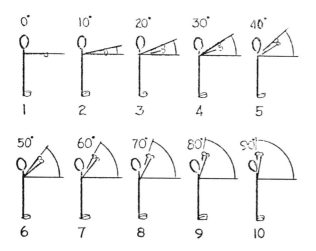

From position 1, where both fists are directly in front of the body and parallel to the ground, to position 10, where the top fist is directly overhead and perpendicular to the ground, the student's fists traverse 90 degrees of arc. It follows that each closed fist approximates 10 degrees and each finger 2 degrees. With this fundamental and readily available measuring device the class can now estimate the balloon's altitude above the horizon.

They should be able to observe some simple relationships between the number of fists measured (altitude) and the wind speed. For example: few fists—much wind; many fists—little wind.

Questions for discussion and further experimentation:

1. How much helium is needed to fill one 11-inch balloon?
2. Will three balloons tied together go three times as high or far?
3. Will the balloons increase or decrease in volume as they rise?

4. What will eventually cause the balloon to burst?
5. What direction do the balloons generally seem to go in your area (besides up)?
6. Can the heights of clouds be determined from the rate of ascent of the balloon if it is timed as well as measured in altitude?
7. How many balloons would be needed to lift you off the ground?

This may be found indirectly, but only approximately, by calculating how much weight one balloon can lift and then figuring out how many would be required to lift X pounds, or the weight of one student. Remember that this will be only an approximation for with a large number of balloons required the weight of the balloons and string will influence the results.

All kinds of additional questions may arise from this one activity, and imagine the excitement of the youngsters when a card is found and returned from some distant town or state.

UNKNOWN OBJECTS—ECOLOGY

How to Begin

From all corners cries of concern may be heard about the quality of our environment. Many are echoing the cry and rushing off in all directions at once, not always too sure of where they're going. Generally, little effort is given to an understanding of what the problem is really all about. Much of the initial reaction and concern are based upon fear and emotion. These may prove to be necessary ingredients if progress is to be made in preserving our environment, but it remains to be seen what real accomplishments can be made if criticism and emotion for their own sake are offered up as the means to justify the end.

Much hope for the future lies with the younger generation, for the present population, while concerned with root problems, has all it can do to treat symptoms and may have little time to devote directly to causes. Perhaps, as described in the unit on air pollution elsewhere in this book, the time has come to begin to treat causes, not just symptoms. This implies more than reaching the present adult population through shock-type statistics. It means properly educating today's youngsters who must address themselves to the problem since they will be more squarely confronted with it in the future.

Why Do It This Way?

In dealing with teachers and students at the intermediate grade levels it soon becomes evident that a majority of them experience difficulty in understanding ecology and ecological problems. There are probably a number of reasons, but one of the most salient is that ecology has just recently become a commonly used term, and like

most unfamiliar fields, it has a language all its own. Ironically, it is in danger of becoming a trite

212

and abandoned word before it is clearly understood. The apparently confusing terminology tends to frighten most students as well as their teachers away.

The language of science is a very precise and exact language, with each word conveying a specific meaning. Trained scientists readily understand this language, but for the young tyro this new language poses a completely new problem. By way of comparison, consider a doctor confronted with having to remove an infected appendix. Before doing so it's reasonable to expect that he should have some idea of what a healthy one looks like. Now in distinguishing the potential or actual harm that man can wreak upon his environment he must make an effort to understand the natural processes in action in much the same way the doctor is trained to perceive the abnormal from the normal.

Ecological problems often require an understanding of the interrelationships of living things, which requires an ability to identify and become familiar with the names of the various types of organisms one is working with. This may be accomplished through direct comparisons with known organisms, but in most cases, particularly with untrained students, identification keys are used. At this point some teachers make the mistake of assuming that keys are easy to use and thrust them upon children with little explanation or instruction. This almost guarantees failure of the lesson, for an inordinate amount of time is spent in just figuring out how the key works and often the student never gets down to attacking the problem he started out to solve.

This unit will focus upon a basic understanding of the construction and use of simple plant and animal keys with an emphasis upon sharpening a youngster's classification organizing and observing skills. This is accomplished by actually constructing and developing simple keys of various kinds and progressing toward more complex ones.

This unit is divided into activities for convenience only and it is not necessary to follow the exact sequence. One activity does not constitute a period. Some activities may take several class periods to complete.

We know that early man always searched for

ways of sorting or organizing things into groups that made some sense to him. It may have started quite simply when he separated things he could eat from things which he could not eat. An early Greek philosopher separated all things in the universe into fire, air, earth, and water. Language is grouped into the parts of speech, and in arithmetic we group numbers. Early man probably separated himself and other living creatures from non-living things. In our own daily lives we may be surprised to discover how much we group items all around us. We may group our clothes in our closet, the things on our desk, phonograph records in a collection, items in a notebook. Even the stars in the heavens are grouped into familiar patterns called constellations. Man compartmentalizes and categorizes much of his knowledge of the environment, perhaps to help keep his sanity. In nature there are groupings and patterns that are not always so readily discernible and it may take considerable skill to unravel their interrelationships. Things may be put into groupings because of their physical similarities as compared to one another or on the basis of their dissimilarities.

This process is generally termed classification; more specifically in the life sciences it is referred to as taxonomy. By its simplest definition, taxonomy deals with the identification and classification of plants and animals by natural relationships.

One of the most useful tools in decoding these relationships is a biological key, which is an instrument designed to help one quickly and easily find the genus and species name of the organism being examined (see the Where to Find Out section for a list of various keys).

In learning how to design, construct, and use a biological key students will become fluent in the language of ecology and be alerted to recognizing the natural processes and patterns surrounding them.

From this new vantage point their view will be clearer and the larger problem of how to preserve and understand the environment will be placed in proper perspective. Akin to the doctor, with his special language and training, students of ecology will then be better able to discern the *normal* from the abnormal.

How To Do It

Begin by placing a group of metal keys on an overhead projector or hold them up in front of the class. Ask the class what keys are used for. There will probably be a multitude of answers. Challenge a specific youngster to determine which of your group of keys will open the door of your car. Often he can readily deduce this by direct

examination of the keys using the most salient characteristics of size, shape, and color.

Question whether the car key can be used to open other locks or doors in the room. The class will generally agree that this is not possible and that only the right key will do this and only the car key will unlock your car.

Biological keys are very similar to keys on a key chain. Each key is specific and unlocks only the identity of a particular group of plants or animals. Remember that a key does not always definitely identify a specimen, it gives only a hint of what it might be. The only sure identification is made by comparing the specimen examined with another specimen that is already identified, or with a good drawing or detailed description.

Keys are very useful, for they help children to observe plants and animals closely and to see how they are similar or different from one another. Keys are also helpful in aiding the teacher and student to identify groups of plants and animals and to understand some of the patterns actually used by scientists in classifying organisms.

Activity 1

Materials: cigar boxes or containers and a large assortment of objects such as paper clips, metal fasteners, chalk, wood, etc.

Give each student a cigar box or container holding a dozen or so varied objects. Seal the boxes so that the identity of the objects will initially be unknown to the holder. Let the class play with the containers using all their ingenuity to discover what is inside without actually opening the container. When their curiosity is sufficiently stimulated, allow them to open the containers and spread their objects out on the desk.

Instruct the class to try to divide their objects into two approximately equal numbered groups, based only upon characteristics they can observe directly, not upon function. Groupings may be based on characteristics such as hard or soft, rough or smooth, big or little, heavy or light, dark- or light-colored, metal or nonmetal, and so on. Secondly, ask them to further subdivide their

objects by using a pair of characteristics other than the ones chosen initially. Continue this process until each individual object has been isolated and identified.

Activity 2

Now that the class has gained some experience in classifying familiar objects, suggest that they try a similar procedure with themselves, using physical characteristics as the basis of grouping

each other. The most common division decided upon is boys from girls. Then such things as eye color, size, hair color, and so on may be used. It becomes real fun when there are twins in the class and the last division has to be made between the two (discretion must be exercised by the teacher in cases where race, weight, height, or a physical handicap may be chosen as the basis of grouping and cause embarrassment to some individuals).

Activity 3

This activity is relatively simple and the only materials necessary are large pieces of construction paper, preferably of two colors, scissors, rulers, compasses or round shapes for drawing circles (An overhead projector and colored cellophane or plastic sheets are helpful for demonstration.)

Give each child a set of eight paper objects as follows: two red squares, one large and one small; two red circles, large and small; also distribute a set of black (or another color) squares and circles. It might be fun to have the students cut out their own shapes. Variations of increasing complexity may be devised by adding other shapes, such as triangles or rectangles or diamonds, to the group. Still other variations may be introduced by additional colors.

Ask each child to divide his pieces of paper into two groups. The teacher may want to demonstrate with a set made from colored cellophane or plastic acetate shown on the overhead projector. The children will often select color as the primary characteristic to divide their groups—for example, red versus black. A few may choose size, and others shape, but it should be emphasized that any of these characteristics may be used as long as the selection is based upon a characteristic that each object shows in its group. For a little fun select one of the paper patterns and pretend it is a truly *unknown object* and ask the class to try to figure out which one you picked by a series of questions concerning its shape, size, or color. Questions which might be asked are, "Is it red?" "Is is black?" "Is it large?" "Is it square?" Each question eliminates the paper pattern from one group until the answer to the last question completely identifies it. Try building a "key outline" which resembles a tennis tournament schedule in reverse. In a tennis tournament you start out with all the contestants or players and end up with a winner. A biological key outline, or in this case a paper pattern one, is structured similarly except that you start out with all the unknown objects, things, or organisms as a group and end up with each individual one identified. For example, see page 218.

A simple key may now be constructed utilizing this outline. The key is divided into pairs or couplets and is so constructed that there are two alternatives to each sequence. This is also called a biramous key. It works by the process of elimination,

gradually narrowing down the number of possible choices. All the paper objects can be divided into two colors, red or black, and then two sizes, big or small, and lastly two shapes, circle or square.

The first two alternatives are both numbered one and the two alternatives are red and black. The number after the color tells you where to go next on your key. For example:

1. Black . . . . .go to number 2
1. Red .go to number 5

2. Large . . . . .go to number 3
2. Small . . . . .go to number 4

3. *Square*
3. *Circle*

4. *Square*
4. *Circle*

5. Large . . . . .go to number 6
5. Small . . . . .go to number 7

6. *Square*
6. *Circle*

7. *Square*
7. *Circle*

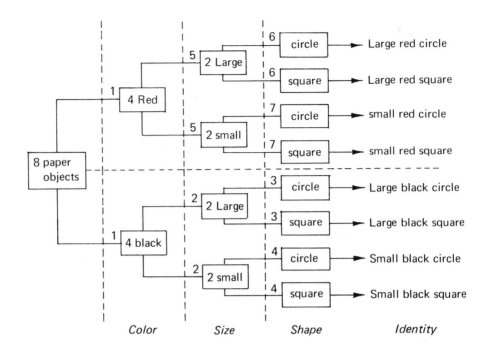

Color	Size	Shape	Identity

8 paper objects → 1 → 4 Red → 5 → 2 Large → 6 → circle → Large red circle

4 Red → 5 → 2 Large → 6 → square → Large red square

4 Red → 5 → 2 small → 7 → circle → small red circle

2 small → 7 → square → small red square

8 paper objects → 1 → 4 black → 2 → 2 Large → 3 → circle → Large black circle

2 Large → 3 → square → Large black square

4 black → 2 → 2 small → 4 → circle → Small black circle

2 small → 4 → square → Small black square

The student can now select one of the eight pieces and "run the key" to find out where it belongs according to its characteristics or physical properties. Since these are familiar shapes, more challenging ones may be devised or others added as suggested earlier. One ingenious teacher assigned nonsense names or cartoon characters' names to the shapes and the children enjoyed ending up with Batman instead of a big black circle and Robin instead of a small red square.

More difficult keys can be made by using such items as screws of different sizes and color, nails, paper fasteners, or any other readily available materials.

Activity 4

In this activity a dittoed sheet or an overhead projection of the following list of animals and things may be used.

Think of a way to separate the following list of objects into two separate groups based upon only those characteristics you could directly observe if the animal or object were available.

1. Turtle	7. Monkey
2. Moth	8. Hunk of lead
3. Fir tree	9. Grain of sand
4. Rose	10. Rock
5. Nail	11. Screw
6. Maple tree	12. Grain of salt

The usual decision is to separate the living from the nonliving things.

GROUP A Living	*GROUP B Nonliving*
1. Turtle	1. Nail
2. Moth	2. Salt
3. Fir tree	3. Rock
4. Maple tree	4. Lead
5. Rose	5. Screw
6. Monkey	6. Sand

218

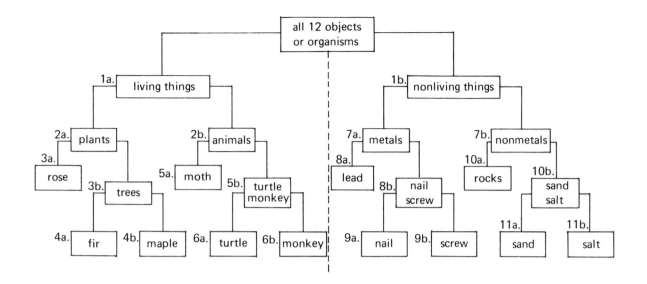

The "tennis tournament" in reverse outline can now be made. Remember, any number of characteristics could have been used initially to break the objects into two distinct groups. There is no "wrong" selection per se but some criteria work better than others. The outline above represents one possible approach.

The complete game may now follow and individual characteristics can be developed for each of the couplets. The sequence of numbers might be first applied to the outline and then used in organizing the couplets.

Activity 5

By this time the class has acquired considerable skill in constructing and running the key. Perhaps a simple key dealing with the trees surrounding the school can be constructed. The teacher might divide the class into several groups and assign an initial characteristic to each group. For example, group A must use evergreen versus deciduous trees, group B, simple versus compound leaves, group C, alternating versus opposite leaves, and so on. The following key is an example of a simple key for eight trees. Always keep in mind that a key is useful only for the organisms or objects it is designed for. The tree key on page 220 will work for only those trees noted. It can be adapted or modified to fit the trees in your area (see Where to Find Out section for a list of additional tree keys).

This key can be used for oak, maple, elm, ash, cedar, pine, hemlock, and spruce trees (you can modify this key for the trees around your school).

A plan or pattern now begins to emerge for constructing and designing a key. First attempt to group the animals, plants, or unknown objects into two distinct categories having some characteristics in common. Make a Data Chart or table of information about the objects or organisms being classified (see sample chart on page 221). Then develop an outline in the form of a flow chart as shown in the samples with this unit.

Develop couplets in which choices are offered by giving alternatives such as: leaves simple in structure versus leaves compound in structure. When the specimens are very similar, such as two kinds of frogs or birds, more than one set of characteristics is usually necessary. Lastly, select one of the plants, animals, or unknown objects and key it in reverse, that is, run it backwards, making sure that it fits every one of the couplets it was derived from. This last check will usually turn up errors which may go unnoticed when the key is used normally from the beginning.

A simple flow chart or "Tennis Tournament" in reverse outline for eight trees

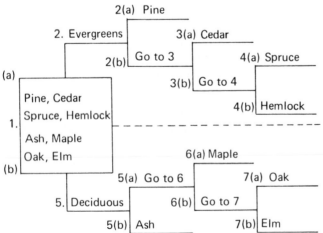

Terms used in the key:

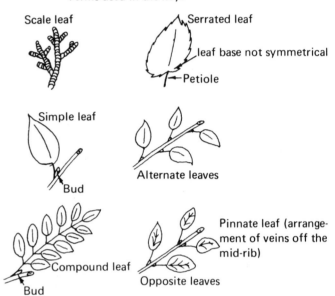

Scale leaf

Serrated leaf

leaf base not symmetrical

Petiole

Simple leaf

Bud

Alternate leaves

Compound leaf

Bud

Pinnate leaf (arrangement of veins off the mid-rib)

Opposite leaves

KEY

1. Evergreen trees, leaves scalelike or needlelike (2)
1. Broad leaves, lost in fall of the year (5)

2. Leaves needlelike, 2 to 5 needles in a bundle   PINE
2. Leaves not in bundles (3)

3. Leaves scalelike   CEDAR
3. Leaves not scalelike (4)

4. Short, stiff leaf, 4-sided leaf, found on all sides of the twig   SPRUCE
4. Short leaves, flat and blunt at the free end   HEMLOCK

5. Simple leaf (6)
5. Compound leaf   ASH

6. Leaves arranged opposite on the twig   MAPLE
6. Leaves arranged alternately on the twig (7)

Data Chart

Name of Animal	Backbone	No Backbone	Having Fur	No Fur	Having Wings	No Wings	Shell	No Shell	8 Legs	6 Legs	5 Legs	4 Legs	2 Legs
1. ROBIN	X			X	X			X					X
2. BAT	X		X		X			X					X
3. SPIDER		X	X			X		X	X				
4. BUTTERFLY		X		X	X			X		X			
5. STARFISH		X		X		X	X				X		
6. HORSE	X		X			X		X				X	
7. FISH	X			X		X		X					
8. SNAKE	X			X		X		X					
9. TURTLE	X			X		X	X					X	
10. BEAR	X		X			X		X				X	
11. FROG	X			X		X		X				X	
12. CLAM		X		X		X	X						

7. Leaf pinnate and deeply notched or lobed   OAK

7. Leaf not lobed, serrated (jagged) edge, leaf base near petiole not symmetrical   ELM

There are keys for all kinds of plants and animals. There are keys for insects (one is inserted here for reference—another is located in the Hexapod Unit). Keys may be made for turtles, snakes, amphibians, mollusks, worms, microscopic life, wild flowers, etc. The authors even developed one for the identification of rocks which may be found in *Guppies, Bubbles, and Vibrating Objects.*[1]

The real fun in developing keys is in the application. Plan field trips with a specific goal in mind such as classifying and labeling the trees surrounding the school. Perhaps a nature trail can be undertaken as a project by the class with all the trees and wild flowers identified.[2] Visitors to the trail could be given copies of student-devised keys to use as they walk the trail.

Have the children practice by attempting to trace an animal or plant through someone else's key.

With this newfound information the class is now prepared to do some real exploring in the environment and while this is just the beginning of understanding ecology it is at least undertaken by an attempt to speak the language.

A Key to Eight Common Orders of Adult Insects (See Hexapod Unit for another version of an insect key)

This key can be used for Isoptera, Hymenoptera, Diptera, Orthoptera, Odonata, Coleoptera, Hemiptera, and Lepidoptera.

Insect characteristics: Three pairs of jointed legs, three main body parts, no wings or one pair, or two pairs of wings.

[1] McGavack and LaSalle, *Guppies, Bubbles,* and *Vibrating Objects*, New York, John Day, 1969, Rock Sorting Unit, pp. 112-113.

[2] A tree key designed by a junior high student is included at the end of this unit. It is for the trees on Talcott Mountain in Avon, Connecticut.

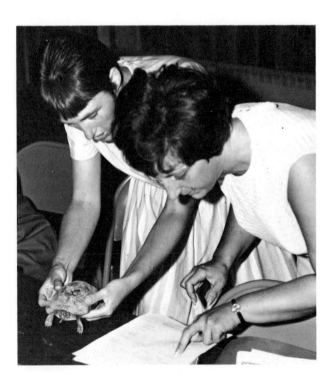

A. Insects without wings or one pair of wings (B)

  B. Insects with one wing pair (other pairs vestigial) DIPTERA (flies, mosquitoes)

  B. Ants or antlike insects with no wings, except during mating season (C)

    C. White insects (gray with two wing pairs when mating), live in wood, thorax and abdomen are not wasp-waisted as in ants ISOPTERA (termites)

    C. Red or black insects, abdomen-thorax connection *very* restricted, wings during mating season HYMENOPTERA (ants)

A. Insects with two pairs of wings (D)

    D. Wings not covered with "powder" (scales) (E)

      E. Both wing pairs entirely membrane-like (F)

        F. Large insects with long thin abdomen ODONATA (dragonfly)

        F. Small to large insects with restricted (wasp-waist) thorax to abdomen connection HYMENOPTERA (bee, wasp, hornet)

      E. Outer wings not membranelike or only outer part is membranelike (G)

        G. Insects with outer wings as hard covers COLEOPTERA (beetle)

        G. Insects without hard outer wings as covers (H)

          H. Outer wings thickened near base, remainder membrane-like, mouth parts for sucking, wings fold on back across each other HEMIPTERA (stink bug)

          H. Outer wings leathery, mouth parts for chewing, wings not folded across back ORTHOPTERA (grasshopper, cricket, cockroach)

NATURE TRAIL

at the

TALCOTT MOUNTAIN SCIENCE CENTER for STUDENT INVOLVEMENT

TREE KEY

1   If the tree has needles . . . IT IS HEMLOCK
1   If the tree has small green scales and sharp pointed brown scales . . . IT IS JUNIPER
1   If the tree has leaves . . . go to 2

---

2   If the leaves are opposite . . . go to 3
2   If the leaves are alternate . . . go to 4

---

3   If the leaves are compound . . . IT IS WHITE ASH
3   If the leaves are simple and round . . . IT IS DOGWOOD
3   If the leaves are simple and have lobes . . . go to 5

---

4   If the leaves are compound and the branches have thorns . . . IT IS LOCUST
4   If the leaves are compound and there are no thorns, and there are at least eleven leaflets . . . IT IS STAGHORN SUMAC
4   If there are five to seven leaflets . . . IT IS SHAGBARK HICKORY
4   If the leaves are simple . . . go to 6

---

5   If the leaves have many teeth between the lobes and are silvery white underneath . . . IT IS RED MAPLE
5   If the leaves are fairly smooth between teeth and green on both sides . . . IT IS SUGAR MAPLE

---

6   If the leaves have lobes . . . IT IS RED OAK
6   If the leaves have large rounded teeth . . . go to 7
6   If the leaves are not like either of these . . . go to 8

---

7   If the bark is a smooth yellow green and the leaf is rather heart shaped . . . IT IS BIGTOOTH ASPEN
7   If the twig has clustered end buds . . . IT IS CHESTNUT OAK

---

8   If the leaf base is lopsided (lower on one side than on the other) . . . go to 9
8   If the bases are about even . . . go to 10

---

9   If the leaves are large and heart shaped . . . IT IS BASSWOOD
9   If the leaves are smaller, oblong, and fuzzy . . . IT IS ELM

---

10   If the leaves are somewhat narrow, finely toothed, and there are two small glands on the leaf stalk near the leaf base . . . go to 11
10   If the leafstalk is very flat . . . go to 12
10   If it is neither . . . go to 13

This key was designed by a student at the Talcott Mountain Science Center for Student Involvement.

11   If the leaves are long, narrow, and the main vein on the underside has a lot of brown hair on it . . .
      IT IS BLACK CHERRY
11   If the leaves are wider, smaller, and lack the brown hair . . . IT IS CHOKE CHERRY

---

12   If the leaves are green on both sides, and the leafstalks are pinkish with two (2) small glands near
      the leaf base . . . IT IS COMMON COTTONWOOD
12   If the leaves are pale underneath and lack the glands . . . IT IS QUAKING ASPEN

---

13   If the bark is white . . . IT IS GRAY BIRCH
13   If the teeth of the leaves are deep cut and sharp . . . IT IS BEECH
13   If the teeth are smaller and the crushed twigs smell like wintergreen . . . IT IS BLACK BIRCH

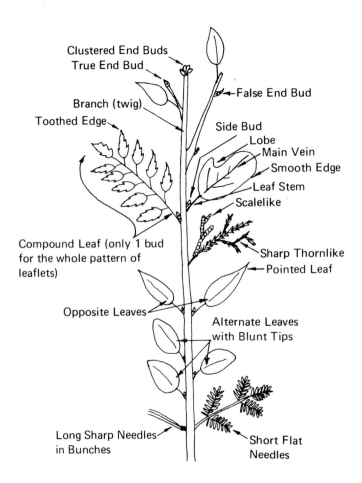

Composite plant showing the various kinds of characteristics
one might be confronted with while working this key.

WATER CHARACTERISTICS

How to Begin

Chemistry is the study of the composition of matter (ingredients present), the properties of matter (qualities by which materials are recognized), and the changes in composition of matter (transforming one material to another).

Intermediate school children do not have this understanding of chemistry. There is no reason why they should. They do know that their world is made of "things"—objects, materials, or substances. "Things" put together make new "things." and it takes energy to make these new "things."

A chemical which is certainly not a new "thing" to students is the substance water. Because it may not be considered a new thing and it has become such an accepted part of our everyday life we may have overlooked its interesting characteristics. Possibly this unit will stimulate greater interest in this commonplace, yet abused substance, water.

Why Do It This Way?

Direct contact with simple experiences related to water can develop a greater appreciation for its important role in sustaining our civilization. Investigations in this unit will focus primarily on water as an interesting commonplace substance.

How to Begin

For convenience this unit is subdivided into activities. Materials required are listed at the beginning of each activity. Each activity does not necessarily represent one class period for science.

Activity 1

Materials needed: sugar, salt, baking soda, vinegar, liquid detergent, cooking oil, drinking straws,

baby food jars, masking tape, and newspaper to cover desktops.

Students should work in pairs. Each pair of students should receive four baby food jars (or any other small transparent container) and some straws. The other ingredients (salt, vinegar, baking soda, etc.) should be centrally located in the room for easy access by all pairs of students.

One of the most common chemicals on earth and one of the most important to us is water.

Water can dissolve many materials. See for yourself by trying to dissolve some common kitchen chemicals in water. Fill each jar half full with water and then add to each jar one teaspoonful of one of the substances your teacher has in front of the room.

Stir each jar with the drinking straw. Label each jar—using the masking tape—so you will know what you placed in each jar.

Observations

Mixture	Today	Tomorrow
1. water and salt		
2. water and sugar		
3. water and baking soda		
4. water and detergent		
5. water and cooking oil		
6. water and vinegar		

Record your observations today and then again tomorrow.

A. After stirring your mixture can you see any:
   1. salt   4. baking soda
   2. sugar   5. detergent
   3. cooking oil   6. vinegar

B. The next day can you see any:
   1. salt
   2. sugar
   3. baking soda

C. How did the three mixtures of water and vinegar, water and cooking oil, and water and detergent look the next day?
   1. Is there any vinegar, oil, or detergent visible?
   2. Are these liquids mixed through the water, on top of the water, or on the bottom?
   3. Did any liquid *not* mix with the water?

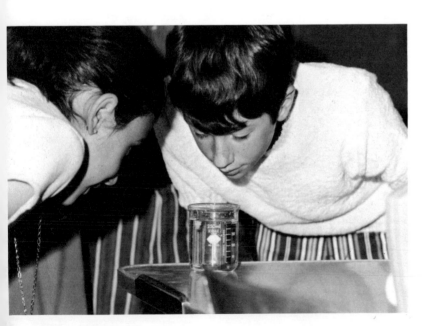

D. Fill a clear jar half full of water and add about a teaspoonful of cooking oil. Now add less than a teaspoonful of liquid detergent. Stir the mixture slowly. What happens to the oil?

After the experimentation in this activity is completed you should encourage class discussion. The following information should help you in stimulating an active discussion.

In this activity you are using water as a dissolving agent. In some cases, either all or some of the substance added to the water disappeared—that is, dissolved. Although you cannot see them, there are billions of tiny spaces between the molecules in a glass of water. It is into these spaces that the molecules of some of the chemicals go. A chemical that dissolves in water is called a **solute**.

Salt, sugar, and baking soda are **solutes** when they dissolve in water. The water which dissolves the chemicals is called a **solvent**. Water will dissolve many, but not all, things.

Many factors affect how much solute will be dissolved by a solvent. One important factor is temperature—the temperature of the solvent (water). Discuss this with the students and possibly run a demonstration in which you dissolve salt, sugar, and baking soda in warm and cold water, noting under which condition more chemical was dissolved. As the water temperature increased more substance could be dissolved.

The cooking oil did not dissolve in the water. It remained on the top because it is lighter. Water does not dissolve oily or greasy substances. When the liquid detergent was added to the oil and water mixture the oil appeared to be spread throughout the water in the form of tiny droplets. The detergent **emulsifies** grease and oil—that is, it breaks grease into tiny droplets that do not stick together. Because of this action by a detergent, water can easily wash away grease. Water is not a solvent for cooking oil. Water by itself cannot wash grease away. Mixed with a detergent it will break the grease up into tiny droplets which then are easy to wash away (not dissolve). Note some of the commercial advertisements about detergents and grease.

When water contains many dissolved minerals it is called **hard water**. Soap helps to remove these minerals as well as to emulsify fats. The ring around the bathtub may not all be dirt—some of it is minerals removed by the soap.

Many foods in the kitchen contain fats that have been emulsified so they no longer stick together in gobs but are evenly distributed throughout the liquid. Milk is an **emulsion**. The small particles of butterfat are distributed through the water that makes up most of the milk. Mayonnaise is also an emulsion.

Each of these substances needs a chemical to act as an emulsifying agent to make the fat mix with the water. In milk, it is a chemical called **casein** (produced by the cow to emulsify butterfat). In mayonnaise, egg yolk is beaten into a mixture of vinegar and oil to emulsify the fat.

Activity 2

Materials needed: baby food jars, foil, rubber bands, small pieces of cloth (old sheet or pillowcase) or paper towels, sugar, and salt.

Because water can dissolve many chemicals it will act as a "carrier" of chemicals.

A. Place a piece of cloth or paper towel over the mouth of a baby food jar—use the rubber band to hold it.
   1. Put a teaspoon of salt or sugar on the cloth. Does the salt or sugar go through the cloth?
   2. Dissolve a teaspoon of salt or sugar in some water (fill the baby food jar halfway with water). Slowly pour this mixture on the cloth or paper towel which covers the baby food jar. Does the mixture go through the cloth?

B. Water can act as a "carrier" of chemicals. In the soil, water dissolves many chemicals, and some of these chemicals are necessary for plant growth. The water with the dissolved chemicals is taken in through the roots of the plant.
   1. Place a few drops of salty water on a small piece of foil. Put it in a safe spot and observe it later in the day or on the next day. What happened to the salty water? Try the same thing with sugar and water.
C. Can you now develop a theory about a "water cycle" which explains how plants receive nourishment?
   1. Start with rain—
   2. What it does to chemicals in the soil—
   3. How the plant gets the chemicals—
   4. How the water returns to the air—

Solutions are extremely important to man's existence and water certainly acts as one of the most important solvents. For the plant kingdom water is the agent which transports necessary chemicals for growth. In section C of this activity students are encouraged to develop a "water cycle." They are asked to explain in their own words how chemicals are dissolved by rainwater, transported to and absorbed by the roots, carried up the stem to all cells in the plant, carried to the leaves where some of the chemicals are deposited as the water evaporates back into the air, thus completing the cycle. Not all students will require the leading questions provided in C. Teacher judgment must determine which students would profit from having them on the activity sheet.

Activity 3

Materials needed: baby food jars, bell wire, flashlight batteries, masking tape, sodium carbonate (washing soda), waxed paper.

A solution made of washing soda and water will conduct electricity. Make this solution by dissolving two teaspoons of washing soda in a baby food jar half filled with water. Students should work in pairs on this lesson. Each pair should receive two batteries, two 8-inch pieces of wire, one baby food jar, and a small piece of waxed paper.

1. Fill a small jar halfway with water. Add two teaspoons of washing soda and stir carefully. What happens to the washing soda?
2. Connect two batteries in series and tape one wire to the positive terminal and one wire to the negative terminal (see diagram).

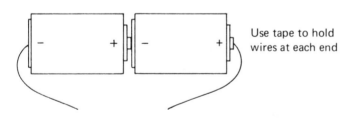

Use tape to hold wires at each end

   a. Place the two ends of the wire in the solution you made earlier. What do you observe?

   b. Do you observe the same thing at the end of each wire?

   c. What happens if only one wire is in the solution?

3. Place a few drops of the solution on a piece of waxed paper. Keep your wires connected to the batteries as in question 2. Put the ends of the wire in a drop. What do you observe? Can you "stretch" the drop with the wires still in the drop? What happens when the drop "breaks"?

4. Can you mix other "things" with water and observe the same things you saw with the washing soda–water solution?

This activity should culminate with a demonstration of electrolysis by the teacher. Extra equipment required is one 500-milliliter beaker and two test tubes. Mix a solution of water and washing soda (two tablespoons of washing soda mixed in the beaker completely filled with water). Fill each test tube completely with the solution and invert the test tubes in the beaker. This last step is tricky. To accomplish this, after completely filling each test tube place a small piece of paper over the test tube mouth and then invert it rapidly while you submerse it into the filled beaker (remove the paper). Insert one wire into each inverted test tube (strip back the insulation on the ends about ½ inch before inserting). Connect the wires to two flashlight batteries connected in series. Bubbles of gas (oxygen and hydrogen) will begin to collect in the top of the test tubes, displacing the washing soda-water solution (see diagram).

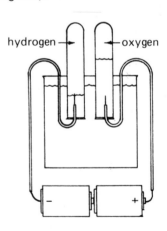

hydrogen —   — oxygen

Electric currents flow easily through some solutions. There seem to be electrically charged "carriers" available in some solutions. The name for these carriers we guess are in the solution is **ions**, from the Greek word for "travel."

In many solutions, any small voltage drives a current without trouble or delay, so it seems likely that the ions are already "swimming" around in the water. The solution of washing soda and water appears to make more ions available—ions of hydrogen (H+) and oxygen (O⁻).

The current passed through the washing soda-water solution causes the hydrogen ions to go to the negative wire and the oxygen ions to go to the positive wire, where the gases form bubbles and are collected in the test tubes. The gas that forms in greater amount is hydrogen—the lightest gas known. The other gas is oxygen. These two gases were water before the passage of an electric current through the solution.

Chemists learned some time ago that when water breaks down it forms twice as much hydrogen as oxygen. To express this ratio the chemist writes a formula for water as follows: H_2O. This means there are two parts of hydrogen to one part of oxygen in water.

After you have collected the gas in the test tubes, a simple test will demonstrate the presence of the two gases, oxygen and hydrogen. Remove the test tube containing hydrogen (one with negative wire from battery inserted), keeping it inverted (hydrogen is very light), and bring a lighted match near the mouth of the test tube. You will hear a small "pop" or "whoosh." Remove the other test tube. Light one end of a thin wooden stick. As soon as it burns well, blow out the flame and insert the glowing stick into the test tube. It will glow more brightly or even burst into flame. Hydrogen is explosive and oxygen supports combustion.

Both of these gases are commercially important. These gases stored in tanks under pressure (compressed gas tanks) supply oxy-hydrogen blowtorches that produce a flame that can melt steel. Hydrogen is added to vegetable fats to make shortening such as Spry and Crisco. Hydrogen serves as an agent in helping to remove oxygen from some valuable ores in the mining process. Oxygen helps to keep us alive—about 20% of the air is composed of oxygen. Liquid oxygen is used in giant rockets both as a fuel and as a coolant. Fuels need oxygen to burn. Gasoline is a chemical combination of hydrogen and carbon. When the hydrogen burns, water is formed. Water can sometimes be seen dripping from an exhaust pipe of an automobile.

Activity 4

In this activity an assortment of experiments is suggested. Each will emphasize one or more important characteristic of water.

Materials needed for each pair of students:
medicine dropper (straws can be used in place of the droppers), waxed paper, plastic wrap, foil, newspaper, hand magnifier, baby food jar, toothpicks, cooking oil, and liquid detergent

1. Place a drop of water on a piece of waxed paper. Does the drop spread out or remain in a rounded pile? Using your hand magnifier, observe small and large drops you place on the waxed paper. Place drops on other substances—foil, paper, and plastic wrap—what do they look like?

2. Can you do the same experiments with a liquid detergent? Try them.

3. Place a few water drops on waxed paper. Push the drops around with a toothpick—record your observations. Place the toothpick in some liquid detergent and then touch the drops as you did above—record your observations.

4. Fill a baby food jar with cooking oil. Fill the dropper with water and place it in the oil. Carefully squeeze out some water and observe the drops of water. What is their shape?

What happens to the drops? Do all the drops move at the same speed?

Drops of water will look almost spherical, especially the smaller drops. The larger the drop the flatter is the upper surface. When the drops touch they instantly form one drop. Touching the drops with a toothpick should not disturb them. The drops act as though they are surrounded by a film and although the toothpick punctures this film there is no noticeable effect. Touching the water drop with a toothpick which is covered with a small quantity of detergent seems to puncture the film and the water drop tends to flatten out.

Water drops squeezed into the cooking oil will assume a spherical shape and sink to the bottom. The larger the drop the faster it will sink. Very small drops will remain almost stationary.

The film around a water drop is like a skin enclosing the water. This is caused by the surface tension that results from the attraction of molecules for similar molecules. Molecules of a given liquid attract molecules of the same liquid with an equal force in all directions. Molecules in a drop are attracted equally in all directions. At the surface of a water drop molecules in the air do not attract the molecules of water with the same force as do other molecules of water inside the drop. Hence, the major attraction is inward, toward the interior, and the outer perimeter of water molecules seems to act like a membrane or skin surrounding the drop. The introduction of a detergent reduces the magnitude of the inward molecular force and the drop flattens out.

Surface tension forces are fascinating to study. Some encouragement from you could get students to do some special project work in this area.

Activity 5

Materials needed: hand magnifier, small pie plates, baby food jars, strips of cloth, strips of newspaper, strips of oak tag, food coloring, and masking tape.

Water sticks not only to itself but to other things also.

1. Fill a jar partway with some water. Place one or two drops of food coloring in the water. What do you observe? Look at the surface of the water where it touches the sides of the jar. What does it look like? Draw a picture of what you see—the hand magnifier may be helpful.
2. Fill a jar partway with clean water. Add one or two drops of food coloring to the water. Place a ruler over the jar as indicated in the

diagram and dangle pieces of cloth and paper from the ruler into the colored water.

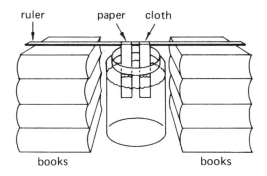

ruler   paper   cloth

books   books

Observe what happens and record your observations. Try this experiment with different pieces of material (newspaper, tissue paper, hand towels, etc.) and record your observations. Try this experiment with pieces of material of different sizes—long pieces, wide pieces—and record your observations.

3. Fill a jar partway with colored water. Place it on a pie pan. Cut a strip of paper toweling 1 inch wide and 7 inches long. Put one end of the strip in the jar and let the other end drop down against the bottom of the pan. Observe carefully what happens. Leave the jar and paper in this position overnight and observe the results the next day.

Water molecules are attracted to other substances. Water not only **coheres** but also **adheres**. Water can climb up the sides of some containers and can climb through materials that are porous.

Where the water surface meets the glass the edges of the water curve upward, forming a **meniscus.** This curving edge results from the water adhering to the glass and then pulling itself up a little. Not all liquids do adhere to glass. Mercury does not and, therefore, does not form an upward curving edge where it encounters the glass side. Rather it curves downward because it **coheres** only to itself.

Water exhibits adhesion and cohesion characteristics. When the paper, cloth, etc., are dangled into the water it seems to climb up the strips. The water climbs faster in some substances than in others.

Water does not always move up through porous substances. It can also move down. In time a considerable amount of water will move from the jar onto the pie plate.

The following experiments can be done as demonstrations or student activities. They are related to the melting and freezing of water and can develop interesting discussion topics.

1. Put an ice cube in a cup and fill it to the *very top* with warm water (use a dropper to add the last amount of water). What does the class think will happen when the ice is completely melted?

Water expands (fortunately) when it freezes. In fact, water expands about one-tenth of its volume during freezing. Hence a cubic foot of water on freezing becomes more than a cubic foot. This makes ice lighter than water and it floats. After the ice cube melts completely the water level in the cup will be unchanged. The volume of water displaced by the floating ice cube is the same as the volume of water resulting from the melting of the ice.

2. Fill a styrofoam cup half full with cracked ice. Place a thermometer in the ice and then add several tablespoons of salt. Stir the mixture slowly and observe the change in temperature.

The addition of salt lowers the melting point of ice. Instead of melting (or freezing) at 32° F (0° C) it melts (or freezes) at 25°F, or 15°F, or lower, depending on the amount of salt added. For this reason salt is sprinkled on icy roads in the winter time.

The following information about water may be of interest to you in your science or social studies lessons. These facts could stimulate some extra project work on the part of your students.

1. How does water differ from other substances around us?

    Water appears in all three states assumed by matter—gas, liquid, and solid. It is less responsive to heat than other substances. And unlike most materials, it expands when chilled—to form ice.

2. What is the "troposphere"?

    A thin layer which surrounds the earth—the earth's "weather layer" just below the stratosphere. It is where turbulence and moisture are transported around the earth. Compared with the thickness of the earth, the seven-mile thickness of the troposphere is like the skin of an onion compared with the onion itself.

3. How much water is there on earth?

    336 million cubic miles covering three-fourths of the earth's surface.

4. Where is most of the earth's water?

    Oceans hold 97.2%. Glaciers contain 2%. The rest, 0.8%, is available for human needs. Much of it is lodged at great distances from the demand.

5. What portion of the earth's water is available fresh water?

    Only 0.27%.

6. Where is most of the world's fresh water?

    About 74.7% is frozen in the polar icecaps of the Arctic and Antarctic. If it all melted, sea levels would rise about 250 feet. (Farewell to New Orleans, Houston, Miami, and much of Washington, Philadelphia, and New York should this happen.)

7. How much water is in the Antarctic icecap?

    If the icecap melted, its water could feed all the rivers of the world for 800 years.

8. How fast are glaciers melting?

    Slowly. The Atlantic Ocean is rising at the rate of two feet a century. (But at one time, New York City was under an ice sheet hundreds of feet thick, and the Great Lakes were a solid mass of ice.)

9. What percentage of the earth's unfrozen fresh water is in surface water—lakes, rivers, streams, ponds?

    Less than 2%. Over 98% of fluid fresh water is underground.

10. How much of the earth's land has enough water to sustain life?

    A little more than half. According to Unesco, 13,200,000 of the earth's 23,000,000 square miles of firm land can sustain life, including some with inadequate water supply.

11. How much does water expand when it freezes?

    Ten percent, when it turns to ice.

12. At what temperature does water reach its minimum volume?

    At 39° Fahrenheit.

13. Why is ocean water salty?

    Because water, the "great solvent," dissolves and carries salt from land to oceans, as well as to some lakes.

14. Is Great Salt Lake still shrinking?

    No. Climatic conditions tend to stabilize the lake at its present 950 square miles, a drop from 2,400 square miles in 1873.

15. Is the Sea of Galilee fresh or salt water?

    The normally fresh water of the sea contains dozens of salt water springs, which may be capped or their flow pumped off to save freshness.

16. Can seawater be reproduced artificially?

    The Department of Interior reported in 1964 that freshly made seawater "rots" on standing.

17. What cracks titanium, a metal tough enough to resist heat and light for supersonic flights?

    Salt water.

18. In what region of the United States is rainfall greatest?

    The Olympic Mountains of the Pacific Northwest—150 inches a year.

19. Where is rainfall the least in the U. S.?

The Arizona-Nevada-Utah area—10 inches a year.

20. Do raindrops fall separately in a storm?

Raindrops collide with other raindrops about ten times in each mile of free fall during a typical storm.

21. What is the "life" of a drop of fresh water?

About 12 days in the atmosphere. In a glacier, about 40 years. On a lake bottom, perhaps 100 years. Deep in the ground—tens of thousands of years.

22. Where does most rain come from?

From cyclonic storms if you're in the United States. Not to be confused with cyclones, these occur when southward-moving polar air masses meet warmer air masses from the Equator.

23. How much rain falls in a year?

Thirty inches in the United States as rain, snow, sleet, hail, and dew. Of this, soil and vegetation take 21 inches. Man uses three inches of the remainder.

24. What is the daily rainfall in the United States?

About 4,300 billion gallons. Vegetation absorbs 70% directly. Man utilizes 360 billion gallons daily of the "runoff" water.

25. Does most atmospheric water move vertically or horizontally?

Horizontally, as vapor or clouds, often for thousands of miles before it drops to earth as rain.

26. Does the moon affect rainfall?

Yes, according to 1965 corroboration of an early nineteenth-century belief: the moon's gravitational pull on the earth's atmosphere can lift the air a few feet and cause snow or rain on earth when the two bodies are lined up with the sun—at new moon and full moon.

27. What percentage of rainfall in the U. S. can be utilized?

About 30%. The rest evaporates or is absorbed by plants.

28. How much rainfall rises again into the atmosphere?

Almost three-fourths, by evaporation and transpiration from vegetation.

29. What is an important deterrent to rain-making?

Legal restrictions by some of the states.

30. How long can a person live without water?

The longest known time on the ocean is 11 days. An average healthy person can survive only 7 to 10 days without water.

31. What water use requires the largest consumption today?

Irrigation. But by 1980 it is estimated that steam electric plants will require more water, for cooling, than will agriculture.

32. Where does America's useful water come from?

Eighty percent from surface sources, 20% from underground supplies.

33. Where is most fresh water stored in America?

A recent report shows that 47 million cubic feet of ground water are contained in United States' aquafiers (underground storage areas). This is three times as much as our total water from rivers and lakes.

34. How much tap water is used in America?

Right now, 400 billion gallons daily, 57% of all that is available. In 30 years we may require 900 billion gallons daily, more than today's total supply.

35. Is most American water alkaline or acid?

Eighteen of our 100 largest cities, with more than 15,000,000 people, obtain raw water which is mildly acid (pH. 5.8 to 7.0). Eighty have mildly alkaline sources (pH. 7.0 to 9.0), and two have strongly alkaline water. (A pH. of 7.0 is neutral. Lower is acid, higher is alkaline.)

36. In arid areas, does man utilize most fresh water?

No. For example, in 17 western American states, evaporation from reservoirs and transpiration from deep-rooted plants account for more than twice the amount of water used by man in the entire U. S. A.

37. How many community water-producing facilities are there in America?

About 20,000, serving 21,000 communities and 158 million people.

38. How much water does each American require daily?

About 155 gallons.

39. How much hot water is used in the average American home?

About 120 gallons daily.

40. How much water does the average child drink?

In America, less than a pint a day as water. Soft drinks, juices, and milk supplement the liquid intake.

41. What is the highest dam in the world?

The Oroville Dam in California has an embankment wall towering 735 feet above the bed of the Feather River, making it 9 feet higher than the Hoover Dam. The Nouek Dam on the Vaksh River, southeast of the Caspian Sea, has a height of 985 feet. For comparison, the Empire State Building is 1,472 feet high to the tip of its TV tower.

42. What is the largest number of people to be used on one water project?

In India, 125,000 men and women are employed constructing the 302-foot Nagarjuve Dam and related canals.

43. Where is the oldest water supply system still in use?

Vetulonia, Italy, a famous Etruscan city from the seventh to fifth centuries B.C. Its 800 inhabitants today use the same water system. The city is on top of a hill, yet its wells never go dry.

44. What river has the world's largest flow?

The Amazon accounts for about 2% of the total discharge of all the world's rivers to the sea. Measured 400 miles upstream, the flow was at the rate of 7,600,000 cubic feet per second. Another method measured 3.6 billion gallons a minute, 14 times the flow of the Mississippi.

45. Is there water on other planets?

A thin layer of water vapor was measured on Venus by instruments of unmanned balloon flights and satellite orbits.

46. What has been happening to "Old Man River"?

The Mississippi is sort of "down in the mouth." So much of the river was flowing into the Atchaflaya River, it looked like New Orleans and Baton Rouge might be left without enough water. A $70 million project corrected the flow.

47. How many families earn their livelihood fishing in the Mississippi River and its tributaries?

A recent census lists 434 families, compared with 2,000 families in 1900.

48. Is the Mississippi River rising or falling?

The Mississippi's level has been falling one foot every ten years for the last few decades. This is not due to less rainfall, but to the river's gouging out a wider channel.

49. What was the water intake of the first group that scaled Mount Everest?

Six pints per day per man.

50. When was New York's first aqueduct put to use?

The 30-mile-long Croton Aqueduct was completed in 1842, sending 35 million gallons of water daily into a reservoir then located at Fifth Avenue and 42nd Street.

51. How many lakes are actually in "the land of 10,000 lakes"?

Minnesota, so identified, has 13,871 lakes of more than ten acres each.

52. What is the largest structure ever built by man?

An earth dam, Fort Peck Dam in Montana, with a volume of 130,000,000 cubic yards.

53. What is an artesian well?

A deep well in which water is forced up by underground pressure.

54. What does "bod" mean?

"Bod" is the biochemical oxygen demand—the rate at which the microbe population in water consumes oxygen. When bod is high, it means the oxygen content of water is low, making survival difficult for fish, plant, insect, or microbe life.

55. Is all water H_2O?

Almost none of it. All the fresh water on earth is about 99.7% H_2O. The rest may be some or all of 52 separate substances found in water, mostly dissolved minerals.

56. How much water is used in agriculture?

Forty percent of the total supply used, four times as much as all communities used.

57. Do water softeners add sodium?

Yes. Some add as much as 351 milligrams per liter of sodium to water. One glassful of this water per day could upset a low-salt diet advised by physicians for certain disorders.

58. Does dew come from the atmosphere?

No. Dew comes from the earth, not out of air.

59. How many minerals are in ocean water?

At least 52 elements have been found in seawater.

60. What industry uses the most water?

The American pulp and paper industry uses over 4 trillion gallons a year. This is more water than our 400 largest cities require, not including industrial use.

61. Is it true that "it takes 100 tons of water to make a ton of steel"?

No. The same water can be reused. Real consumption can be small.

62. Is water from subterranean sources in popular use?

Yes, in some nations. Denmark gets almost all of its water from underground reservoirs. In Belgium, 90% of the water used is from underground. West Germany and The Netherlands tap ground water for 75% of their totals.

63. What was "man's first medicine"?

Water. Natural springs of consistent goodness became focal points for health resorts. Some, popular today, are thousands of years old.

64. Is hard or soft water better for man?

Hard water is better, according to some recent reports in the United States, Great Britain, and Sweden. (Hard water is usually described as water with 100 parts per million or more dissolved solids.)

65. What American cities have the hardest tap water?

Lubbock, Phoenix, and San Diego each has over 500 p.p.m. dissolved solids in tap water.

66. Are all trace elements in water good?

Some may not be. As one example, one part in 5 billion of a particular pesticide is deadly to fish.

67. Can tap water reduce the itch of poison ivy and other inflammations?

Hot water—hot enough to cause discomfort but not hot enough to burn—applied briefly on the affected area, may give immediate relief.

68. Does weather affect arthritis?

Rising humidity with falling barometric pressure exerts a detrimental effect on arthritis symptoms, according to one controlled test. Researchers added that changing conditions were responsible.

Conversely, some physicians advise certain types of bottled health waters to reduce pain, swelling, and stiffness for certain types of arthritis. (Diagnosis and treatment should always be by a doctor.)

69. Are you fatigued? What's a quick remedy?

A glass of refreshing water, some U. S. State Department employees were advised after a study. Inadequate water in your system sets off the "fatigue cycle," and the best remedy is frequent sips of good water, the report added.

70. Is water always good for bathing?

Some bathers suffer from "water allergy," according to American and British reports. Remedies include antihistamines, coating skin with oil, not bathing.

71. What are some physical illnesses attributed to impure water?

The list keeps growing and includes typhoid fever, infectious hepatitis, cholera, bacillary dysentery, gastro-enteritis, and skin infections. Tularemia and the virus of poliomyelitis may be water-borne. The World Health Organization reported that five million people suffer disabling diseases associated with water each year.

72. Can water be "reused"?

It often is. As an example, by the time the Ohio River flows into the Mississippi, the water has been reused 3.7 times.

73. What percentage of treated tap water is used by human beings?

Only 10%—and just a small percentage of that is consumed.

74. When did chlorination—today's main reliance for making tap water safe—start in America?

In the Jersey City reservoirs in 1908. (Paisley, Scotland, may have been the first community with water filtration, installed by fabric bleacher John Gibb in 1804.)

75. Do Americans desire fluoridation of public water supplies?

One poll taker reported 70% to 80% favor it, but two-thirds of local referendums have voted against it.

76. Are septic tanks and private wells feasible?

Septic tanks and private wells have caused problems in almost every urban area where they have been used, endangering public health, according to the Surgeon General a few years ago.

77. How long will a detergent stay in water?

At least five weeks, according to one government test.

78. Is much tap water lost by leaks?

According to a 1964 estimate by New York City, 100 million gallons of water were lost daily by that one city. A Martinsburg, W. Va., report stated that 48.6% of all its tap water was lost through leaks.

79. Are fresh water fishing areas increasing?

Yes, man-made reservoirs, now covering 13 million acres, will cover 23 million acres by A.D. 2000. The demand for reservoir fishing has increased because of pollution of natural streams, but fluctuations of the water level in reservoirs don't help the supply of fish.

80. Are coastal fish resources increasing?

Resources from Maine to Florida dropped 50% in five years because of pollution in marshes, rivers, and bays where some popular varieties of fish are spawned, according to a private study.

81. What are the principal water pollutants?

1. Natural pollution—the leaching action of runoff water on natural deposits, forest soil, animal effluent, and chemically treated farmland.

2. Thermal pollution—the additon of hot waters, upsetting the oxygen balance, opening the door to other pollutants.

3. Sewage pollution, from raw or partly-treated domestic waste.

4. Industrial waste, including all manufacturing or other commercial waste which finds its way into water.

5. Chemical changes in water receiving refuse. Example: 2 parts per million copper won't hurt fish, nor 8 parts zinc. But combine one-tenth of these amounts and all the fish in a stream will die.

82. How much fresh water is polluted in the United States?

In 1967, President Johnson stated that every major water system is polluted.

83. What chemical is the principal water pollutant?

Nitrogen, mostly in nitrates. Water gets it both from urban industrial waste and from agricultural fertilizers.

84. How much does animal life contribute to water pollution?

In 1967 it was estimated that the wastes from a total of 7,250,000 cattle, hogs, and sheep in Kansas were equivalent to untreated wastes of 70,000,000 people.

85. What is a safe nitrate limit in drinking water?

A Public Health report indicates 45 p.p.m. Some scientists have written that more than 10 p.p.m. may affect infants adversely.

86. Who is the worst offender in water pollution?

Industry now pours twice as much organic material into U. S. streams as all municipalities combined.

87. Is water pollution increasing?

It's up 600% in American rivers since 1900, according to one report.

88. Does pollution destroy fish?

Yes. One example is a 2,600-square-mile polluted area in the center of Lake Erie which, in 1966, was reported almost devoid of oxygen and fish.

89. What is the best "cleanser" of polluted water?

Stems of ordinary water reeds, according to a German research institute.

90. What's the cost of sewer systems to avoid some water pollution?

A billion-dollar sewer system has been planned for one county—Suffolk in New York—where the Water Department warned that the water is dangerously close to being destroyed by pollution from cesspools.

91. Is man-made water pollution America's problem only?

No, indeed. Every so-called civilized nation has the problem. The French figure it would take 10,000 trains, each carrying 600 tons, to haul the polluted matter dumped into French waters each year.

92. What is the most polluted river on earth?

One author nominates the Merrimack River of New England, "where there is less oxygen than most fish require to live." The Buffalo River is also in the running. A federal report calls it "not even as good as a cesspool."

93. What quantities of pesticides are used annually?

The yearly production in America totals 500 million pounds. Quite a bit finds its way into fresh surface waters.

94. How "clean" is the water tumbling over Niagara Falls?

It contains sewage from 25 Canadian municipalities with sewer systems, according to a Provincial Government report. But wastes are greater from American shores, say Canadian experts, citing as one example the daily dumping of 40 million gallons of industrial waste from the city of Niagara Falls, N. Y.

95. Where does polluted air go?

What goes up must come down. You guessed it—a lot of air pollutants settle on soil, and find their way into water.

96. Is a deep or shallow water reservoir preferable for combating pollution?

Shallow—to permit greater oxidation through water flow.

97. How much is the United States expected to spend each decade to stop water pollution?

Estimates vary from $75 billion to more than $100 billion.

98. Can water pollution be corrected by law?

Only if it were possible to enforce regulations to the letter. That's impossible for many reasons, and of course would not stop natural pollution. Practical solutions must consider the type and quantity of waste in each area, and the quantity, depth, flow, and ultimate disposition of pollutants which now enter the water.

99. If water pollution is curbed, how long will it take our waterways to clear?

Rivers—not long at all. But lakes are a different story. As examples, Lake Erie could purge itself in 6 years, Lake Ontario in 20. Lake Michigan would take 100 years, and Lake Superior from 500 to 800 years. Differences are due to depth and rate of flow.

WHAT IS FOOD?

How to Begin

Food is the fuel that makes the human machine work. Similar to a machine or engine, the human body is burning up energy when it is functioning. Energy is needed to breathe, to talk, to walk, to run, to stand, or even to think.

Man gets his energy from the various foods he consumes; he burns food in much the same manner as a steam engine burns coal or a gasoline engine burns fuel. The amount of energy that foods can provide determines the quantity of food needed by the human body.

We measure food energy in calories. A food calorie is defined as the amount of heat required to raise the temperature of 1,000 grams (1 kilogram) of water one degree centigrade.

Thus, in a slice of white bread containing approximately 63 calories there is enough potential heat energy to raise 63,000 grams of water (about 65 quarts) one degree in temperature centigrade.

An average man needs about 2,900 calories of food each day.

Theoretically, there is enough energy in a steak to kill a man if it were released all at once. Naturally, this energy is released slowly and no harm is done. However, on a comparative scale it is quite surprising to see how much equivalent energy there is in food.

The table on page 239 serves to illustrate some comparisons.

Why Do It This Way?

Every child should be able to make wise decisions about his food intake now and in later life. His decisions should be based upon knowledge of the nutrient composition of the plant, animal, and formulated foods in his environment as well as his physiological needs.

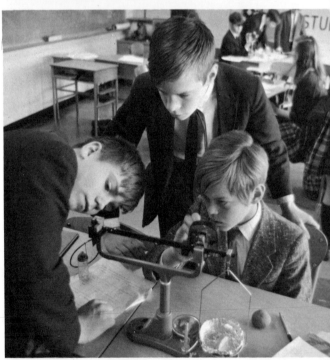

A hundred years ago most people ate food they had grown at home.

Portions of Food	Number of Calories	Energy Equivalents
cup of orange juice	108	1/3 pound of coal
2-inch square of fudge	185	7/10 stick of dynamite
piece of apple pie	310	1" × 2" × 4" piece of wood
hamburger	316	1/6 cup of gasoline
double dip of ice cream	334	1/2 cubic foot of cooking gas

Today much food comes from thousands of miles away and reaches the dinner table only after a number of complex processes have transformed it into handy packages to delight the housewife and stimulate the palate. Each day American families consume the contents of 20 million cans and jars and 32 million pounds of freezer packages. The food industry is larger than the aerospace, automobile, and steel industries combined. It has become the largest single industry in the country.

How to Begin

Materials needed:

15 alcohol burners
roll of aluminum foil
simple weighing scales
1 100 milliliter graduate
gallon of alcohol (methyl)
hot plate
blue glass (cobalt glass)
15 test tubes
Lugol's solution
Benedict's solution
potassium iodide
lithium chloride

Also needed are the following variety of foods and minerals: table salt, garlic salt, celery salt, glucose, maltose, lactose, sucrose, milk, corn starch, potato starch, egg albumin, gelatin, food seasoning, grated cheese, corn oil, butter, vegetable shortening.

Divide the class into teams of two and encourage each team to perform all of the experiments.

In this activity students will learn to do simple analyses of various materials to determine which ones are foods and to which particular category of food each one belongs. Tests for certain minerals are also included.

239

The results of these tests will specifically illustrate such things as the amount of water in various foods, mineral and carbon content. All results will be unmistakably apparent if performed as directed. In the event that sufficient materials or time is lacking, any section may be omitted without affecting other sections.

There is no prescribed time limit for this investigation but it is suggested that at least one full class period be allotted to each test, allowing sufficient time for discussion and additional student-designed experiments.

CAUTION: Alcohol burners should be placed on asbestos mats and the main supply bottle of alcohol stored far away from any open flame. Carelessness may result in a serious accident.

Foods may be generally classed into five groups: water, minerals, carbohydrates, proteins, and fats and oils. In biological systems water serves as the medium of transport for all other compounds in the system. It is not a food in the true sense of the word, but it is nonetheless important. In addition it also enters into many chemical reactions with other compounds. Starches, for instance, may be broken down to sugars by the *addition* of water in the presence of appropriate enzymes (hydrolysis), which are biological catalysts (compounds which change the rate of chemical reactions). Conversely, sugars may be changed to starch by the removal of water molecules (dehydration) in the presence of appropriate enzymes. From this, it can be understood why starches and not sugars are the main *storage carbohydrates* in plants and animals—*they take up less room than do sugars because they are dehydrated*.

Minerals are necessary in biological systems for a multitude of reasons. Some such as sodium and potassium help to regulate the acid-base balance of the system. Many are used in the construction of the system. Calcium and phosphorus are notable in this respect, since they contribute greatly to the formation of teeth and bones. Iron is necessary for many animals and plants to transport oxygen throughout their systems, for the synthesis of vitamins, enzymes, and hormones.

Carbohydrates are a varied and complex group of compounds composed of *carbon, hydrogen, and oxygen*. Their general formula—$(CH_2O)_n$— suggests their name—carbo-hydrate—which literally means compound of carbon and water. The two most familiar carbohydrate groups are the sugars and starches. Sugars are composed of 5 or 6 carbon atoms and enough oxygen and hydrogen to satisfy their structures. The structural formula for glucose (blood sugar), for instance, is as follows:

$$
\begin{array}{c}
H \\
| \\
H-C-OH \\
| \\
H-C-OH \\
| \\
H-C-OH \\
| \\
HO-C-H \\
| \\
H-C-OH \\
| \\
H-C-O
\end{array}
\qquad
\begin{array}{l}
\text{or } (CH_2O)_6 \\[4pt]
\text{or } C_6H_{12}O_6
\end{array}
$$

Activity 1 (optional)

Have students construct as many organic compounds as possible. Use molecular model kits; styrofoam balls, springs, and toothpicks or any reasonable facsimile will do if kits are not available.

Starches are composed of hundreds of glucose molecules joined end to end. As mentioned previously, starch is formed by dehydration of sugar (glucose) in the presence of appropriate enzymes. A formula for starch could be written therefore as:

$$(CH_2O)\,600 - 100\,H_2O = \text{starch}$$
glucose minus water equals starch

One of the most commonly occurring carbohydrates is cellulose (wood, paper, cardboard, etc.). This compound is composed of even longer chains of glucose—up to 50,000 or so molecules joined end to end. One can see that as the molecular chains get longer and longer, the properties of the carbohydrate change considerably. Sugars, for instance, are quite soluble in water, starches less soluble, and cellulose insoluble.

Activity 2

Proteins are composed of carbon, hydrogen, oxygen, and nitrogen. Like the carbohydrates, they are made up of basic molecular units, in this case called amino acids. Unlike the carbohydrates, however, proteins do not have a general formula. They are built up and torn down in the same fashion as are the carbohydrates, that is, by the dehydration or addition of water molecules respectively in the presence of appropriate enzymes.

$$\text{amino acids} \xrightarrow[\overleftarrow{+H_2O}]{-H_2O} \text{proteins}$$

Whereas carbohydrates are used by living systems only for energy, proteins may be used both for energy or construction. The gristle of bone is composed of protein, as is cartilage, tendon, ligament, skin, muscle, and other connective tissues.

Fats and oils are composed of carbon, hydrogen, and oxygen only. They are built up from two types of molecules, glycerol and fatty acids.

$$\text{glycerol} + 3 \text{ fatty acids} \longrightarrow \text{fat}$$

or

$$\xleftarrow{\hspace{2cm}}$$
oil molecule

Again it can be seen that dehydration (removal of water) and hydrolysis (addition of water) in the presence of suitable enzymes are necessary processes in the synthesis of fats and oils.

There is no basic difference between a fat and an oil except their degree of fluidness at room temperature. Both fats and oils are used by living systems as energy sources and are the most condensed stored food products found in many plants and most animals.

Carbohydrates, proteins, and fats and oils may be changed into one another within biological systems with the aid of the right enzymes.

Food Tests (refer to Student Record Sheets)

1. Determination of water in various foods.
   A. Weigh food sample.
   B. Evaporate water from crushed sample over low heat on electric hot plate for a minimum of 2 hours. Complete drying may take two or three class periods.
   C. Reweigh sample.
   D. Help students calculate percentage of water.

2. Determination of minerals in foods.
   A. To show that the presence of sodium causes the yellow flame rather than chlorine in sodium chloride, place another compound containing a chloride but not sodium in the flame. Examples of suitable compounds are cupric (copper) chloride, lithium chloride, and strontium chloride. These compounds will produce colors characteristic of their own atoms. The flame colors are due to excitement of atoms, causing them to emit protons (radiant energy in visible form) in particular wavelengths. This test requires a Bunsen burner or propane torch, and will have to be done either as a demonstration or by small student groups if only one Bunsen burner is available.
   B. To show that the presence of potassium causes the purple flame rather than the chlorine in potassium chloride, place another compound containing chlorine but not potassium in the flame. Examples of suitable compounds are cupric (copper) chloride, lithium chloride, and strontium chloride.

3. Determination of carbon in foods.
   A. To determine if carbon is present, have the students burn the food in stainless steel teaspoons over alcohol lamps. The carbon will show up as a black residue.
   B. To determine the percentage of carbon present in a food:
      1. Weigh the food in a teaspoon.
      2. Burn the food in a teaspoon over an alcohol lamp or Bunsen burner.
      3. Reweigh the carbon residue.
      4. Divide the weight of the residue by the original weight and multiply the result by 100.
   C. Advanced students can determine both the percentage of water and the percentage of carbon in a sample of fresh food. Have the students place a small amount of freshly crushed potato in a teaspoon and weigh it. Evaporate the water over low heat on a hot plate for 2 or 3 hours and reweigh it. Calculate the percentage of water in the potato. Then have the students burn the dried potato, reweigh the residue, and calculate the percentage of carbon in the original potato.

Original weight - dry weight = water lost.

$$\frac{\text{Weight of water lost}}{\text{Original weight of sample}} \times 100 = \% \text{ of } H_2O \text{ sample}$$

4. This section and the next section involve the use of test tubes and solutions. Each student should be provided with at least one test tube. Solutions should be dispensed from one place in the room for convenience and reasons of safety.

   Benedict's solution may be used as purchased. Lugol's solution is made up as follows: Dissolve 10 grams of potassium iodide (KI) in 100 ml. of water; add 5 grams of iodine to the above solution; mix thoroughly and store in a dark bottle.

   Note: To perform the experiments in sections 4 and 5 have students use **very small** amounts of food and solution. A few trials will allow the teacher and students to judge the minimum amounts necessary to achieve satisfactory results.

Food Tests: Student Record Sheets

Foods may be generally classified into five groups:

1. Water
2. Minerals
3. Carbohydrates
4. Proteins
5. Fats and oils

The presence of these food groups can often be detected by simple physical and chemical tests. For example: Can you think of a simple way to find out if a food contains water? Can you think of an experiment to find out *how much* water a particular food contains?

1. Percentage of water in certain foods.
   With the teacher's help, perform an experiment to determine how much water is contained in a

chosen amount of:

apple	milk
bread	dried milk
potato	salt

To find out the percentage of water in a food sample, divide the weight of the water lost after the experiment by the weight of the original sample and multiply the result by 100.

Percentage of water in apple
Percentage of water in bread
Percentage of water in potato
Percentage of water in milk
Percentage of water in dried milk
Percentage of water in salt

2. Mineral tests.

   A. The presence of minerals in foods can be detected in a variety of ways. One of the easiest minerals to detect is sodium, an element which is found in large amounts in common table salt, sodium chloride. Place a small amount of salt on the end of a metal scoop and put it into a Bunsen burner flame. What color does the flame turn?

   Since the compound sodium chloride (NaCl) also contains the element chlorine, can you think of an experiment you could perform to show that the color of the flame is due to the element sodium and not due to the chlorine?

   B. The element potassium is present in all living matter and may also be detected by a flame test. In this case the characteristic blue color of potassium is often masked by the yellow in the flame. So in order to see it clearly, one must look at the flame through a *blue glass* filter. With your teacher's aid, flame-test the compound potassium chloride. What is the color of the flame? Can you think of an experiment to show that the color is due to the presence of potassium and not to the presence of the chlorine?

test tube. For this test you will use a blue solution called Benedict's solution, which contains dissolved copper. If a simple sugar is present, this solution will turn copper color (brick red) after being heated. This same test will also show the presence of protein. If protein is present in the food, the solution will turn deeper blue after being heated.

Now determine whether or not the following foods contain simple sugars or proteins. (Note: Not all sugars are "simple" sugars, and therefore will not show in this test.)

If you finish early, ask your teacher how to determine the percentage of carbon in a food. Then find the percentage of carbon in a sample of dried potato. Show how you found out.

If you still have time, determine the percentage of (A) water and (B) carbon in a sample of raw potato. Show how you found these percentages.

Starches, another form of carbohydrate, can be detected by means of another color test. In this test you will use Lugol's solution, which contains dissolved iodine. If starch is present, the food will turn dark purple immediately after adding Lugol's solution. No heating is necessary to perform this test.

Now determine if starch is present in the foods listed on your summary sheet. (See opposite.)

3. Tests for carbohydrates.

Carbohydrates, fats, and proteins all contain atoms of carbon, hydrogen, and oxygen. Proteins have one more kind of atom in addition to these three—nitrogen. A few proteins also contain sulfur. It is rather difficult to show that hydrogen and oxygen are present in these foods, but carbon can be detected rather easily. Can you think of a possible method?

Can you think of a way to determine the **amount**, or **weight** of carbon in a food?

Carbohydrates occur in many forms. Two of the most common forms are simple sugars and starches. To determine if a food is a simple sugar there is a color test which can be performed in a

4. Test for protein.

Follow the same procedure as outlined for carbohydrates. Benedict's solution will turn deeper blue if protein is present.

5. Tests for fats and oils.

The presence of fats and oils in foods may be determined by a very easy test. If the food is a liquid, simply place a drop of the liquid on a piece of white paper and hold the paper up to a light. If there is fat or oil in the food, the paper will appear translucent. That is, it will let more light through than plain paper. Some semi-solid foods can also be tested for fats and oils by simply placing them on paper for a short time and observing the paper later. For example, butter can be tested like this. If the food is powdered, however, it is necessary to dissolve the food in water first, and then place a drop of the liquid on the paper. After the paper has dried, examine the spot to see if it is translucent. If the paper is not changed, there is no fat or oil present in the food.

Now set up a special page similar to one shown here and test the foods listed for the presence of fats or oils in the spaces as provided. Put your results in the appropriate place on the summary sheet when completed. Remember that when testing for one substance the presence of others may mask the results if combinations such as sugar and protein exist together in your sample.

FOOD TESTS — STUDENT SUMMARY SHEET

Material Tested	Simple Sugar	Starch	Protein	Fat or Oil	K (Potassium)	Na (Sodium)	C (Carbon)
A. Table Salt							
B. Garlic Salt							
C. Celery Salt							
D. Glucose (Karo Syrup)							
E. Lactose							
F. Maltose							
G. Sucrose							
H. Milk							
I. Corn Starch							
J. Potato Starch							
K. Egg Albumin							
L. Gelatine							
M. Food Seasoning							
N. Grated Cheese							
O. Corn Oil							
P. Olive Oil							
Q. Butter							
R. Vegetable Shortening							

Check the appropriate box or boxes to the right of the materials listed if the substance was discovered to be present in your test.

Food Tests: Student Record Sheet for fats and oils.

A. Table Salt	B. Garlic Salt	C. Celery Salt
D. Glucose	E. Maltose	F. Lactose
G. Sucrose	H. Milk	I. Corn Starch
J. Potato Starch	K. Egg Albumin	L. Gelatine
M. Food Seasoning	N. Grated Cheese	O. Corn Oil
P. Olive Oil	Q. Butter	R. Vegetable Shortening

Where to Find Out

Where to Find Out

There are a tremendous number of science curriculum resources available to the intermediate school teacher. National curriculum groups are currently producing generous quantities of materials. Most of these materials emphasize student involvement and have as their central theme the process of science. Commercial publishers and equipment manufacturers have been greatly influenced by these national curriculum groups and are becoming more involved in the development of classroom materials to implement science programs.

Adoption of a science textbook series can no longer be considered sufficient to meet the needs of intermediate school science. Textbook publishers realize this and school systems are gradually coming to this decision. In fact, the multiple text idea coupled with a generous assortment of resource books (frequently paperback) and the material objects (supplies and equipment) are becoming the required classroom complement of curriculum materials.

The following material is resource material for the science units in this book. It should not be considered complete, for new and exciting materials are constantly being produced.

Reading and Visual Aid Material

Aerospace

A. Reading material for children

1. Adler, Irving, *Man-Made Moons: The Earth's Satellites and What They Will Tell Us* (John Day 1957)
2. Asimov, Isaac, *Satellites in Outer Space* (Random House 1960)
3. Bendick, Jeanne, *The First Book of Space Travel* (Franklin Watts 1963)
4. Chester, Michael, *Let's Go on a Space Trip* (G. P. Putnam 1963)
5. Dietz, David, *All About Satellites and Space Ships* (Random House 1962)
6. Goodwin, Harold L., *All About Rockets and Space Flight* (Random House 1964)
7. Gottlieb, William P., *Space Flight and How It Works* (Doubleday 1964)
8. Hyde, Margaret O., *Flight Today and Tomorrow* (McGraw-Hill 1962)
9. Hyde, Margaret O., *Off into Space* (McGraw-Hill 1959)
10. Holsaert, Eunice, *Outer Space* (Holt, Rinehart and Winston 1959)
11. Kane, Elmer R., and Fellger, Merrill C., *What Is Space?* (Benefic Press 1963)

B. Reading material for teachers

1. Adams, Carsbie C., *Space Flight* (McGraw-Hill 1958)

2. Del Rey, Lester, *Rockets Through Space* (Holt, Rinehart and Winston 1960)
3. Ley, Willy, *Our Work in Space* (Macmillan 1964)
4. Parker, Bertha M., *Satellites and Space Travel* (Golden Press 1963)
5. Schneider, Leo, *Space in Your Future* (Harcourt, Brace and World 1961)
6. Stambler, Irwin, *Build the Unknown* (W. W. Norton 1964)
7. Swezey, Kenneth M., *Science Shows You How* (McGraw-Hill 1964)
8. Wells, Robert, *Electronics, Key to Space Exploring* (Dodd, Mead 1964)

C. Films

1. *Rockets: How They Work*, Encyclopaedia Britannica Films
2. *Rockets: Principles and Safety*, Film Associates of California
3. *Satellites: Stepping Stones To Space*, Film Associates of California
4. *What Is Space?*, Encyclopaedia Britannica Films

D. Filmstrips

1. *Flight Around the Moon*, Encyclopaedia Britannica Films
2. *Man in Space*, Encyclopaedia Britannica Films

Air Pollution

A. Reading material for children

1. Adler, Irving and Ruth, *Air* (John Day 1962)
2. Adler, Irving and Ruth, *Storms* (John Day 1963)
3. Allen, Shirley Watler, and Leonard, Justine Wilinson, *Conserving Natural Resources* (McGraw-Hill 1966)
4. Barr, Jene, and Chopin, Cynthia, *What Will the Weather Be?* (Albert Whitman and Co. 1965)
5. Bendick, Jeanne, *The Wind* (Rand McNally 1964)

6. Fisher, James, *The Wonderful World of Air* (Doubleday 1958)
7. Kavaler, Lucy, *Dangerous Air* (John Day 1967)
8. Lewis, Howard R., *With Every Breath You Take* (Crown Publishers 1965)
9. Palmer, Woods Jr., *Air and Water* (Grosset and Dunlap 1967)
10. Pine, Tillie S., and Levine, Joseph, *Weather All Around* (McGraw-Hill 1966)

B. Reading material for teachers

1. American Association for the Advancement of Science, *Air Conservation* (1966)
2. Battan, Louis J., *The Unclean Sky* (Doubleday 1966)
3. Carlson, Carl Walter, and Carlson, Bernice Wells, *Water Fit to Use* (John Day 1966)
4. Carr, D. E., *The Breath of Life* (W. W. Norton 1965)
5. Herber, Lewis, *Crisis in Our Cities* (Prentice-Hall 1965)
6. Ramsey, William L., and Buckley, Raymond A., *Modern Earth Science* (Holt, Rinehart and Winston 1965)

C. Films

1. *Air of Disaster*, United States Public Health Service
2. *Conservation of Natural Resources*, Encyclopaedia Britannica Films
3. *How Weather Is Forecast*, Coronet Films
4. *It's the Humidity*, Cenco Educational Films
5. *It's the Only Air We've Got*, United States Public Health Service
6. *Our Natural Resources*, Pat Dowling Pictures
7. *Something in the Wind*, United States Public Health Service
8. *Take a Deep Breath*, National Medical Audiovisual Center
9. *The Air Around Us*, Encyclopaedia Britannica Films
10. *The Poisoned Air*, United States Public Health Service
11. *To Clear the Air*, American Petroleum Institute

12. *Winds and Their Causes*, Coronet Films

D. Filmstrips

1. *Air and Its Properties*, McGraw-Hill Films
2. *Air Pollution and You*, The National Center for Air Pollution Control
3. *Atmosphere and Its Circulation*, Encyclopaedia Britannica Films
4. *Sunlight and the Earth's Temperature*, D. C. Heath
5. *The Air*, Encyclopaedia Britannica Films
6. *Water Conservation Today*, Society for Visual Education

Commonplace "Things"

A. Reading material for children

1. Adler, Irving, *Man-Made Moons: The Earth's Satellites and What They Will Tell Us* (John Day 1957)
2. Adler, Irving and Ruth, *Things That Spin* (John Day 1956)
3. Adler, Irving and Ruth, *Your Ears* (John Day 1963)
4. Branley, Franklyn M., *A Book of Satellites for You* (Thomas Y. Crowell 1958)
5. Branley, Franklyn M., *A Book of Moon Rockets for You* (Thomas Y. Crowell 1959)
6. Gottlieb, William P., *Space Flight and How It Works* (Doubleday 1964)
7. Huey, Edward G., *What Makes the Wheels Go Round?* (Harcourt, Brace and World 1962)
8. Irving, Robert, *Sounds and Ultrasonics* (Alfred A. Knopf 1959)
9. Kettelkamp, Larry, *Flutes, Whistles and Reeds* (William Morrow 1962)
10. Mandell, Muriel, and Wood, Robert E., *Make Your Own Musical Instruments* (Sterling Publishing 1958)
11. Pine, Tillie S., and Levine, Joseph, *Gravity All Around* (McGraw-Hill 1963)

B. Reading material for teachers

1. Branley, Franklyn M., *Experiments in the Principles of Space Travel* (Thomas Y. Crowell 1955)
2. Gamow, George, *A Planet Called Earth* (Viking Press 1963)
3. Leonard, Jonathan N., *Exploring Science* (World Publishing 1959)
4. Mann, Martin, *How Things Work* (Thomas Y. Crowell 1960)
5. Pierce, John R., and David, Edward E., *Man's World of Sound* (Doubleday 1958)
6. Swezey, Kenneth M., *Science Shows You How* (McGraw-Hill 1964)

C. Films

1. *Gravity, the Mighty Pull*, United World Films
2. *How We Know the Earth Moves*, Film Associates of California
3. *Moving Things on Land*, Churchill Films
4. *Time*, Indiana University Audio Visual Center
5. *What's So Important About the Wheel?*, Journal Films
6. *You and Your Ears*, Walt Disney Productions

D. Filmstrips

1. *Friction at Work*, Young America Films
2. *Our Earth Is Moving*, Curriculum Materials Corporation
3. *Overcoming Gravity*, Young America Films

Currents and Charges

A. Reading material for children

1. Bendick, Jeanne, *Electronics for Young People* (McGraw-Hill 1955)
2. David, Eugene, *Television and How It Works* (Prentice-Hall 1962)
3. Epstein, Sam and Beryl, *The First Book of Electricity* (Franklin Watts 1953)
4. Holden, Raymond, *Magnetism* (Golden Press 1963)
5. Irving, Robert, *Electronics* (Alfred A. Knopf 1961)
6. Mandelbaum, Arnold, *Electricity: The Story of Power* (G. P. Putnam's 1960)

7. Morgan, Alfred, *Boy's Third Book of Radio and Electronics* (Charles Scribner's 1962)
8. Neal, Charles D., *Safe and Simple Projects With Electricity* (Childrens Press 1965)
9. Oddo, Nick, and Carini, Edward, *Exploring Electromagnetism* (Holt, Rinehart and Winston 1964)
10. Oddo, Nick, and Carini, Edward, *Exploring Static Electricity* (Holt, Rinehart and Winston 1964)
11. Pine, Tillie S., and Levine, Joseph, *Electricity and How We Use It* (McGraw-Hill 1962)
12. Podendorf, Illa, *The True Book of Magnets and Electricity* (Childrens Press 1961)
13. Posin, Daniel Q., *What Is Electronic Communication?* (Benefic Press 1960)
14. Reuben, Gabriel, *Electronics for Children* (Sterling Publishing 1961)
15. Shapp, Martha and Charles, *Let's Find Out What Electricity Does* (Franklin Watts 1961)
16. Shepherd, Walter, *Electricity* (John Day 1964)
17. Syrocki, B. John, *What Is Electricity?* (Benefic Press 1961)
18. Tannenbaum, Harold E., and Stillman, Nathan, *We Read About Television and How It Works* (Webster Publishing 1960)
19. Victor, Edward, *Magnets* (Follett Publishing 1962)

B. Reading material for teachers

1. Eaton, Jeannette R., *Beginning Electricity* (Macmillan 1952)
2. Kennedy, John M., *Making Electricity Work* (Thomas Y. Crowell 1957)
3. Morgan, Alfred P., *Adventures in Electrochemistry* (Charles Scribner's 1959)
4. Morgan, Alfred P., *The Boy Electrician* (Lothrop, Lee and Shepard 1957)
5. Seeman, Bernard, *The Story of Electricity and Magnetism* (Harvey House 1967)
6. Sootin, Harry, *Experiments in Magnetism and Electricity* (Franklin Watts 1962)

7. Wells, Robert, *Electronics, Key to Space Exploring* (Dodd, Mead 1964)
8. Willman, William R., *Elementary Electricity* (Van Nostrand 1959)

C. Films

1. *Communication in the Modern World*, Coronet Films
2. *Electricity from Chemicals*, Coronet Films
3. *Electricity: How to Make a Circuit*, Encyclopaedia Britannica Films
4. *Electricity: Principles of Safety*, Coronet Films
5. *Exploring Electromagnetic Energy*, Film Associates of California
6. *Flow of Electricity*, Young America Films
7. *How Electricity Is Produced*, Pat Dowling Pictures
8. *Magnetic, Electric and Gravitational Fields*, Encyclopaedia Britannica Films
9. *Television in Your Community*, Coronet Films
10. *We Use Power*, Churchill Films

D. Filmstrips

1. *Electricity*, Society for Visual Education
2. *Electricity in Circuits*, Encyclopaedia Britannica Films
3. *Electricity and Magnetism*, Encyclopaedia Britannica Films
4. *How Television Works*, McGraw-Hill
5. *Making Electric Currents*, D. C. Heath
6. *Power for Us*, D. C. Heath
7. *What Is Current Electricity?*, Jam Handy

Drug Abuse

A. Reading material for children

1. Burgdof, Otto P., *Adventure Book of Biology* (Golden Press 1962)
2. Faber, Doris, *The Miracle of Vitamins* (G. P. Putnam's 1964)
3. Finkel, Lawrence S., and Kravitz, Ruth, *You and Drugs* (Ramapo House 1970)
4. Follett, Robert J. R., *Your Wonderful Body* (Follett Publishing 1961)

5. Gess, Diane, *You and Smoking* (Ramapo House 1970)
6. Gilmore, Ann and James, *Understanding Your Senses* (Frederick Warne 1963)
7. Goldenson, Robert M., *All About the Human Mind* (Random House 1963)
8. Horrobin, David F., *The Communication Systems of the Body* (Basic Books 1964)
9. Lauber, Patricia, *Your Body and How It Works* (Random House 1962)
10. Patterson, George, *You and Alcohol* (Ramapo House 1970)
11. Reit, Ann, *The Body in Action* (Golden Press 1962)
12. Riedman, Sarah R., *Your Blood and You* (Abelard-Schuman 1963)
13. Turner, Eloise, *Inside You and Me* (John Day 1961)
14. Weart, Edith L., *The Story of Your Brain and Nerves* (Coward-McCann 1961)

B. Reading material for teachers

1. American Education Publications, *Know About Drugs* (1969)
2. Andrews, G., and Vinkenoog, S., *The Book of Grass* (Grove Press 1967)
3. Asimov, Isaac, *The Human Body: Its Structure and Operation* (Houghton Mifflin 1963)
4. Bacon, Margaret, and Jones, Mary B., *Teenage Drinking* (Thomas Y. Crowell 1968)
5. Bier, William C., *Problems in Addiction: Alcohol and Narcotics* (Fordham University Press 1962)
6. Blakeslee, Alton, *What You Should Know About Drugs and Narcotics* (The Associated Press 1969)
7. Bloomquist, Edward, *Marijuana* (Collier-Macmillan 1968)
8. Castillo, Juan J., *Lung Cancer and Cigarette Smoking* (Carlton Press 1965)
9. De Bold, Richard C., and Leaf, Russell C., *LSD, Man and Society* (Wesleyan University Press 1968)
10. DeRopp, Robert S., *Drugs and the Mind* (Grove Press 1967)

11. Ford, A. S., *Tobacco Poisoning and Your Health* (Carlton Press 1965)
12. Hoffer, Abram, and Osmond, Humphrey, *The Hallucinogens* (Academic Press 1967)
13. Houde, Christian A., and Kalb, William S., *Your Body: Its Anatomy and Nutrition* (C. S. Hammond 1962)
14. Kimber, Diana, *Anatomy and Physiology* (Macmillan 1961)
15. Laurie, Peter, *Drugs: Medical, Psychological, and Social Facts* (Penguin Books 1967)
16. Lindesmith, Alfred R., *The Addict and the Law* (Indiana University Press 1965)
17. Moscow, Alvin, *The Merchants of Heroin* (Dial Press 1968)
18. Oursler, Will, *Marijuana—the Facts—the Truth* (Hill and Wang 1968)
19. Taylor, Norman, *Narcotics: Nature's Dangerous Gifts* (Dell 1963)
20. Williams, John, *Narcotics and Hallucinogenics, A Handbook* (Collier-Macmillan 1965)
21. Wilner, Daniel M., and Kassebaum, Gene G., *Narcotics* (McGraw-Hill 1965)
22. Yablonsky, Lewis, *The Tunnel Back* (Collier-Macmillan 1965)

C. Films

1. *About the Human Body*, Churchill Films
2. *Breaking the Habit*, American Cancer Society
3. *Drugs and the Nervous System*, Churchill Films
4. *Hearts, Lungs and Circulation*, Coronet Films
5. *Hooked*, Churchill Films
6. *Human Body: Nervous System*, Coronet Films
7. *Learning About Our Bodies*, Coronet Films
8. *Our Senses: What They Do for Us*, Coronet Films
9. *The Huffless, Puffless Dragon*, American Cancer Society
10. *The Human Machine*, Moody Institute of Science

11. *The Science of Alcohol*, Sid Davis Productions

D. Filmstrips

1. *How Your Body Grows*, Curriculum Materials Corporation
2. *Human Factories*, D. C. Heath
3. *I'll Choose the High Road*, American Cancer Society
4. *Nervous System*, McGraw-Hill
5. *The World of Our Senses*, D. C. Heath
6. *You, the Living Machine*, Encyclopaedia Britannica Films

Growing Crystals

A. Reading material for children

1. Adler, Irving and Ruth, *Coal* (John Day 1965)
2. Comfort, Iris Tracy, *Earth Treasures: Rocks and Minerals* (Prentice-Hall 1964)
3. Cooper, Elizabeth K., *Discovering Chemistry* (Harcourt, Brace and World 1959)
4. Franke, Herbert W., *The Magic of Molecules* (Abelard-Schuman 1964)
5. Hyde, Margaret O., *Molecules Today and Tomorrow* (McGraw-Hill 1963)
6. Larson, Egan, *Atoms and Atomic Energy* (John Day 1963)
7. Pearl, Richard M., *Wonders of Gems* (Dodd, Mead 1963)
8. Posin, Daniel Q., *What Is Matter?* (Benefic Press 1960)
9. Sanders, Lenore, *The Curious World of Crystals* (Prentice-Hall 1964)
10. Victor, Edward, *Molecules and Atoms* (Follett 1963)

B. Reading material for teachers

1. Anderson, William R., *Living with the Atom* (World 1963)
2. Asimov, Isaac, *Building Blocks of the Universe* (Abelard-Schuman 1957)
3. Compton, Charles, *An Introduction to Chemistry* (Van Nostrand 1958)
4. Hecht, Selig, *Explaining the Atom* (Viking Press 1955)
5. Holden, Alan, and Singer, Phyllis, *Crystals and Crystal Growing* (Doubleday 1960)
6. Irwin, Keith G., *The Romance of Chemistry* (Viking Press 1959)
7. Milgrons, Harry, *Matter, Energy and Change* (Holt, Rinehart and Winston 1960)
8. Wood, Elizabeth A., *Crystals and Light, An Introduction to Optical Crystallography* (Van Nostrand 1964)
9. Wood, Elizabeth A., *Experiments with Crystals and Light* (Bell Telephone Laboratories 1964)

C. Films

1. *Explaining Matter: Atoms and Molecules*, Encyclopaedia Britannica Films
2. *Explaining Matter: Molecules in Motion*, Encyclopaedia Britannica Films
3. *Gold and Gold Mining*, Bailey Films
4. *Rocks and Minerals*, Film Associates of California
5. *Solids, Liquids and Gases*, McGraw-Hill Films
6. *The Earth: Resources in Its Crust*, Coronet Films
7. *The World of Molecules*, Churchill Films
8. *What's Inside the Earth?*, Film Associates of California

D. Filmstrips

1. *All Matter Has Three Forms*, Young America Films
2. *How Crystals Are Formed*, Film Strip of the Month Club
3. *How We Get Our Oil*, Young America Films
4. *Matter and Molecules*, Eye Gate House
5. *Mineral Resources*, Curriculum Materials Corporation
6. *Minerals in the Soil*, Encyclopaedia Britannica Films
7. *Some Things Dissolve*, Young America Films

Hexapods—Insect Trapping

A. Reading material for children

1. Adler, Irving and Ruth, *Insects and Plants* (John Day 1962)
2. Allen, Gertrude, *Everyday Insects* (Houghton Mifflin 1963)
3. Brouillette, Jeanne S., *Insects* (Follett 1962)
4. Conklin, Gladys, *We Like Bugs* (Holiday House 1963)
5. Cooper, Elizabeth K., *Insects and Plants: The Amazing Partnership* (Harcourt, Brace and World 1963)
6. Cooper, Elizabeth K., *Silkworms and Science* (Harcourt, Brace and World 1961)
7. David, Eugene, *Spiders and How They Live* (Prentice-Hall 1964)
8. Doering, Harold, and McCormick, Jo Mary, *An Ant Is Born* (Sterling Publishing 1964)
9. Eeckhoudt, J. P. vanden, *A Butterfly Is Born* (Sterling Publishing 1960)
10. Goudey, Alice E., *Butterfly Time* (Scribner's 1964)
11. Hawes, Judy, *Bees and Beehives* (Thomas Y. Crowell 1964)
12. Headstrom, Richard, *Adventures with Insects* (J. B. Lippincott 1963)
13. Hogner, Dorothy C., *Water Beetles* (Thomas Y. Crowell 1963)
14. Huntington, Harriet E., *Praying Mantis* (Doubleday 1957)
15. Hutchins, Ross E., *The Travels of Monarch X* (Rand McNally 1966)
16. Lavine, Sigmund A., *Wonders of the Beetle World* (Dodd, Mead 1962)
17. Mitchell, Arthur A., *First Aid for Insects and Much More* (Harvey House 1964)
18. Shuttlesworth, Dorothy E., *The Story of Spiders* (Doubleday 1959)

B. Reading material for teachers

1. Crompton, John, *A Hive of Bees* (Doubleday 1958)
2. Disraeli, Robert, *New Worlds Through the Microscope* (Viking Press 1960)
3. Harpster, Hilda T., *The Insect World* (Viking Press 1956)
4. Herbert, Hiram J., *Wonder-workers of the Insect World* (Dutton 1960)

5. Hyde, Margaret O., *Animal Clocks and Compasses* (McGraw-Hill 1960)
6. Klots, Alexander B., *The World of Butterflies and Moths* (McGraw-Hill 1958)
7. Lavine, Sigmund A., *Wonders of the Wasp's Nest* (Dodd, Mead 1961)
8. Life Science Library, *The Insects* (Time-Life Books 1962)
9. Pain, Nesta, *Lesser Worlds* (Coward-McCann 1958)
10. Raskin, Edith, *Watchers, Pursuers, and Masqueraders* (McGraw-Hill 1964)

C. Films

1. *Adaptations of Insects*, Stanton Films
2. *Animals at Work*, Encyclopaedia Britannica Films
3. *Ants*, Encyclopaedia Britannica Films
4. *Insect Collecting*, Pat Dowling Pictures
5. *Insect Foods*, Pat Dowling Pictures
6. *Monarch Butterfly*, Summel-Meservey
7. *The Butterfly*, Coronet Films
8. *The Honeybee*, Coronet Films

D. Filmstrips

1. *How Insects Live and Grow*, Society for Visual Education
2. *Insects Around Us*, Jam Handy
3. *Insect Communities*, Curriculum Materials Corporation
4. *Insects: Man's Greatest Rival*, D. C. Heath

Hydroponics—Soilless Gardens

A. Reading material for children

1. Bulla, Clyde, *A Tree Is a Plant* (Thomas Y. Crowell 1960)
2. Darby, Gene, *What Is a Plant?* (Beckley-Cardy 1960)
3. Green, Ivah, *Conservation From A to Z* (Oddo 1966)
4. Hammond, Winifred, *Plants, Food and People* (Coward-McCann 1964)
5. Hammond, Winifred, *The Riddle of Seeds* (Coward-McCann 1965)

6. Huntington, Harriet E., *Forest Giants: The Story of the California Redwoods* (Doubleday 1962)
7. Hutchins, Ross E., *This Is a Leaf* (Dodd, Mead 1962)
8. Kurtz, Edwin B. Jr., and Allen, Chris, *Adventures in Living Plants* (University of Arizona 1965)
9. Neurath, Marie, *How Plants Grow* (Sterling Publishing 1962)
10. Podendorf, Illa, *True Book of Plant Experiments* (Childrens Press 1960)
11. Queree, Pearl, and Foster, Willene K., *Seeds Are Wonderful* (Melmont 1960)
12. Riedman, Sarah R., *Naming Living Things* (Rand McNally 1963)
13. Wood, Dorothy, *Plants with Seeds* (Follett 1963)
14. Zim, Herbert S., *How Things Grow* (William Morrow 1960)

B. Reading material for teachers

1. Asimov, Isaac, *Chemicals of Life, Enzymes, Vitamins and Hormones* (Abelard-Schuman 1954)
2. Beck, Barbara, *The First Book of Weeds* (Franklin Watts 1963)
3. Cook, J. Gordon, *Our Living Soil* (Dial Press 1960)
4. Hyde, Margaret O., *Plants Today and Tomorrow* (McGraw-Hill 1960)
5. Kreig, Margaret, *Green Medicine* (Rand McNally 1964)
6. Lynch, Patrick, *Man and Nature* (St. Martin's Press 1964)
7. Milne, Lorous J. and Margery, *Plant Life* (Prentice-Hall 1959)

C. Films

1. *Food from the Sun*, Encyclopaedia Britannica Films
2. *Green Plants and Sunlight*, Encyclopaedia Britannica Films
3. *Let's Watch Plants Grow*, Coronet Films
4. *Photosynthesis: Chemistry of Food Making,* Coronet Films
5. *Plants Make Food*, Churchill Films
6. *Seeds Grow into Plants*, Coronet Films
7. *Soil: What It Is and What It Does*, Coronet Films
8. *What Plants Need for Growth*, Encyclopaedia Britannica Films
9. *Wonders of Plant Growth*, Churchill Films

D. Filmstrips

1. *A Plant Through the Seasons*, Encyclopaedia Britannica Films
2. *How a Plant Grows*, Young America Films
3. *How a Plant Makes Food*, McGraw-Hill
4. *How Plants Live and Grow*, Young America Films
5. *How Plants Spread and Reproduce*, D. C. Heath
6. *Seeds and Seed Travel*, Society for Visual Education
7. *Soil for Plants*, Educational Visual Aids
8. *The World of Living Things*, D. C. Heath

Measuring Raindrops

A. Reading material for children

1. Adler, Irving, *Storms* (John Day 1963)
2. Antoine, Tex, *Wonder of the Weather* (Dodd, Mead 1962)
3. Bendick, Jeanne, *The Wind* (Rand McNally 1964)
4. Disney, Walt, *Man and Weather Satellites* (Golden Press 1960)
5. Feravolo, Rocco V., *Junior Science Book of Weather Experiments* (Garrard 1963)
6. Forrester, Frank, *Exploring the Air Ocean* (G. P. Putnam's 1960)
7. Goetz, Delia, *Tropical Rain Forests* (William Morrow 1956)
8. Kirk, Richard, *The Lightning and the Rainbow* (Follett 1962)
9. Larrick, Nancy, *Junior Science Book of Rain, Hail, Sleet and Snow* (Garrard 1961)
10. McKibben, Margaret, *The Story of a Storm* (Coward-McCann 1962)
11. Palmer, Woods, Jr., *Air and Water* (Grosset and Dunlap 1967)

12. Parker, Bertha M., *Clouds, Rain and Snow* (Golden Press 1959)
13. Pine, Tillie S., and Levine, Joseph, *Weather All Around* (McGraw-Hill 1966)
14. Tannenbaum, Harold E., and Stillman, Nathan, *We Read About Lightning and Thunder* (Webster 1960)

B. Reading material for teachers

1. Bell, Thelma H., *Thunderstorm* (Viking Press 1960)
2. Blanchard, Duncan C., *From Raindrops to Volcanoes* (Doubleday 1967)
3. Cook, J. Gordon, *Our Astonishing Atmosphere* (Dial Press 1957)
4. Harris, Miles F., *Man Against Storm: The Challenge of Weather* (Coward-McCann 1962)
5. Krick, Irving P., and Fleming, Roscoe, *Sun, Sea, and Sky* (J. B. Lippincott 1954)
6. Newell, Homer E., Jr., *Window in the Sky* (McGraw-Hill 1959)
7. Wolfe, Louis, *Probing the Atmosphere: The Story of Meteorology* (G. P. Putnam's 1961)

C. Films

1. *Clouds Above*, Bailey Films
2. *Life in Hot, Wet Lands*, Coronet Films
3. *Water in the Air*, Encyclopaedia Britannica Films
4. *Water in the Weather*, Academy Films
5. *Weather: Understanding Storms*, Coronet Films
6. *What Makes Rain?*, Young America Films
7. *Wonder of Water*, Moody Institute of Science

D. Filmstrips

1. *Air, Wind and Weather*, Eye Gate House
2. *Clouds, Rain and Snow*, Society for Visual Education
3. *Our Ocean of Air*, Society for Visual Education

4. *Water and Life*, D. C. Heath
5. *Weather*, Young America Films

Mirrors and Lenses

A. Reading material for children

1. Adler, Irving, *Color in Your Life* (John Day 1962)
2. Adler, Irving, *Your Eyes* (John Day 1963)
3. Beeler, Welson F., and Branley, Franklyn M., *Experiments in Optical Illusion* (Thomas Y. Crowell 1951)
4. Carona, Philip B., *Mirror on the Wall: How It Works* (Prentice-Hall 1964)
5. Disraeli, Robert, *New World Through the Microscope* (Viking Press 1960)
6. Feravolo, Rocco V., *Junior Science Book of Light* (Garrard 1961)
7. Freeman, Mae B. and Ira M., *Fun With Your Camera* (Random House 1955)
8. Harrison, George R., *The First Book of Light* (Franklin Watts 1962)
9. Healey, Frederick, *Light and Color* (John Day 1962)
10. Jupo, Frank, *The Adventure of Light* (Prentice-Hall 1958)
11. Meyer, Jerome S., *Prisms and Lenses* (World 1959)
12. Moore, Patrick, *Telescopes and Observatories* (John Day 1962)
13. Munch, Theodore W., *What Is Light?* (Benefic Press 1960)
14. Neal, Charles D., *Exploring Light and Color* (Childrens Press 1964)
15. Pine, Tillie S., and Levine, Joseph, *Light All Around* (McGraw-Hill 1961)
16. Rainivater, Janette, *Vision* (Golden Press 1962)

B. Reading material for teachers

1. Biren, Faber, *New Horizons in Color* (Reinhold 1955)
2. Bragg, William, *The Universe of Light* (Dover 1959)
3. Efron, Alexander, *Light* (John F. Rider 1958)
4. Minnaert, M., *The Nature of Light and Color in the Open Air* (Dover 1954)

5. Tannenbaum, Beulah, and Stillman, Myra, *Understanding Light: The Science of Visible and Invisible Rays* (McGraw-Hill 1960)

C. Films

1. *Color and Light: An Introduction*, Coronet Films
2. *How to Bend Light*, Encyclopaedia Britannica Films
3. *Learning About Light*, Encyclopaedia Britannica Films
4. *Light and Color*, Encyclopaedia Britannica Films
5. *Light and Shadows*, McGraw-Hill
6. *The Nature of Light*, Coronet Films

D. Filmstrips

1. *Light*, Young America Films
2. *Light and Color*, Jam Handy
3. *Light and How It Travels*, Jam Handy

Observing Cells

A. Reading material for children

1. Ames, Gerald, and Wyler, Rose, *The Giant Golden Book of Biology* (Golden Press 1967)
2. Beeler, Nelson F., and Branley, Franklyn M., *Experiments with a Microscope* (Thomas Y. Crowell 1957)
3. Burgdof, Otto P., *Adventure Book of Biology* (Golden Press 1962)
4. Disraeli, Robert, *New Worlds Through the Microscope* (Viking Press 1968)
5. Eggleston, Joyce S., *Things That Grow* (Melmont 1959)
6. Fletcher, Helen J., *For Junior Doctors Only* (Bobbs-Merrill 1961)
7. Grant, Madeline P., *Wonder World of Microbes* (McGraw-Hill 1964)
8. Horrobin, David F., *The Communication Systems of the Body* (Basic Books 1964)
9. Hyde, Margaret O., *Your Brain: Master Computer* (McGraw-Hill 1964)
10. Kavaler, Lucy, *The Wonders of Algae* (John Day 1961)
11. Lauber, Patricia, *Your Body and How It Works* (Random House 1962)

12. Reidman, Sarah R., *Your Blood and You* (Abelard-Schuman 1963)
13. Reit, Ann, *The Body in Action* (Golden Press 1962)
14. Schatz, Albert, and Riedman, Sarah, *The Story of Microbes* (Harper & Row 1952)
15. Schneider, Leo, *Lifeline: The Story of Your Circulatory System* (Harcourt, Brace and World 1958)
16. Schwartz, Julius, *Through the Magnifying Glass* (McGraw-Hill 1954)
17. Weart, Edith L., *The Story of Your Blood* (Coward-McCann 1960)
18. Zim, Herbert S., *How Things Grow* (William Morrow 1960)

B. Reading material for teachers

1. Asimov, Isaac, *The Human Body: Its Structure and Operation* (Houghton Mifflin 1963)
2. McElroy, William, *Cellular Physiology and Biochemistry* (Prentice-Hall 1961)
3. Sproul, Edith E., *The Science Book of the Human Body* (Franklin Watts 1955)
4. Swanson, Carl P., *The Cell* (Prentice-Hall 1964)
5. Wilson, Mitchell, *The Human Body: What It Is and How It Works* (Golden Press 1959)

C. Films

1. *About the Human Body*, Churchill Films
2. *Exploring Your Growth*, Churchill Films
3. *Heart, Lungs and Circulation*, Coronet Films
4. *How Our Bodies Fight Diseases*, Encyclopaedia Britannica
5. *Human Body: Nervous System*, Coronet Films
6. *Learning About Our Bodies*, Coronet Films
7. *Life in a Drop of Water*, Coronet Films
8. *Life Story of the Paramecium*, Encyclopaedia Britannica Films

D. Filmstrips

1. *How Your Body Grows*, Curriculum Materials Corporation

258

2. *Human Factories*, D. C. Heath
3. *Living Things*, Society for Visual Education
4. *The World of Our Senses*, D. C. Heath
5. *You, the Living Machine*, Encyclopaedia Britannica Films

Snowflake Replicas

A. Reading material for children

1. Adler, Irving and Ruth, *Dust* (John Day 1958)
2. Adler, Irving and Ruth, *Storms* (John Day 1963)
3. Barr, Jene, and Chapin, Cynthia, *What Will the Weather Be?* (Albert Whitman 1965)
4. Bell, Thelma H., *Snow* (Viking Press 1954)
5. Bendick, Jeanne, *The Wind* (Rand McNally 1964)
6. Euller, John, *Arctic World* (Abelard-Schuman 1958)
7. Frank, R. Jr., *Ice Island: The Story of Antarctica* (Thomas Y. Crowell 1957)
8. Gibson, Gertrude H., *About Our Weather* (Melmont 1960)
9. Hitte, Kathryn, *Hurricanes, Tornadoes and Blizzards* (Random House 1960)
10. Larrick, Nancy, *Junior Science Book of Rain, Hail, Sleet and Snow* (Garrard 1961)
11. Lauber, Patricia, *Junior Science Book of Icebergs and Glaciers* (Garrard 1961)
12. McFall, Christie, *Wonders of Snow and Ice* (Dodd, Mead 1964)
13. Neurath, Marie, *The Wonder World of Snow and Ice* (Sterling Publishing 1962)
14. Ogle, Ed, *Getting to Know the Arctic* (Coward-McCann 1961)
15. Parker, Bertha M., *Clouds, Rain and Snow* (Golden Press 1969)

B. Reading material for teachers

1. Adler, Irving, *Weather in Your Life* (John Day 1959)
2. Bell, Corydon, *The Wonder of Snow* (Hill and Wang 1957)
3. Berrill, Jacquelyn, *Wonders of the Arctic* (Dodd, Mead 1959)

4. Cary, Sturgis, *Volcanoes and Glaciers* (Coward-McCann 1959)
5. Harris, Miles F., *Man Against Storm: The Challenge of Weather* (Coward-McCann 1962)
6. Wolfe, Louis, *Probing the Atmosphere: The Story of Meteorology* (G. P. Putnam's 1961)
7. La Chapelle, Edward R., *Field Guide to Snow Crystals* (University of Washington Press 1969)

C. Films

1. *Clouds Above*, Bailey Films
2. *How Weather Is Forecast*, Coronet Films
3. *Let's Learn to Predict the Weather*, Coronet Films
4. *Water in the Weather*, Academy Films

D. Filmstrips

1. *Air, Wind and Weather*, Eye Gate House
2. *Clouds, Rain, Snow*, Society for Visual Education
3. *Information from Satellites*, Films For Education
4. *We Learn About Weather*, Young America Films

Thermobarometers and Other Weather Investigations

A. Reading material for children

1. Adler, Irving and Ruth, *Storms* (John Day 1963)
2. Barr, George, *More Research Ideas for Young Scientists* (McGraw-Hill 1961)
3. Barr, Jene, and Chapin, Cynthia, *What Will the Weather Be?* (Albert Whitman 1965)
4. Bonsall, George, *The How and Why Book of Weather* (Grosset and Dunlap 1960)
5. Brindze, Ruth, *The Story of the Trade Winds* (Vanguard Press 1960)
6. Disney, Walt, *Man and Weather Satellites* (Golden Press 1960)
7. Feravolo, Rocco V., *Junior Science Book of Weather Experiments* (Garrard 1963)

8. Gaer, Joseph, *Everybody's Weather* (J. B. Lippincott 1957)

9. Irving, Robert, *Hurricanes and Twisters* (Alfred A. Knopf 1955)

10. Laird, Charles and Ruth, *Weathercasting* (Prentice-Hall 1955)

11. McGrath, Thomas, *About Clouds* (Melmont 1959)

12. Palmer, Woods Jr., *Air and Water* (Grosset and Dunlap 1967)

13. Pine, Tillie S., and Levine, Joseph, *Weather All Around* (McGraw-Hill 1966)

14. Spar, Jerome, *The Way of the Weather* (Creative Educational Society 1962)

15. Syrocki, B. John, *What Is Weather?* (Benefic Press 1960)

16. Tannenbaum, Harold E., and Stillman, Nathan, *We Read About Lightning and Thunder* (Webster 1960)

17. Wyler, Rose, *The First Book of Weather* (Franklin Watts 1956)

B. Reading material for teachers

1. Adler, Irving, *Weather in Your Life* (John Day 1959)

2. Bell, Thelma H., *Thunderstorms* (Viking Press 1960)

3. Cook, J. Gordon, *Our Astonishing Atmosphere* (Dial Press 1957)

4. Harris, Miles F., *Man Against Storm: The Challenge of Weather* (Coward-McCann 1962)

5. Koeppe, Clarence E., and DeLong, George C., *Weather and Climate* (McGraw-Hill 1959)

6. Newell, Homer E., *Window in the Sky* (McGraw-Hill 1959)

C. Films

1. *Climate and the World We Live In*, Coronet Films

2. *Clouds Above*, Bailey Films

3. *How Weather Is Forecast*, Coronet Films

4. *Let's Learn to Predict the Weather*, Coronet Films

5. *Life in Hot, Wet Lands*, Coronet Films

6. *The Weather Station*, McGraw-Hill Films

7. *Weather: Understanding Storms*, Coronet Films

8. *Winds and Their Causes*, Coronet Films

D. Filmstrips

1. *Atmosphere and Its Circulation*, Encyclopaedia Britannica Films

2. *A Visit to a Weather Station*, D. C. Heath

3. *Clouds, Rain and Snow*, Society for Visual Education

4. *Information from Satellites*, Films for Education

5. *Sunlight and the Earth's Temperature*, D. C. Heath

6. *The Weather*, Curriculum Materials Corporation

7. *What Is Weather?* Jam Handy

Unknown Objects—Ecology

A. Reading material for children

1. Allen, Gertrude, *Everyday Insects* (Houghton Mifflin 1963)

2. Allen, Robert P., *Giant Golden Book of Birds* (Golden Press 1962)

3. Audubon Nature Charts, *Twigs, Simple Leaves, Compound Leaves, Evergreens* (National Audubon Society)

4. Caulfield, Peggy, *Leaves* (Coward-McCann 1962)

5. Earle, Olive L., *Strange Lizards* (William Morrow 1964)

6. Harlow, William M., *Fruit Key and Twig Key to Trees and Shrubs of New England* (Dover 1946)

7. Hurd, Edith, *Starfish* (Thomas Y. Crowell 1962)

8. Hylander, Clarence J., *Fishes and Their Ways* (Macmillan 1963)

9. Jacques, H. E., *How to Know the Insects* (William C. Brown)

10. Jensen, Amy E., *The How and Why Wonder Book of Mushrooms, Ferns and Mosses* (Grosset and Dunlap 1965)

11. Kurtz, Edwin B., Jr., and Allen, Chris, *Ad-*

ventures in Living Plants (University of Arizona Press 1965)

12. McClung, Robert M., *All About Animals and Their Young* (Random House 1958)
13. McGrath, Thomas, *About Clouds* (Melmont 1959)
14. Robinson, William W., *At the Seashore* (Macmillan 1964)
15. Shannon, Terry, *About Food and Where It Comes From* (Melmont 1963)
16. Shuttlesworth, Dorothy E., *The Story of Spiders* (Doubleday 1959)
17. Snedigar, Robert, *Life in the Forest* (Encyclopaedia Britannica 1962)
18. Watts, May T., *Flower Finder* (Nature Study Guild)
19. Watts, May T., *Master Tree Finder* (Nature Study Guild)
20. Watts, May T., *Tree Finder* (Nature Study Guild)
21. Whitehead, Robert, *The First Book of Bears* (Franklin Watts 1966)
22. Zim, Herbert S., *Rocks and How They Were Formed* (Golden Press 1961)
23. Zim, Herbert S., and Martin, A. C., *Trees* (Golden Press 1952)

B. Reading material for teachers

1. Beck, Barbara, *The First Book of Weeds* (Franklin Watts 1963)
2. Burton, Maurice, *Under the Sea* (Franklin Watts 1960)
3. Cronquist, Arthur, *Introductory Botany* (Harper and Row 1961)
4. Edmondson, W. T. (editor), *Fresh Water Biology* (John Wiley 1959)
5. Fernald, M. L. (editor), *Gray's Manual of Botany* (American Book)
6. Fisher, James, *The World of Birds* (Doubleday 1963)
7. Hall, Richard P., *Protozoa: The Simplest of All Animals* (Holt, Rinehart & Winston)
8. Hyde, Margaret O., *Plants Today and Tomorrow* (McGraw-Hill 1960)
9. Lutz, Frank E., *Field Book of Insects* (3d ed.), (G. P. Putnam's 1948)
10. Metcalf, Z. P. and C. L., *Key to the Principal Orders and Families of Insects* (Metcalf)
11. Pennals, Robert W., *Fresh-Water Invertebrates of the United States* (Ronald Press)
12. Zim, Herbert S., and Shaffer, Paul R., *Rocks and Minerals* (Golden Press 1957)

C. Films

1. *About the Human Body*, Churchill Films
2. *Amphibians: Frogs, Toads, and Salamanders*, Film Associates of California
3. *Clouds Above*, Bailey Films
4. *Earthworms*, Pat Dowling Pictures
5. *Fish Family*, Moody Institute of Science
6. *Insect Collecting*, Pat Dowling Pictures
7. *Learning About Leaves*, Encyclopaedia Britannica Films
8. *Minerals and Rocks*, Encyclopaedia Britannica Films
9. *Reptiles and Their Characteristics*, Coronet Films
10. *Seashore Life*, Encyclopaedia Britannica Films
11. *Snakes*, Coronet Films

D. Filmstrips

1. *Adventures with Trees*, Film Strip of the Month Club
2. *Clouds, Rain and Snow*, Society for Visual Education
3. *Common Minerals*, Society for Visual Education
4. *Flowers, Fruits and Seeds*, Society for Visual Education
5. *Foods and Nutrition*, Encyclopaedia Britannica Films
6. *Frogs, Toads, and Turtles*, Society for Visual Education
7. *How Animals Are Grouped*, Young America Films
8. *Insect Communities*, Coronet Films

Water Characteristics

A. Reading material for children

1. Adler, Irving, *Oceans* (John Day 1962)
2. Adler, Irving, *Rivers* (John Day 1962)

3. Bauer, Helen, *Water, Riches or Ruin* (Doubleday 1959)
4. Boyle, E. Marie, *Water: Its Form and Motion* (Beacon Press 1962)
5. Buehr, Walter, *World Beneath the Waves* (W. W. Norton 1964)
6. Eifert, Virginia S., *Wonders of the Rivers* (Dodd, Mead 1962)
7. Elting, Mary, *Water Come—Water Go* (Harvey House 1964)
8. Greenhood, David, *Watch the Tides* (Holiday House 1961)
9. Hagaman, Adaline P., *What Is Water?* (Beckley-Cardy 1960)
10. Harmer, Mabel, *About Dams* (Melmont 1963)
11. Meyer, Jerome S., *Water at Work* (World 1963)
12. Pine, Tillie S., and Levine, Joseph, *Water All Around* (McGraw-Hill 1959)
13. Rose, Elizabeth and Gerald, *The Big River* (W. W. Norton 1964)
14. Schlein, Miriam, *Sun, the Wind, the Sea, and the Rain* (Abelard-Schuman 1960)
15. Winchester, James, *Wonders of Water* (G. P. Putnam 1963)

B. Reading material for teachers

1. Archer, Sellers, *Rain, Rivers and Reservoirs: The Challenge of Running Water* (Coward-McCann 1963)
2. Carhart, Arthur H., *Water—Or Your Life* (J. B. Lippincott 1959)
3. Cook, J. Gordon, *The World of Water* (Dial Press 1957)
4. Gerard, Geoffrey, *The Book of Water Power* (Frederick Warne 1963)
5. Graham, Edward H., *Water for America: The Story of Water Conservation* (Henry Z. Walck 1956)
6. Lewis, Alfred, *This Thirsty World: Water Supply and Problems Ahead* (McGraw-Hill 1964)
7. Piccard, Jacques, and Dietz, Robert S., *Seven Miles Down* (G. P. Putnam 1961)

C. Films

1. *Conservation of Natural Resources*, Encyclopaedia Britannica Films
2. *Dams*, Pat Dowling Pictures
3. *Our Natural Resources*, Pat Dowling Pictures
4. *Pipes in the House*, Churchill Films
5. *Water We Drink*, Coronet Films
6. *Working Water*, Pat Dowling Pictures

D. Filmstrips

1. *Nothing Can Live Without Water*, Young America Films
2. *Soil and Water Conservation*, D. C. Heath
3. *Story of Rivers*, Encyclopaedia Britannica Films
4. *Story of Underground Water*, Encyclopaedia Britannica Films
5. *The Ocean*, D. C. Heath
6. *Water and Its Importance*, Eye Gate House
7. *Water and Life*, D. C. Heath
8. *Water and Its Works*, Young America Films

What Is Food?

A. Reading material for children

1. Burgdorf, Otto P., *Adventure Book of Biology* (Golden Press 1962)
2. Faber, Doris, *The Miracle of Vitamins* (G. P. Putnam 1964)
3. Follett, Robert J. R., *Your Wonderful Body* (Follett 1961)
4. Green Erma, *Everybody Eats* (William R. Scott 1961)
5. Lauber, Patricia, *Your Body and How It Works* (Random House 1962)
6. Martin, Lealon E., *Conquest of Disease: The Challenge of Your Life* (Coward-McCann 1961)
7. Riedman, Sarah R., *Food for People* (Abelard-Schuman 1961)
8. Shannon, Terry, *About Food and Where It Comes From* (Melmont 1963)
9. Turner, Eloise, and Fenton, Carroll Lane, *Inside You and Me* (John Day 1961)

B. Reading material for teachers

1. Asimov, Isaac, *The Human Body: Its Structure and Operation* (Houghton Mifflin 1963)
2. Diehl, Harold S., *Healthful Living* (McGraw-Hill 1963)
3. Hovde, Christian A., and Kalb, William S., *Your Body: Its Anatomy and Nutrition* (C. S. Hammond 1962)
4. Life Science Library, *Food and Nutrition* (Time-Life Books 1967)
5. Taylor, Clara Mae, *Foundations of Nutrition* (Macmillan 1956)

C. Films

1. *About the Human Body,* Churchill Films
2. *How Our Bodies Fight Diseases*, Encyclopaedia Britannica Films
3. *Learning About Our Bodies*, Coronet Films
4. *Exploring Your Growth*, Churchill Films

D. Filmstrips

1. *Food and Nutrition*, Encyclopaedia Britannica Films
2. *How Your Body Grows*, Curriculum Materials Corporation

Publisher	Address
Abelard-Schuman, Ltd.	257 Park Avenue South, New York, N.Y. 10010
Abingdon Press	201 Eighth Avenue South, Nashville, Tenn. 37202
Addison-Wesley Publishing Co.	Reading, Mass. 01867
Allyn and Bacon, Inc.	470 Atlantic Avenue, Boston, Mass. 02110
American Association for the Advancement of Science	1515 Massachusetts Ave., N.W., Washington, D.C. 20005
American Book Company	450 West 33 Street, New York, N.Y. 10001
American Education Publications	55 High Street, Middletown, Conn. 06457
American Library Association	50 East Huron Street, Chicago, Ill. 60611
American Technical Society	848 East 58 Street, Chicago, Ill. 60637
Appleton-Century and Appleton-Century-Crofts Inc.	440 Park Avenue South, New York, N.Y. 10016
Atheneum Publishers	122 East 42 Street, New York, N.Y. 10017
A. S. Barnes & Co.	Forsgate Drive, Cranbury, N.J. 08512
Barnes and Noble Inc.	105 Fifth Avenue, New York, N.Y. 10003
Basic Books Inc.	404 Park Avenue South, New York, N.Y. 10016
Beacon Press	25 Beacon Street, Boston, Mass. 02108
Beckley-Cardy Company	See Benefic Press
Benefic Press	10300 West Roosevelt Road, Westchester, Ill. 60153
Chas. A. Bennett Company, Inc.	809 West Detweiller Drive, Peoria, Ill. 61614
Benziger Brothers Publishing Co.	7 East 51 Street, New York, N.Y. 10022
The Bobbs-Merrill Co. Inc.	4300 West 62 Street, Indianapolis, Ind. 46206

William C. Brown Company	135 South Locust Street, Dubuque, Iowa 52002
The Bruce Publishing Company	400 North Broadway, Milwaukee, Wis. 53201
Capitol Publishing Co., Inc.	850 Third Avenue, New York, N.Y. 10022
Chandler Publishing Co.	124 Spear Street, San Francisco, Calif. 94105
University of Chicago Press	5750 Ellis Avenue, Chicago, Ill. 60637
Childrens Press, Inc.	1224 West Van Buren Street, Chicago, Ill. 60607
Chilton Book Company	401 Walnut Street, Philadelphia, Pa. 19106
Cornell University Press	124 Roberts Place, Ithaca, N.Y. 14851
Coward-McCann, Inc.	200 Madison Avenue, New York, N.Y. 10016
Criterion Books	257 Park Avenue South, New York, N.Y. 10010
Thomas Y. Crowell Company	201 Park Avenue South, New York, N.Y. 10003
Crown Publishers, Inc.	419 Fourth Avenue, New York, N.Y. 10016
The John Day Company, Inc.	257 Park Avenue South, New York, N.Y. 10010
T. S. Denison & Company, Inc.	315 Fifth Avenue South, Minneapolis, Minn. 55415
Dial Press, Inc.	750 Third Avenue, New York, N.Y. 10017
Dodd, Mead & Company	79 Madison Avenue, New York, N.Y. 10016
Doubleday and Company, Inc.	Garden City, N.Y. 11530
Dover Publications	180 Varick Street, New York, N.Y. 10014
Duell, Sloan and Pearce, Inc.	See Hawthorn Books
Earth Science Curriculum Project	Boulder, Colorado, 80301
E. P. Dutton & Company, Inc.	201 Park Avenue South, New York, N.Y. 10003
Encyclopaedia Britannica, Inc.	425 North Michigan Avenue, Chicago, Ill. 60611
Feron Publishers, Inc.	2165 Park Boulevard, Palo Alto, Calif. 94306
The Fideler Company	31 Ottawa Avenue N.W., Grand Rapids, Mich. 49502
Follett Publishing Company	1010 West Washington Boulevard, Chicago, Ill. 60607
W. H. Freeman and Company	660 Market Street, San Francisco, Calif. 94104
Friendship Press	475 Riverside Drive, New York, N.Y. 10027
Garden City Books (see Doubleday)	
Garrard Publishing Co.	1607 North Market Street, Champaign, Ill. 61820
Ginn and Company	Statler Building, Back Bay P.O. 191, Boston, Mass. 02117
Globe Book Company, Inc.	175 Fifth Avenue, New York, N.Y. 10010
Golden Press, Inc. (Education Division)	850 Third Avenue, New York, N.Y. 10022
Goodheart-Willcox Co.	18250 Harwood Avenue, Homewood, Ill. 60430
Grossett & Dunlap, Inc.	51 Madison Avenue, New York, N.Y. 10010

E. M. Hale and Company	1201 South Hastings Way, Eau Claire, Wis. 54701
C. S. Hammond and Co.	Hammond Building, Maplewood, N.J. 07040
Harcourt, Brace & World, Inc.	757 Third Avenue, New York, N.Y. 10017
Harper and Row, Publishers, Inc.	49 East 33 Street, New York, N.Y. 10016
Harvey House, Inc.	5 Buckhout Street, Irvington-on-Hudson, N.Y. 10533
Hastings House Publishers, Inc.	151 East 50 Street, New York, N.Y. 10022
Hawthorn Books, Inc.	70 Fifth Avenue, New York, N.Y. 10011
D. C. Heath & Company	285 Columbus Avenue, Boston, Mass. 02116
Hebrew Publishing Company, Inc.	79 Delancy Street, New York, N.Y. 10002
Hill and Wang, Inc.	141 Fifth Avenue, New York, N.Y. 10010
Holiday House Inc.	18 East 56 Street, New York, N.Y. 10022
Holt, Rinehart & Winston, Inc.	383 Madison Avenue, New York, N.Y. 10017
Houghton Mifflin Company	2 Park Street, Boston, Mass. 02107
International Publishers, Inc.	381 Park Avenue South, New York, N.Y. 10016
International Text Book Co.	Scranton, Pa. 18515
Alfred A. Knopf, Inc.	501 Madison Avenue, New York, N.Y. 10022
Laidlaw Brothers	Thatcher & Madison Streets, River Forest, Ill. 60305
J. B. Lippincott Company	East Washington Square, Philadelphia, Pa. 19105
Little, Brown and Company	34 Beacon Street, Boston, Mass. 02106
Lothrop, Lee & Shepard Company, Inc.	381 Park Avenue South, New York, N.Y. 10016
Lyons & Carnahan	407 East 25 Street, Chicago, Ill. 60616
The Macmillan Company	866 Third Avenue, New York, N.Y. 10022
David McKay Company, Inc.	750 Third Avenue, New York, N.Y. 10017
Macrae Smith Co.	225 South 15 Street, Philadelphia, Pa. 19102
Manufacturing Chemists Association	1825 Connecticut Avenue N.W., Washington, D.C. 20009
McCormick-Mathers Publishing Company	P.O. Box 2212, 1440 East English Street, Wichita, Kans. 67201
McGraw-Hill Book Company	330 West 42 Street, New York, N.Y. 10036
McNight & McNight Publishing Co.	Bloomington, Ill. 61701
Melmont Publishers, Inc.	1224 West Van Buren Street, Chicago, Ill. 60607
Meredith Press	1716 Locust Street, Des Moines, Iowa 50303
Charles E. Merrill Books, Inc.	1300 Alum Creek Dr., Columbus, Ohio 43216
Julian Messner (Division of Simon & Schuster, Inc.)	1 West 39 Street, New York, N.Y. 10018
University of Michigan Press	Ann Arbor, Mich. 48106

University of Minnesota Press	2037 University Avenue S.E., Minneapolis, Minn. 55455
William Morrow & Company, Inc.	425 Park Avenue South, New York, N.Y. 10016
National Center for Air Pollution	U.S. Government Printing Office, Washington, D.C. 20402
National Science Teachers Association	1201 16 Street, Washington, D.C.
Thomas Nelson & Sons	1626 Copewood, Camden, N.J. 08103
The New American Library Inc.	1301 Avenue of the Americas, New York, N.Y. 10019
New York Graphic Society, Ltd.	104 Greenwich Avenue, Greenwich, Conn. 06830
Noble and Noble Publishers, Inc.	750 Third Avenue, New York, N.Y. 10017
W. W. Norton & Company, Inc.	55 Fifth Avenue, New York, N.Y. 10003
Pantheon Books	22 East 51 Street, New York, N.Y. 10022
Penguin Books Inc.	7110 Ambassador Road, Baltimore, Md. 21207
J. Lowell Pratt & Co. Inc.	15 East 48 Street, New York, N.Y. 10017
Prentice-Hall, Inc.	Englewood Cliffs, N.J. 07632
G. P. Putnam's Sons	200 Madison Avenue, New York, N.Y. 10016
Ramapo House	235 East 45th Street, New York, N.Y. 10017
Rand McNally & Company	P.O. Box 7600, Chicago, Ill. 60680
Random House, Inc.	457 Madison Avenue, New York, N.Y. 10022
Reader's Digest Services, Inc.	Educational Division, Pleasantville, N.Y. 10570
The Reilly & Lee Co.	114 West Illinois Street, Chicago, Ill. 60610
Reinhold Publishing Company	See Van Nostrand Reinhold Company
John F. Rider Company, Inc.	116 West 14 Street, New York, N.Y. 10011
Roy Publishers	30 East 74 Street, New York, N.Y. 10021
W. B. Saunders Co.	West Washington Square, Philadelphia, Pa. 19105
St. Martin's Press, Inc.	175 Fifth Avenue, New York, N.Y. 10010
Scholastic Book Services	50 West 44 Street, New York, N.Y. 10036
Science Research Associates, Inc.	259 East Erie Street, Chicago, Ill. 60611
William R. Scott, Inc.	333 Avenue of the Americas, New York, N.Y. 10014
Scott, Foresman & Company	1900 East Lake Avenue, Glenview, Ill. 60025
Charles Scribner's Sons	597 Fifth Avenue, New York, N.Y. 10017
Silver Burdett Company	Morristown, N.J. 07960
Simon & Schuster Inc.	630 Fifth Avenue, New York, N.Y. 10020
L. W. Singer Company (Division of Random House)	501 Madison Avenue, New York, N.Y. 10022

South-Western Publishing Co.	512 North Avenue, New Rochelle, N.Y. 10801
Sterling Publishing Company, Inc.	419 Park Avenue South, New York, N.Y. 10016
Teachers Publishing Corporation	23 Leroy Avenue, Darien, Conn. 06820
Frederick Ungar Publishing Co. Inc.	250 Park Avenue South, New York, N.Y. 10003
Vanguard Press, Inc.	424 Madison Avenue, New York, N.Y. 10017
Van Nostrand Reinhold Company	450 West 33 Street, New York, N.Y. 10001
The Viking Press, Inc.	625 Madison Avenue, New York, N.Y. 10022
Time-Life Books (Division of Time, Inc.)	Time & Life Building, Rockefeller Center, New York, N.Y. 10020
University of Washington Press	Seattle, Wash. 98105
Harr Wagner Publishing Co.	609 Mission Street, San Francisco, Calif. 94105
Wadsworth Publishing Co., Inc.	Belmont, Calif. 94002
Henry Z. Walck, Inc.	19 Union Square West, New York, N.Y. 10003
Frederick Warne and Company, Inc.	101 Fifth Avenue, New York, N.Y. 10003
Watson-Guptill Publications, Inc.	165 West 46 Street, New York, N.Y. 10036
Franklin Watts (Division of Grolier)	575 Lexington Avenue, New York, N.Y. 10022
Webster Publishing (Division of McGraw-Hill Book Co.)	Manchester Road, Manchester, Mo. 63011
Wesleyan University Press	100 Riverview Center, Middletown, Conn. 06457
John Wiley and Sons, Inc.	605 Third Avenue, New York, N.Y. 10016
Whitman Publishing Co.	1220 Mound Avenue, Racine, Wis. 53404
Whittlesey House (Division of McGraw-Hill Book Company)	330 West 42 Street, New York, N.Y. 10036

Film and Filmstrip Distributors

Academy Films, 1145 Las Palmas Avenue, Hollywood Calif. 90038

Almanac Films, 29 East 10 Street, New York, N. Y. 10036

American Petroleum Institute, 1271 Avenue of the Americas, New York, N. Y. 10020

Audio-Visual Productions Inc. 630 Ninth Avenue, New York, N. Y. 10036

Avalon Daggett Productions (Films distributed by Modern Learning Aids, 1212 Avenue of the Americas, New York, N. Y.)

AV—ED Productions, 7939 Santa Monica Boulevard, Hollywood, Calif. 90046

Avis Films, Inc., P. O. Box 643, Burbank, California

Bailey Films, Inc., 6509 DeLongpre Avenue, Hollywood, Calif. 90028

Arthur Barr Productions, 1029 North Allen, Pasadena, Calif. 91104

Stanley Bowman Co., Inc., 12 Cleveland Street, Valhalla, New York

Canadian National Film Board, 1271 Avenue of the Americas, New York, N. Y.

Charles Cahill and Associates, Inc., Box 3220, Hollywood, Calif. 90028

Cenco Educational Films, 1700 Irving Park Road, Chicago, Ill. 60607

Childrens Press, Inc., 1224 West Van Buren Street, Chicago, Ill. 60607

Churchill Films, 662 North Robertson Boulevard, Los Angeles, Calif. 90069

Classroom Film Distributors, Inc., 5620 Hollywood Boulevard, Hollywood, Calif. 90028

Coast Visual Education Company, 5620 Hollywood Boulevard, Hollywood, Calif. 90028

Coronet Instructional Films, 65 East South Water Street, Chicago Ill. 60601

Creative Education Inc., 340 North Milwaukee Ave., Libertyville, Ill.

Curriculum Materials Corporation, 1319 Vine Street, Philadelphia, Pennsylvania

Dallas Jones Productions, Inc., 430 West Grand Place, Chicago, Illinois

Walt Disney Productions, 800 Sonora Avenue, Glendale, Calif. 91201

Pat Dowling Pictures (Distributed by Bailey Films

Educational Horizons, 3015 Dolores Street, Los Angeles, California

Educational Visual Aids, Inc., E. 64 Midland Ave., Paramus, N.J. 07652

Encyclopaedia Britannica Educational Corporation, 425 N. Michigan Avenue, Chicago, Ill. 60611

Eye Gate House Inc., 146-01 Archer Avenue, Jamaica, N.Y. 11435

Film Associates, 1159 Santa Monica Boulevard, Los Angeles, Calif. 90025

Films for Education, Inc., Audio Lane, New Haven, Connecticut

Filmstrip House, 347 Madison Avenue, New York, N. Y. 10017

Filmstrip of the Month Clubs, 355 Lexington Avenue, New York, N. Y. 10017

Gateway Productions, Inc., 1859 Powell Street, San Francisco, Calif. 94133

Grover-Jennings Productions, Inc., P. O. Box 303, Monterey, Calif. 93940

Jam Handy Organization, 2821 E. Grand Boulevard, Detroit, Mich. 48211

Heath Science Filmstrips, 285 Columbus Avenue, Boston, Mass. 02116

Indiana University, Audio Visual Center, Bloomington, Indiana

International Film Bureau Inc., 332 South Michigan Avenue, Chicago, Ill. 60614

Journal Films, 909 West Diversey Parkway, Chicago, Ill. 60614

McGraw-Hill Films, 330 West 42 Street, New York, N. Y. 10036

Moody Institute of Science, 12000 E. Washington Boulevard, Whittier, Calif. 90606

Nate Quillen Instructional Systems, Inc., 620 East Smith Road, Medina, Ohio 44256

National Educational Television (See Indiana University)

National Medical Audiovisual Center, Film Distribution, Chamblee, Ga. 30005

Rampart Productions, 401 Taft Building, Los Angeles, California

Society for Visual Education Inc., 1345 West Diversey Parkway, Chicago, Ill. 60614

Stanton Films, 7934 Santa Monica Boulevard, Los Angeles, Calif. 90046

U. S. Department of Agriculture, Motion Picture Services, Washington, D.C. 20250

United States Public Health Service, Department of Health, Education and Welfare, Washington, D.C.

United World Films, 1445 Park Avenue, New York, New York

Universal Education and Visual Arts, Division of Universal City Studios, Inc., 221 Park Avenue South, New York, N.Y. 10003

Young America Films (distributed by McGraw-Hill Book Co.), 330 West 42 Street, New York, N.Y. 10036

Equipment and Supply Distributors

Aero Service Corporation, 210 East Courtland Street, Philadelphia, Pa. 19120

Ainsworth & Sons, 2151 Lawrence Street, Denver Colorado

Allied Chemical & Dye Corp., 40 Rector Street, New York, N.Y. 10006

Aloe Scientific, 1831 Olive Street, St. Louis, Mo. 63103

American Optical Co., Box A, Buffalo, N. Y. 14215

American Type Culture Collection, 2112 M Street N. W., Washington, D. C. 20007

Applied Sciences, Inc., 12435 Euclid Avenue, Cleveland, Ohio 44106

Atomic Accessories, Inc., 811 West Merrick Road, Valley Stream, N. Y. 11582

Bausch & Lomb Inc., 635 St. Paul Street, Rochester, N.Y. 14602

The Bendix Corporation, 3625 Hauck Road, Cincinnati, Ohio 45241

Biddle & Company, 1316 Arch Street, Philadelphia, Pa. 19107

Biological Research Products Co., 243 W. Root Street, Chicago, Ill. 60648

Biological Supply Company, 1176 Mount Hope Avenue, Rochester, New York

Bioscope Manufacturing Company, P. O. Box 1492, Tulsa, Okla. 74101

Black Light Planetarium Company, 329 North Elmwood, Oak Park, Ill. 60302

Buck Engineering Company, Inc., Lab-Volt Division, 37-41 March Street, Freehold, N. J. 07728

California Biological Service, 1612 W. Glenoaks Boulevard, Glendale, Calif. 91201

California Botanical Materials Co., 861 E. Columbia Avenue, Pomona, Calif. 91767

Cambosco Scientific Company, Inc., 342 Western Avenue, Boston, Mass. 02135

Carolina Biological Supply Company, Burlington, North Carolina, and Gladstone, Oregon

Central Scientific Company, 1700 Irving Park, Chicago, Ill. 60613

Certified Blood Donor Service, 146-16 Hillside Avenue, Jamaica, N.Y. 11435

Charles Beseler Company, 219 South Eighteenth Street, East Orange, N.J. 08818

Chemical Rubber Company, 2310 Superior Avenue, Cleveland, Ohio 44114

Chem-Products, Inc., 1619 East First Street, Austin, Texas 78700

Chicago Apparatus Co., 1735 N. Ashland Avenue, Chicago, Ill. 60622

Cole-Parmer Instrument and Equipment Co., 7330 North Clark Street, Chicago, Ill. 60626

College Biological Supply, Inc., 9230 Woodlawn Avenue, Seattle, Wash. 98125

Conso-Lab Supply Co., 7 Endo Boulevard, Garden City, N.Y. 11533

Corning Glass Works, Corning, N. Y. 14830

The George F. Cram Company, Inc., 730 East Washington Street, Indianapolis, Ind. 46204

Creative Playthings, Edinburg Road, Cranbury, N.Y. 08512

Criterion Manufacturing Company, 331 Church Street, Hartford, Conn. 06109

W. H. Curtin and Co., P. O. Box 1546, Houston, Texas 77001

Denoyer-Geppert Company, 5235 Ravenswood Avenue, Chicago, Ill. 60640

Difco Laboratories Inc., Detroit, Mich. 48201

Dow Chemical Co., Midland, Mich. 48640

The Ealing Corporation, 2225 Massachusetts Avenue, Cambridge, Mass. 02140

Eastman Kodak Co., 343 State Street, Rochester, N. Y. 14604

Eckert Mineral Research, 110 East Main Street, Florence, Colo. 81226

Edex Corporation, 3940 Fabian Way, Palo Alto, Calif. 91303

Edmund Scientific Company, Barrington, New Jersey

Eimer and Amend, Greenwich and Morton Streets, New York, N.Y. 10014

Elgeet Optical Co., Inc., 838 Smith Street, Rochester, N. Y. 14606

Encyclopaedia Britannica Inc., 1150 Wilmette Avenue, Wilmette, Ill. 60091

Erb & Gray Co., 854 S. Figueroa Street, Los Angeles, Calif. 90014

Essex International, 308 Springfield Avenue, Berkeley Heights, N. J. 07922

Farquhar Transparent Globes, 5007 Warrington Avenue, Philadelphia, Pa. 19143

Faust Scientific Supply, Ltd., 5108 Gordon Avenue, Madison, Wis. 53716

Fisher Scientific Co., 717 Forbes Avenue, Pittsburgh, Pa. 15200

General Biochemicals, Inc., 677 Laboratory Park, Chagrin Falls, Ohio 44022

General Biological Supply House, 8200 South Hoyne Avenue, Chicago, Ill. 60620

Gradwohl Laboratories, 3514 Lucas Avenue, St. Louis, Mo. 63103

The Graf-Apsco Company, 5868 Broadway, Chicago, Ill. 60626

Henry J. Green Instruments, Inc., 2500 Shames Drive, Westbury, N. Y. 11590

Hail Corporation, 210 S. Fourth Street, St. Louis, Missouri

Hamden Engineering Corporation, 99 Shaker Road, East Longmeadow, Mass. 01028

Harshaw Scientific Division, Harshaw Chemical Co., 1945 E. 9th Street, Cleveland, Ohio 44114

H. C. Hazel and Sons, Eustis, Fla. 32726

Heath Company, Benton Harbor, Mich. 99022

T. N. Hubbard Scientific Company, P. O. Box 105, 109 Pfingsten Road, Northbrook, Ill. 60062

Jewel Aquarium Company, Inc., 5005 West Armitage Avenue, Chicago, Ill. 60639

Kelly-Koett Manufacturing Co., 24 E. Sixth Street, Covington, Ky. 41011

Ken-A-Vision Manufacturing Company Inc., 5615 Raytown Road, Raytown, Mo. 64133

Kimbel Glass, P. O. Box #1035, Toledo, Ohio 43601

Klinger Scientific Apparatus Corp., 83-45 Parsons Boulevard, Jamaica, N. Y. 11432

Knickerbocker Blood Donor Service, 300 West 43 Street, New York, N. Y. 10036

Kuy-Sheerer Corporation, 2109 Borden Avenue, Long Island City, New York

Lab-Aids, Inc., Cold Spring Harbor, Long Island, N. Y. 11100

Lab-Line Instruments, Inc., Fifteenth and Bloomington Avenues, Melrose Park, Ill. 60160

La Pine Scientific Company, 6001 South Knox Avenue, Chicago, Ill. 60629

Leahy Manufacturing Co., Higginsville, Mo. 64037

Lederle Laboratories, Div. American Cyanamid Co., Midtown Road, Pearl River, N.Y. 10965

E. Leitz Inc., 468 Park Avenue South, New York, N.Y. 10016

The Lemberger Co., 1222 W. So. Park Avenue, P. O. Box 482, Oshkosh, Wis. 54901

Los Angeles Biological Laboratories, 2977 W. Fourteenth Street, Los Angeles, Calif. 90006

The Lumiscope Company, 836 Broadway, New York, N.Y. 10003

Macalaster Bicknel, Inc., 181 Henry Street, New Haven, Conn. 06511

Macalaster Scientific Corp., 60 Arsenal Street, Watertown, Mass. 02172

Malge Co., Inc., Rochester, N.Y. 14602

Marine Biological Laboratories, Woods Hole, Mass. 02543

Merck & Co., Rahway, N.J. 07065

Misco Biological Corporation, 6780 Jackson Road, Ann Arbor, Mich. 48103

Monsanto Chemical Co., 1700 S. Second Street, St. Louis, Mo. 63104

National Biological Laboratories Inc., P. O. Box 511, Vienna, Va. 22180

National Biological Supply Company, Inc., 2325 South Michigan, Chicago, Ill. 60616

National Teaching Aids, 386 Park Avenue South, New York, N. Y. 10016

New York Biological Supply, 609 West 51 Street, New York, N. Y.

New York Scientific Supply Co., 28 West 30 Street, New York, N. Y. 10001

Northern Biological Supply, Box 222, New Richmond, Wis. 54017

Northwest Biological Laboratories, 3581 Shelbourne Street, Victoria, British Columbia, Canada

Nuclear Chicago Corporation, 333 East Howard Avenue, DesPlaines, III. 60016

Nutrional Biochemicals Corp., 21010 Miles Avenue, Cleveland, Ohio 44128

A. J. Nystrom & Company, 3333 Elston Avenue, Chicago, III. 60618

Ohaus Scale Corporation, 1050 Commerce Avenue, Union, N.J. 07083

Oregon Biological Supply Co., 1806 S. E. Holgate Boulevard, Portland, Ore. 97202

Pacific Laboratory Apparatus Co., 3555 Whittier Boulevard, Los Angeles, Calif. 90023

Charles Pfizer & Co., 11 Bartlett Street, Brooklyn, N.Y. 10006

Phipps and Bird, Inc., 6th at Byrd Streets, P. O. Box 2V, Richmond, Va. 23205

Physicians and Hospitals Supply Co., 1400 Harmon Place, Minneapolis, Minn. 55403

Pickett & Eckel, Inc., 542 South Dearborn Street, Chicago, III. 60605

Polaroid Corp., Cambridge, Mass. 02139

Preiser Scientific, Inc., 900 MacCorkle Avenue S. W., Charleston, W. Va. 25322

Product Design Co., 2796 Middlefield Road, Redwood City, Calif. 44063

Research Specialties Co., 2005 Hopkins Street, Berkeley, Calif. 94707

E. H. Sargent and Company, 4601 W. Foster Avenue, Chicago, Illinois

Schaar Scientific Company, 7300 W. Montrose Avenue, Chicago, III. 60634

Schlueter Scientific Supplies, Inc., 8609 Lincoln Avenue, Morton Grove, III. 60053

Science Electronics Inc., 195 Massachusetts Avenue, Cambridge, Mass. 02139

Science Kit, Inc., 2299 Military Road, Tonawanda, N.Y. 14140

Science Materials Center, 59 Fourth Avenue, New York, N.Y. 10003

Science Teaching Aids, Box 386, Pell Lake, Wis. 53157

Scientific Glass Apparatus Co., Bloomfield, N.J.

Scientific Products, 1210 Leon Place, Evanston, III. 60621

Scientific Supplies Co., 173 Jackson Avenue, Seattle, Washington

Sherer-Gillett Company, 604 South Kalamazoo Avenue, Marshall, Mich. 49068

Sherwin Scientific Co., 1112 North Ruby Street, Spokane, Wash. 99202

Southern Biological Supply Co., 517 Decatur, New Orleans, La.

Southern Precision Instrument Co., 710 Augusta Street, San Antonio, Texas 78215

Sprague-Dawley, Inc., P. O. Box 2071, Madison, Wis. 53705

Standard Scientific Corp., 34 West Fourth Street, New York, N.Y. 10018

Standard Scientific Supply Corp., 808 Broadway, New York, N.Y. 10003

Stansi Scientific Company, 1231 North Honore Street, Chicago, III. 60622

E. G. Steinhilber and Co., Inc., P. O. Box 888, Oshkosh, Wis. 54902

Swift Instruments, Inc., 1190 North Fourth Street, San Jose, Calif. 95112

Taylor Instrument Companies, 95 Ames Street, Rochester, N.Y. 14611

Teaching Materials Corp., 575 Lexington Avenue, New York, N.Y. 10022

Testa Manufacturing Company, 10126 East Rash Street, El Monte, Calif. 91733

The Torsion Balance Company, 35 Monhegan Street, Clifton, N.J. 07013

Trippensee Planetarium Company Inc., 2200 South Hamilton Street, Saginaw, Mich. 48602

United Scientific Co., 204 Milk Street, Boston, Mass. 02108

Unitron Instrument Company, 66 Needham Street, Newton Highlands, Mass. 02161

Universal Scientific Company Inc., 120 Alexander Street, Princeton, N.J. 08540

University Apparatus Co., 2229 McGee Avenue, Berkeley, California

Van Waters and Rogers, Inc., P. O. 5287, Denver, Colo. 80206

Ward's Natural Science Establishment Inc., 3000 Ridge Road East, P. O. Box 1712, Rochester, N. Y. 14603

The Welch Scientific Company, 7300 N. Linder Avenue, Skokie, Ill. 60076

Western Laboratories, 826 Q Street, Lincoln, Neb. 68508

Western Seed Testing Service, 439 Pierce Street, Twin Falls, Idaho 83301

Wilkens-Anderson Company, 4525 West Division Street, Chicago, Ill. 60651

Will Corporation, P. O. Box 1050, Rochester, N. Y. 14603